4/12/66

T
15
F 7.2

MAN THE MAKER

Man
THE MAKER

A History of
Technology and Engineering

R. J. FORBES

ABELARD-SCHUMAN LIMITED
London and New York

Printed in the United States of America

PREFACE

THIS BOOK was written as an attempt to show how certain of our material achievements arose and became part of that complex of culture traits we call civilization. It is the story of *Homo faber*, a sociological species distinct from *Homo sapiens*, and covers his accomplishments in the field of discovery, invention, and engineering from prehistoric times to the present day.

In discussing the meaning of history, the late Dr. F. S. Marvin once wrote: "The learner must turn his eyes to his progenitors of the spirit . . . they will be found in every age and country, strengthening the skillful hand, informing the brain, weaving immortal images of love and beauty. In the spirit of these he must himself learn and work, yet he cannot work only for himself or for his own country, for this would be treachery to the name he bears and the heritage he has acquired. He looks round the world for confirmation and assistance, but is appalled by the many crimes, the long stretches of darkness, the hurrying streams of folly and indifference. Yet if he looks steadily, he cannot mistake the figure of humanity arising in the mists."

The writer believes that the thought so well expressed by Dr. Marvin holds good for engineering and technology as well as for the world of the spirit. Long before man's written records show us his mind and his plans for the future, he acted as Man the Maker, assuming the role of both craftsman and engineer in addition to that of artist, philosopher, and teacher. The engineering and technology of the present is nothing more than the accumulated heritage of the past, the combined experiments and technical creations of hundreds of generations. The figure of humanity rises as clearly in this field as in the fields of literature and art.

In order to make this clear and to show how deeply such mechanical arts as engineering and technology are embedded in the spiritual life of mankind, we have followed up a few threads of this history from the dawn of human life to the dawn of the Atomic Age. A complete history of technology and engineering, however much wanted by students in this field, would require many volumes. In keeping with the general design of *The Life of Science Library* we have accordingly restricted ourselves to the story of such essential topics as power resources, transportation and communication, metallurgy, textiles, glass, chemical technology, and some aspects of civil engineering. This selection may seem more arbitrary as we approach modern times, but we have tried above all to stress the continuity of our story even if this meant neglecting, because of space limitations, many new conquests of modern engineering.

The conquest of nature is the work of mankind as a whole. The nationality of an inventor will be found to be of much less importance than his capacity to make his invention or discovery part of the total cultural heritage of mankind. The scene of our story therefore shifts from country to country as the history of technology advances, so that we obtain a broad panoramic view of the inventive process in terms of world progress rather than nationalistic boundaries. No part of the world can claim to be more innately gifted than any other part; the differences we observe are differences in the culture complex or social heritage of different groups.

If this book helps to make this point clear and to place the story of technology and engineering in proper perspective as a part of the world's cultural heritage, it will have accomplished its purpose. It is hoped that it may also contribute to the general acceptance, by those who are interested in our modern technical world, of the fundamental unity of mankind.

R. J. FORBES
Amsterdam, Netherlands

CONTENTS

ILLUSTRATIONS

MAN THE MAKER

MAN AND NATURE

IN OUR modern world both technology and engineering are branches of applied science; they follow very closely in the footsteps of scientific research as conducted in laboratories and universities. But pure science was not always the fostermother of applied science, nor did engineers always follow up scientific discoveries. During many periods in history craftsmen and engineers had to proceed by trial and error, collecting and evaluating facts in their own workshops. If we go back far enough in history we even find a time when no written science existed and when craftsmen were the only scientists who gathered the harvest of experience that was later to form the foundation of modern science.

For science is the body of knowledge by means of which man accounts for all he observes in the world about him. From his observations and experiences he builds up a picture of nature; he fashions a system out of what he sees, feels, and smells and arranges these observations in some semblance of order. The more he learns about natural objects the more intricate is his picture of the world, until this "second nature" (as Leonardo da Vinci called it) becomes the field of the specialist. The modern scientist studies, measures, and calculates the forces of nature and thus provides the engineer and technologist with physical data. Ever since man first walked the earth he has tried to understand and control the forces of nature in order to survive. Primitive man, no less than modern man, was *Homo sapiens*, Man the Thinker.

But the picture that early man made from what he saw and felt was always mixed up with other aspects of his life. Today even the most primitive aborigine lives in a society in which material factors such as food, shelter, warfare, population density, geography, and climate partly determine its structure—a structure, however, that is also determined by the prevailing religion, philosophy, and art. Spiritual and material forces are closely interwoven in any society. The same social interrelationship holds true for the modern scientist or engineer, who cannot avoid putting something of his own personality into his theory or technical achievement.

Yet were it not for the fact that Man the Thinker was at the same time *Homo faber*, Man the Maker, we would perhaps have no knowledge today of man's prehistoric existence. The earliest traces of primitive man are largely made up of his tools, the remains of his campfire and hut, and whatever artifacts his hands may have fashioned. Man did not seek to understand nature merely to satisfy his curiosity. He had to survive in a strange, hostile world. He had to come to grips with nature, using as his main weapon the intellect that distinguished him from the animals. The primary thing he had to do was to find and collect food, and food was not always in plentiful supply. All his long life on earth man has had to use his intelligence, to observe nature around him, to remember the facts he perceives, and to try to apply them in a way that will increase his security and comfort.

Discoveries and Inventions

THE story of man's conquest of nature is the story of his discoveries and inventions rather than of his political achievements. His understanding of nature and his philosophy of life have molded his actions. As his knowledge of what we now call applied science increased, he strengthened his control over nature. In no field of human action can we speak more truly of evolution. In the world of the spirit, ideas and dogmas died and were reborn, but man's conquest of nature was a constant ascent.

Every discovery and invention added to his knowledge; so did every experiment and observation. A fact or a technique might lie unused for years and might even seem to be forgotten, but the memory of it remained a part of the growing social heritage. Man's scientific knowledge was additive, each generation picking up the torch where the preceding generation had left it. Children then as now learned the essential facts from their parents' experience and started their own campaign for the conquest of nature.

We often tend to forget the subtle distinction between discovery and invention. Man discovered only what already existed in nature—new types of animals such as fowl, horses, and camels, or new plants like wheat and potatoes. He discovered the powers of nature in fire, water, and wind, though it took him a long time to harness these to serve him. He did not change the form of these discoveries but took them as he found them, adapting them to his purposes in various ways.

Man slowly discovered the properties of metals after having used them for centuries; he knew of the magnet and the strange properties of amber when it was rubbed with a cloth. He discovered the methods of working clay and learned to make pottery by applying this knowledge.

But as soon as man used these objects or created something different from the materials of nature, he had made something that had not existed before. Herein lies the difference between discovery and invention. The properties of clay existed long before man appeared on earth, but it was man who applied these properties and made pottery. In inventing, Man the Thinker combines scraps of his knowledge of nature to form a new substance or object that previously did not exist and therefore could not be uncovered or discovered.

It is often difficult, however, to decide whether a new

substance or product is an invention or a discovery. As material civilization becomes more complex, the percentage of inventions grows. There is a natural limit to the number of discoveries possible, but there seems to be no limit to man's capacity of combining existing materials with known properties to form new products with different properties. The facts of nature form the warp, man's imagination and inventiveness the woof of the tapestry of our material civilization. The pattern seems to become more intricate with the passage of time; necessity, invention's mother, stimulates new demands and new inventions. This was particularly true when arts and crafts, once the part-time jobs of ancient farmers and hunters, became the full-time occupation of separate groups in more developed forms of civilization. Inventions and discoveries increased rapidly with the rise of the artisan class and of scientists.

Though the conquest of nature has made tremendous strides since man first appeared, its progress has been less gradual than most people assume. It has not been a uniform evolution; mankind seems to have climbed the ladder of civilization rung by rung. With each step we have seen new perspectives and new possibilities. We have achieved a certain purpose and have discovered or invented what we strove for. But once the new facts, the new means, and the new procedures have been conquered, we are faced once more with new problems and new possibilities. We struggle forward to cope with these new problems; we investigate and experiment along certain lines. No uninformed inventor can sit down and invent something out of the blue. Research is always based on what is already known; the better the grasp of these facts, the more effective research is.

Our achievements feed our search for something better, something different, something that we vaguely discern in our dreams. "For each age is a dream that is dying or one that is coming to birth." The inventor often seems far ahead of his contemporaries, yet this is only partly true. For he, like all his fellow men, is chained to the past and present, and in pursuit of his dreams he can reach out only a little farther than others.

The inventor is a man of imagination, as every scientist should be at heart. He believes in his quest, though he may go beyond his intentions. He is sure that there is always something more to be found in the problem or tool he is pondering over. His genius is his creative imagination, his ability to see things in a different light. Yet imagination alone does not create. When Newton was asked how he had discovered the universal law of gravity, he answered, "By pondering constantly over the problem of falling bodies." His genius made him believe that a single principle would be found to govern both the movements of the planets and the fall of an apple. But only experimenting, collecting the facts, and thinking logically brought the solution. The genius of the inventor must be combined with sound scientific research and reasoning. The unscientific inventor, like the alchemist of old, wastes his efforts in trying to achieve the impossible.

Inventions therefore represent a greater intellectual achievement than discoveries, for the latter merely bring to light existing facts. The scientist may discover new things by using more adequate instruments, whereas the inventor creates something new by "reaching for the power of the gods," as the ancients expressed it. Yet while we know much of the psychology of the inventive process, we are very often ignorant of the names of the great inventors of antiquity, and of the way certain things came to be invented before the dawn of recorded history.

From a study of the earliest forms of pottery shaped like woven bags or like calabashes, we conclude that the art of the potter was discovered when such vessels were made fireproof by covering them with a layer of clay and baking them in the fire. This "plaster theory" may be true, but we have no evidence to confirm it, except the remains of old pots and the fact that similar methods are still in use today among primitive peoples. The example given is only one instance where nothing is known about the original inventor. We don't know his name, can barely guess where he lived, and have only a vague idea of his dates.

7

Let us take another example from the dawn of history. Through the discoveries of archeology we can trace the steps that led to modern metallurgy. We see mankind using natural metals as precious stones, then hammering and cutting them. Following this comes the casting and deformation of

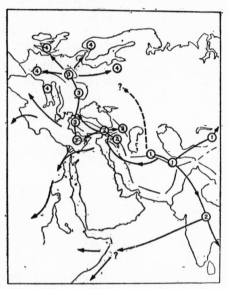

Map showing the diffusion of metallurgy from its earliest beginnings in the Ancient Near East (1), the sequence of figures indicating its spread to (2) the Middle East and India, (3) the Eastern Mediterranean and Balkan peninsula areas and thence up into Central Europe, and (4) through Central Europe to the British Isles and the Baltic Area.

metals by hammering at high temperatures, the processing of copper ores, for example, and many more steps until bronze metallurgy is discovered. But even the last step—the manufacture of bronze—was not a single invention but rather a complex of discoveries and inventions.

First the new alloy was made accidentally and its specific properties noted. These properties then guided the search for the means of manufacturing the alloy. In turn, the search

8

for raw materials from which to prepare the new "impure copper" led to the discovery of cassiterite, or copper ores mixed with tin ore. The tin ore and the metal it contained were recognized as something quite different only many centuries later.

The casting of bronze became possible only through the knowledge of many facts that might seem disconnected to the untrained observer. A well-known ancient method of casting is the "cire-perdue" or wax-casting process, in which the model is molded in wax over a core of sand and clay and again covered by a layer clay and sand, whereupon the molten wax is poured out, leaving an empty space into which the metal can be cast. This method of bronze casting involves a knowledge of handling and preparing bronze alloys, of sand-clay mixes suitable for cores, and of the properties of waxes that can be modeled and melted.

Thus we see that every step in the conquest of nature involves the application of widely divergent facts and experiences. As the conquest of nature proceeds, the mechanism of technology becomes more complex.

Diffusion of Inventions

THIS brings us to a question that is still widely discussed. Can a particular invention or discovery be made more than once, either simultaneously or at different periods, or should we assume that the apparent duplication is due to the diffusion of the original discovery or invention from a central point? There is evidence to prove that many simple inventions and discoveries have been made more than once, either simultaneously or independently at different times. Simple tools, primitive types of ships, dwellings, weapons, and the like, are largely determined by the properties of the materials used. The dugout canoe was probably invented independently in various places and at different periods of history. Smoking the leaves of different plants was a custom in a number of widely separated tribes in antiquity, but the pipe as a specific in-

9

strument used in smoking followed the introduction of tobacco from America to Europe and Asia.

The more intricate an invention is, the less chance there is of its being duplicated elsewhere. When there is an apparent duplication we can usually trace the lines along which the original invention was diffused. The very early stages of metallurgy are common to all primitive peoples. The Indians of the North American Plains have known copper and have handled it in a primitive nonmetallurgical way, but they never knew the true copper metallurgy (smelting and casting) until they learned it from the white men who invaded their country. Metallurgy and its complex processes of ore dressing and smithing or casting were diffused from the ancient Near East, where they were originally invented.

As civilization spread and as contacts between distant parts of the earth became more frequent, this diffusion of ideas grew more important and more common. Today there is very little chance that an invention will be duplicated by two inventors working in complete independence of each other. When scientists in different countries appear to hit on the same discovery or invention at the same time, it is mainly due to the closer contact between them and their common knowledge of the available facts or materials. With modern methods of communication, our periodicals, books, and patent-office publications, it is easy for scientific and technological facts to spread fairly quickly. Scientists are familiar with each other's work and share certain lines of thought in common.

The steps in the conquest of nature have grown smaller but they have become more involved. The facts are presented in detail and all the links in the chain of reasoning, except the last, are available to the most important centers of science and industry. There is a need to solve certain problems and many scientists are trying to solve them at the same moment, though perhaps prompted by different motives. The chances are great for two or more workers to hit upon the missing link at about the same time. Newton in 1665 and Leibnitz in 1679, each working independently, devised methods of the calculus that were essentially similar. The planet Neptune was discovered simultaneously but independently by several astronomers who were all convinced of its existence from certain perturbations observed in the motions of other planets.

As recorded history unfolds, we find better information on the lives and methods of discoverers and inventors, who in the remote past are either unknown or disguised under elaborate myths and legends. It is only in the last twenty centuries that we can follow in closer detail the threads that lead to inventions and the way in which they were used in the new design. But as we study the pages of history of technology and engineering, we are more and more impressed by the close bond between these and other human activities.

The history of technology and engineering is, in the first place, the story of the conquest of materials. The effects of this conquest make themselves felt in all fields of human endeavor. Let us take a few examples from the development of glass. Smelting sand with caustic soda and other ingredients not only served to produce prettily colored baubles, but also provided man with beautiful vessels for holding liquids and gave him windowpanes to shield his dwelling from cold and rain while admitting the light of the sun. Learning to cast and grind glass, man proceeded to produce lenses for spectacles and then turned these lenses to use for telescopes and microscopes. These instruments in turn opened up the universe to science and made it possible for man to study the distant nebulae as well as the microbes in a drop of water and the molecular structure of matter.

Glass vessels not only served man in his houses or palaces; they also held the corrosive chemicals of the pharmacists and alchemists and thus contributed to the evolution of chemistry. Without glass vessels the chemistry of gases—the search for their nature and properties—would have been impossible, and some fundamental laws of physics and chemistry might have remained undiscovered.

On the other hand, technology and engineering were not the only factors contributing to the growth of science, nor was science the only source of the technologist apart from his practical experience. Both fields are intimately linked up with other human activities and both give and take from these aspects of human life. In wartime both may be stimulated and activated, but we must remember that the results thus achieved belong to the narrow field of warfare, and that the new military weapons and other inventions discovered at great cost and lavish expense could just as well have been procured in peacetime with much less cost. Ideally, in order to benefit the whole of mankind, theoretical and applied science should not be bound by limited supplies of money; moreover, in order for science to expand naturally, peaceful conditions are necessary. Peace furthers the natural expansion of all human activities, including trade, the growth of which is intimately connected with that of science and industry.

Trade aims at stable economic conditions, the promotion of sound coinage (for which scientific tests are needed), and of standard weights and measures acceptable in the largest possible area. In promoting this standardization, trade helped the evolution of a world-wide exchange of scientific and technical data. In addition, trade thrives when goods can be produced abundantly and cheaply; in our modern world the mass production of goods has served this end effectively.

Mass production of goods started in the artillery schools of Austria and Spain and in the dockyards of Venice and Holland. Industry soon adopted these mass-production methods and trade strongly promoted the evolution of standard parts and tools. Without the stimulating effects of the demands formulated by a growing world trade, which created the mass market and the mass demand in its own interests, modern mass production would not have grown nor would its benefits have raised the standard of living for so many people. Even before the eighteenth century, when these trends began to appear, trade had attracted the scientists and engineers, who moved with the centers of trade toward those peaceful areas where they found the proper surroundings for technological development.

Not only are all aspects of mankind connected by visible or invisible bonds, but the conquest of nature can be shown to belong to the whole world rather than to any particular nation. In any period a certain national group may seem to hold the key to knowledge, but at close inspection this will prove to be a surface impression only. Knowledge is something that cannot be monopolized, for if kept secret it is useless and if disseminated it will inspire others to spread it to ever-widening circles. The story of industry and invention is one of the lessons demonstrating the oneness of mankind, the inherent unity that exists in spite of such artificialities as frontiers or sectarian beliefs.

THE DAWN OF HISTORY

(BEFORE 3000 B.C.)

IT is often little realized that the fundamental discoveries and inventions on which our modern civilization is based were made before the dawn of history. History is usually said to begin with the advent of written documents, and writing was first conceived in the ancient Near East in the latter half of the fourth millennium B.C. We can trace man's activities before that time only by the remains found by the archeologist. We can only try to reconstruct his beliefs, theories, and reasonings from those remains, for we possess none of his documents, assuming that there were any. Hence we can only state that he employed this or that tool or method at such a period, and are left to guess at the steps that led to its discovery or invention.

The period we refer to is called prehistory. A Danish archeologist, Christian Jörgensen Thomsen, who lived about a hundred years ago, tried to subdivide this rather diffuse period and suggested in 1836 the names "Stone Age," "Bronze Age," and "Iron Age" for these subdivisions, based on the principal material from which man had fashioned his tools and weapons during each of the periods. We know that this sequence as given by Karl Ottfried Müller (1797–1840) holds good only for a limited number of areas, but we can safely adopt it for Europe and for the ancient Near East, where civilization seems to have had its origin. However, we are now aware of the limitations of this scheme. In the Near East the Bronze Age is already a historical period illustrated by documents, while the Bronze Age in Europe remains prehistory. Civilization radiated from the Near East once recorded history began there some five thousand years ago.

The Old Stone Age

THE earliest of these three periods is subdivided into an Old Stone Age and a New Stone Age. The former produces the oldest remains of mankind. Traces of anthropoid or manlike creatures of both earlier and later date have been found, but true prehistory begins with man. From these early remains it is clear that man had already made two important conquests —the use of fire and the fashioning of stone tools.

The conquest of fire as a source of heat and light was a vital one. As man learned to produce fire by rubbing, drilling, or percussion (the same methods still used by primitive people today), he cast off many shackles. He was free to feed or extinguish his fire, to transport and rekindle it. His diet became more varied, for he no longer had to depend only on what nature produced in a directly edible form. He could cook food and preserve it for the winter by heating or drying it. He could make more efficient tools by heating and thus satisfy his growing needs. The fire protected him from wild beasts and cold blasts; it gave him the means of hardening the point of his wooden spear and helped him to make a dugout canoe.

With fire, man investigated the mysteries of all colored and strangely shaped materials. In the earliest documents this fire test already takes an important place and we still use it in modern chemistry and geology. Heating stones and suddenly cooling them with water enabled man to disintegrate them, and with fire he could achieve other wonders.

It is clear that the glory of this conquest was branded into man's memory and that nearly all primitive and ancient peoples practiced some form of fire worship. The Vestals at

15

Rome guarded the fire which once a year was extinguished, to be rekindled with great ceremony. The Parsees of India considered fire too holy an element to burn the bodies of their dead. Many other ceremonies and rites in which fire plays a major part remind us of the awe in which man once held his first conquest.

Just as important for man was the art of fashioning stone tools. It began with his discovery that flint nodules (small lumps of flint) when struck together or with other stones would split and yield flakes along certain planes. By proper percussion and the application of pressure to the edges of the flint, either flakes or cores could be shaped to suit certain purposes. The flakes were usually more suitable for knifelike tools, saws, scrapers, and the like, while the cores could be used as daggers, borers, and axes.

As we study the remains of early man we can even distinguish "core cultures" and "flake cultures," if we name such groups according to the principal type of tool used. Much depended on the geographical features of the country in which man lived. In forest regions he was likely to adopt the "core" axe, but in grassy regions or on steppes the knife-shaped flakes would be more appropriate.

From the beautiful rock drawings, and from the graves and other remains, we know that man of the Old Stone Age had already acquired a considerable body of practical knowledge of nature. He observed the sun, the moon, and the stars, and knew of the cycle of the seasons. He apparently studied closely the animals and plants that he hunted or collected, for the paintings show an intimate knowledge of these animals at every stage of their growth. They depict his hunting techniques, and at the same time show that he was able to make pigments by mixing minerals or plants with other ingredients like bear fat. The stones and minerals he collected and often buried in the graves of the dead indicate that he was attracted by bright colors and strange shapes. Other evidence tends to prove that he possessed the rudiments of astronomy, geology, and natural history. His care for the

dead, as well as other indications, convinces us that he also had a philosophy of life, or religion, although we know very little of his actual beliefs or attitudes.

The New Stone Age

THE New Stone Age is heralded by a complete change of civilization and a gradual disappearance of the older groups of mankind. The new civilization is usually characterized by the beginnings of hoe and digging-stick agriculture. Beyond this we perceive new techniques like the polishing of stone, spinning and weaving, pottery, and the earliest form of mining. New groups of hunters, nomads, and peasants displaced the older types of hunters and food collectors.

The archeological remains prove that even this primitive form of agriculture was the cause of a quick growth of population. The cultivation of certain wild grasses like emmer led to the storage of grain and consequently greater security during unproductive seasons. Life became somewhat more stable, although primitive farming technique forced the earliest peasants to move fairly often when the surface soil of their fields became exhausted.

Toward the end of the New Stone Age another revolution occurred. Modern forms of agriculture appeared, using the plow and irrigation. As far as the Near East was concerned, this also meant the migration of new tribes into this area, while the grasslands stretching from the Atlantic along the Mediterranean through Persia into Central Asia got less and less rain. This change of climate forced the population gradually into the river valleys, which, being covered with trees, shrubs, and reeds as well as swamps and marshes, had to be cleared and drained before they were fit for habitation. The end of the New Stone Age, which in the Near East may cover the period from 3500 to 3000 B.C., was an age of fundamental importance in the history of mankind. Apart from the new forms of agriculture, this period saw the rise of mining, metallurgy, and architecture, and the invention of the wheel,

the ship, and writing—in fact, all the fundamental crafts of modern civilization. This period preceded the historical dynasties of Egypt and Mesopotamia and is therefore usually called the predynastic period.

In agriculture the fundamental invention was that of the plow, which was still generally made of wood with a wooden or stone plowshare and was drawn by oxen. It had the great

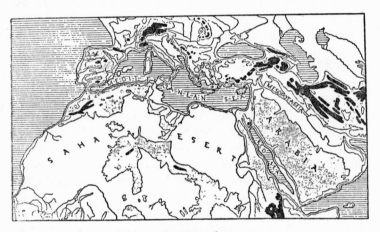

The cradle of modern man.

advantage over both digging-stick and hoe in that, generally speaking, it plowed the soil much deeper and hence the land did not become exhausted so quickly. The peasant became a permanent settler and introduced the rotation of fields wherever he was unable to irrigate his land. The wooden or stone plowshare, occasionally tipped with bronze, remained in use throughout antiquity—another example of the fact that a new material like copper or bronze may not always oust older materials. For copper and bronze were not tough enough for plowing, and the ancient peasant continued to use stone until Roman times, when iron had become cheap enough to be forged into plowshares.

18

Irrigation and Its Effects

THE second great achievement of the ancient peasant was irrigation. Primitive forms of irrigation had been practiced for some time. They were probably improved as man gradually withdrew from the desiccating higher grounds into the river valleys of the Near East. His task in clearing the river valleys of the Nile, Euphrates, Tigris, and Indus must have been formidable. He had to drain the swamps, cut down the bush and reed lands, and hunt the wild animals. But he also had to tame the rampaging floods and guide the fertile waters of the river over his new fields at planting time.

The irrigation systems of the river valleys were no longer the task of any individual peasant. The digging of canals, the building of dikes, dams, and the construction of proper drainage systems were beyond one man's power; they could be achieved only through cooperation and teamwork. Irrigation therefore was one of the most powerful forces in ancient history toward the formation of nations and a strong central power. In Egypt we find that the old hieroglyphic sign for "province," which the Greeks called "nome," is actually a pictograph of such an irrigation and drainage unit. Such units or "polders," as they are now called in Holland, also form the background of the city-states of ancient Mesopotamia. The combining of such units for the most efficient use of the fertile waters of the flooding rivers was only a matter of time. The ancient Egyptians begin their real history with the amalgamation of Upper and Lower Egypt. The conquest that achieved this union was certainly not attributable to lust for power alone.

The influence of irrigation went far beyond political life. It stimulated mathematics and astronomy. Applied mathematics, especially geodesy (measurement of large areas of land), were invaluable because the seasonal floods effaced the boundaries between the fields and the boundary stones had to be re-erected. The fields had to be correctly measured, for taxes were usually based on the area flooded and the level reached by the inundation. Hence we find from the oldest historical times an Egyptian department of "dikes and irrigation." In every province it had a special "water house," an office that sent its inspectors to control the dikes, to observe the level of the Nile, and to cut the dikes when the river had risen to the proper level. There were special courts to hear conflicts on irrigation laws. The destruction of dikes, the neglect of canals, and the abuse of irrigation water were the main problems dealt with by this "water tribunal."

The Egyptians also had a land registry office which in the season of "shortage of water" sent out its surveyors to measure the fields and settle boundary disputes. Every two years a careful survey of all the fields, called "calculation" by the Egyptians, established whatever taxes were to be levied. There are many contemporary drawings of these surveyors showing them accompanied by scribes and slaves carrying the knotted rope with which they measured the fields. Indeed, the classical authors like Herodotus and Strabo correctly remark that the surveyor must have stimulated the development of mathematics and of geometry in particular.

Astronomy also profited from irrigation. Turning again to Egypt, we know that at prominent points along the Nile, often in temple courts, there were water gages in wells connected with the river. These gages were observed with great care and one of the first things the Egyptian kings would mention in their annals was the record level reached by the Nile. It was well known that the Nile had to reach the height of 12–16 ells (40–54 feet) at Memphis to ensure a proper harvest. The Egyptian year began the day when the flood coincided with the rising of the star Sirius at dawn. Observation of the stars, therefore, would give a proper approximation of the beginning of the flood. This stimulated astronomical observations and forced the Egyptians to recognize at an early date that the length of a year was slightly over 365 days. It was well known in historical times that the calendar had to be corrected so that the rising of Sirius would con-

tinue to coincide with New Year's Day. A similar interdependence between irrigation and astronomy is known to
have existed in Mesopotamia.

There were other arts that profited from irrigation—civil
engineering, for example. The digging of canals and the making of dikes meant moving large masses of earth, and this
operation had to be calculated and planned. Many ancient
mathematical texts from Egypt and Mesopotamia deal with
such problems. In fact, if a Babylonian wanted to indicate
that a certain figure represented a cubic measure, he added
the words "mass of earth." We know of many big canals built
in the ancient Near East in early historical times; the irrigation systems were then already so far developed that many
must have been built in predynastic times. Kings and priests
took great pride in the construction of dikes and canals and
gave details in their annals or on the walls of their tombs.
The handling of such large masses of earth entailed organizational problems and practical techniques that were of great
importance later when pyramids and temple mounds were
built. Without the experience gained in irrigation, these enduring monuments might never have been erected.

Irrigation was also linked up with the evolution of machinery, for the smallest fields and especially those higher up along
the desert ridges had to be flooded artificially from the outer
ditches and canals. This stimulated the development of such
machines as the water swipe and several forms of water wheels
either man- or animal-driven. As pictures of primitive forms
of such machines are known to occur on very early seals, it is
quite certain that their invention goes back into the dawn
of history.

Apart from stimulating technology, this oldest "plow and
irrigation" agriculture also had profound social effects. Earlier
forms of agriculture had already increased the population but
now this increase was greatly enhanced, for the new agriculture gave much better yields and permitted the storage of
surplus harvest for bad times. It also helped the rise of classes
of the population who no longer spent most of their time

on the land, as the New Stone Age peasant had done. It was now possible to feed groups such as craftsmen and merchants from the surplus harvest, thus leaving these groups free to produce clothing, tools, and other durable goods that the peasants had formerly been obliged to make for themselves. The surplus of grain could be exchanged for the products of the nomad and mountain dweller. We also learn from the excavations of New Stone Age settlements that the peasant population must have increased far beyond that of the earlier periods.

Again, the new farming methods had increased man's diet. Out of the original wild grasses and early types of corn, such as emmer, man learned to cultivate more valuable foods like barley, wheat, and rye, later adding oats in Northern Europe. He had tamed dogs, cows, pigs, fowl, sheep, and goats, and he even tried to tame antelopes and gazelles, as we can see on certain Egyptian mural paintings. Apart from the obvious uses of the manure, milk, and leather, he was able to use the wool for his clothing. He already cultivated many herbs and vegetables and now added the cultivation of dates, figs, olives, and several fruit trees. It is also fairly certain that the culture of the vine and perhaps the production of wine started in this period. This large extension of diet made the supply of food fairly certain. Accordingly we observe that hunting loses its early vital importance and now becomes the pastime of the rich; now only farmers or pastoral groups have to be reckoned with. In the districts bordering on the river valleys, occasional hunts for predatory animals survived; the Kings had scenes from these hunts depicted on their monuments.

Spinning and Weaving

EARLY in the New Stone Age we find the beginnings of spinning and weaving techniques. These thrived as man not only cultivated flax to make his linen but also began shearing animals of their wool. The technique of basketmaking and matting was already well understood. The gradual improvement of spinning and weaving, partly derived from these earlier techniques, can be followed from the remains of looms and other implements excavated.

Spinning and weaving entail three major inventions. Neither flax nor wool were immediately ready for spinning. The flax was pulled up by the roots and the seeds had to be rippled or shelled off the stems by means of a comblike tool. Then the bundles of flax were retted—that is, the woody part of the fibers was allowed to rot so that they could easily be separated from the fibers inside the stem. By scutching the flax—beating it with wooden mallets on flat stones—the woody parts were eliminated.

In the same way the wool was collected after the sheep had been shorn. The fleece was then carefully washed to remove all dirt and fat. The wool was then carded (combed or brushed with leather-backed brushes called cards). The wool fibers were thus stretched parallel and cleaned to form a fleece or sliver, which was then placed on a forked staff (the distaff) for spinning. The fact that women have always been identified with spinning accounts for the expression "the distaff side."

The long flax fibers were joined while being twisted into a loose, half-twisted thread called a roving. Balls of roving or slivers of wool were now ready for the second major operation, spinning. Its main feature was a combined twisting and stretching of the roving or sliver into a thread of uniform thickness and strength. This was achieved by attaching the sliver to a spindle, a long thin stick weighted by a disk of clay or stone called a whorl. Dropping this spindle caused a length of sliver to be stretched and twisted by the whirling spindle. The thread thus obtained was wound on the spindle and the operation repeated. Thus spools of linen or woolen yarn were obtained. The yarn was then washed, bleached, or dyed as required.

Finally came the third operation, weaving. The simplest form of loom was a frame holding a parallel set of yarns usually attached over the head of the weaver to a horizontal stick and stretched by fastening a weight to each yarn. This set of yarns held in place on the loom was called the warp, and this early type of loom is known as a "warp-weighted loom."

The experience gained in basketmaking and weaving mats was used in making the earliest types of cloth. Through the stretched warp threads the weft or filling yarn was now woven to form a fabric. Weaving was very soon simplified by someone who had the bright idea of running every other warp thread through a little loop of yarn fastened to a stick. When this stick (or heald rod) was pulled forward, the alternate threads were lifted and the filling yarn could easily be passed through the shed (the passage between the two sets of threads) in one movement, and pressed against the other filling threads to make a firm cloth.

The loom gradually developed into a more complicated piece of machinery. The filling thread was enclosed in a boat-like shuttle that moved more easily. By using several heald rods, each attached to different sets of warp threads, more difficult and intricate patterns could be woven. When these "heddles" or "harnesses" were worked by foot pedals, the weaver's hands were free to move the shuttle and to beat the weft into a firm cloth by means of the weaver's sword.

The subsequent development of spinning and weaving techniques did not involve the introduction of any new basic principles but was merely the mechanization of these primitive New Stone Age inventions. Under favorable conditions bits of ancient textiles have been preserved, allowing us to study the technique employed and to gage the strength of the material when new. Remarkable results can be achieved with the primitive looms that Egyptian and Mesopotamian pictures show us. Measurements on samples of ancient cloth show that the thread obtained by Egyptian weavers was often finer than anything we can make on modern machinery; some samples have as many as 540 warp threads to the inch. No wonder the Egyptian linen was world-famous in antiquity.

Pottery

ONE of the great gains of the New Stone Age was the art of the potter. It hinged on the remarkable qualities of clay, which when mixed with water can be molded and dried to form pots, jugs, and other receptacles. But dried-clay vessels can be destroyed again by water. If, however, clay is heated beyond a certain temperature it becomes hard and brittle, no longer susceptible to water and capable of withstanding great heat. At even higher temperatures a kind of vitrification takes place, but primitive kilns hardly ever reached these temperatures. In fact, the earliest pottery gives evidence of having been baked in an open fire. Pottery kilns seem to have evolved from the bread oven shortly before the appearance of the potter's wheel.

We do not know exactly how pottery originated, but the earliest examples have the form of woven bags, leather vessels, and gourd-shaped containers. It seems that the original articles were covered with layers of clay to make them more watertight. This procedure, incidentally, allowed the container to be heated and thus provided man with the possibilities of increasing and improving his menu. The potter's art and that of the cook are closely allied. When used for cooking, these clay-smeared vessels must have got baked in the heat of the fire. Imprints of the original container on which the clay was applied can sometimes be detected on old potsherds (pieces of broken earthen pots). Observations and repetitions of these experiments must have led to the discovery of the potter's art.

Very soon pottery departed from its original forms and adopted those that were more consistent with the nature of clay. New Stone Age man fashioned his pottery according to methods still used today by primitive peoples in America, Africa, and Oceania. He formed a vessel from a single piece of clay or from superposed clay rings. Before long he also made spouts and attached handles to this pottery. He adapted his ideas of natural or geometrical designs to decorate his bowls, jugs, and other clay vessels. He began to use different kinds of clay to obtain colored ware, and knew how to bake at different temperatures to obtain iridescent glazes and other color effects. He also learned to add sand or crushed shards to his clay in order to obtain a more porous vessel. Pottery grew so greatly varied that its forms, decorations, and textures can actually be used by the archeologist, along with early tools and weapons, to distinguish between different cultures.

The second phase of the pottery story started with the introduction of the potter's wheel. This device enabled the potter to make more symmetrical and more original forms. It gave him better means of controlling the thickness of his pots and urns. There seems no end to the forms that the potter now created, yet they can be arranged in series and types which give us some lead as to the spread and course of migrations. In some regions, as in Northwestern Europe, the potter's wheel did not penetrate until about 500 B.C.

Here again we have an example of an art that left its stamp on religious and philosophical beliefs. Just as the new agriculture and its cycle of vegetation gave rise to many religions that worshipped a god of vegetation who dies and is reborn, so there are many allusions to the potter's craft in every religion; thus man is compared to the brittle pot, or the god is credited with having shaped man from clay.

Working Stone

IT WAS also in the New Stone Age that man began to polish stone. No longer was he limited to the use of wood, horn, or flint for his tools. He could now collect hard stones such as granite and diorite and shape them by patient grinding with sand. This meant that he was no longer dependent on the planes of fracture of flint but could develop new stone tools in shapes more appropriate for his purpose. Hence we see definite forms like the pick, the axe, and the sickle being shaped from hard stones. On the other hand, flint was not entirely abandoned as a material for tools; actually the manufacture of flint articles was perfected and transformed into a real art. Beautiful miniature tools and weapons made of flint are found very frequently in certain types of graves of the New Stone Age period.

It is interesting to note that modern research has found that the cutting edges and shapes of tools, as far as the intrinsic design is concerned, resemble rather closely those of our modern tools. Thus the archeologist has a better means of distinguishing the use to which these tools were put. It also permits us to conclude, for example, that certain tools were used by carpenters and therefore that the origin of carpentry dates back to about this period.

The new methods of stoneworking were important for the creation of yet another art, that of the seal cutter. Seals were very useful in antiquity, serving as a means of labeling private property and of authenticating official documents. At a very early date beautifully cut seals appear in graves and excavations. We also have many impressions of these seals on clay tablets or stoppers. In Mesopotamia these seals took the form of engraved cylinders with a hole drilled through the center so that they could be worn or carried on a cord or ring. In Egypt the cylinder seal was superseded at an early date by the signet type that we know today, which in Egypt often took the form of the sacred beetle or scarab.

Another stonecutting craft was the carving and engraving of stone vases and pots of most intricate design. Beautiful examples of these, often executed in translucent stones such as alabaster, can be seen in many of our museums today. It was an art that flourished in Egypt, where natural stone was abundant in the valleys reaching from the Nile to the desert. In Mesopotamia, where such materials had to be imported from the mountain regions which were often in enemy hands, sculpture and stonecutting, except for seal cutting, was never a very thriving art.

The new methods of handling natural stone had stimulating effects in two other directions; they developed the art of mining and contributed to the rise of architecture.

The earliest forms of mining go back to the Old Stone Age. Flint, though fairly abundant on earth, is usually found in nodules concentrated in certain geological formations. Hence flint mining took certain industrial forms at a very early date. In the several centers of Stone Age flint mining that have been discovered, the flint pits have yielded many remains of the crude lamps, horn picks, and even the bones of the miners themselves who had been buried alive when a pit collapsed.

New Stone Age man not only mined many types of natural stone for tools or building, as well as precious and semiprecious stones for ornament or good-luck charms, but also began to develop the primitive pits into extensive mines not unlike those that are dug today. Galleries were driven into the strata of ores and a whole system of corridors was developed within the mine. Exhausted galleries were filled with rubble, and the method of leaving pillars of natural stone to support the roof of the mine began to be employed. Special shafts were now built for ventilation. The earliest mining tools were made of horn and stone, but as the metallurgy of copper and bronze progressed, more adequate tools were created, very often on the spot in mining camps and ore-dressing shops.

Water was one factor that set a limit to early mining. It was still impossible to get rid of subsoil water efficiently. Even the Romans much later could solve the problem only in a rather cumbersome fashion by building a series of water wheels, mostly driven by slaves, which raised the water out of a mine in stages of about twelve feet each. In most cases it was impossible to work under the subsoil water level, and ancient mines seldom were carried below a hundred feet. With the limited demand for ores and minerals in early times, this depth was entirely adequate. There were still plenty of outcroppings and surface pockets of ores and stones to be worked in the Near East; these did not become exhausted until Roman times. It was only when these supplies failed that man was forced to go far underground when he wanted to obtain ores or precious stones.

Apart from the flint and flintlike materials that were used for tools, prehistoric man mined precious and semiprecious stones, which were traded over considerable distances. One of the oldest minerals used for beads and amulets was amber. This was later followed by jade, agate, turquoise, malachite, lazurite, jasper, lapis lazuli, and many other gem materials. Lapis lazuli, then very much in demand in Egypt, was obtained largely from the Afghanistan area. Amber came down from the coasts of the Baltic and the North Sea to the shores of the Mediterranean. Certain shells of the Red Sea coast traveled far into Europe, where they were greatly treasured.

Then as now it was widely believed that many of these stones had some particular power or "mana" that was imparted to the wearer. This belief in the magical potency of stones is one of the strongest forms of superstition in the world; it is still strongly held today. But the widespread use and trade of precious stones does not mean that man traveled over these relatively vast distances to procure them. They were mined locally and handed on by barter from tribe to tribe until they reached their final destination. Here, as in the case of early metallurgical objects, many finds can be recognized as wayside burials made by tradesmen or perhaps caches hidden when danger threatened. By their geographical relation these finds show us the routes along which prehistoric trade moved.

Metallurgy

AT THE end of prehistoric times two new branches of mining gained prominence—the mining of ores, and the science of metallurgy. Certain natural forms of metals were already well known. Copper, gold, silver, and meteoric iron occur in nature in the form of small deposits found near their ores. During the entire period of the New Stone Age small nuggets of these metals were collected and used as beads or amulets. As they could be shaped by cutting, grinding, and hammering, they were often fashioned into ornaments and trinkets. Of course, metalworking of this type is not true metallurgy, but merely the application of woodworking and stoneworking techniques to a material whose real properties were not yet recognized.

The first phase of true metallurgy began when it was realized that these glittering stones had some mysterious power—they could be deformed and fashioned with ease when they were heated in the fire. At higher temperatures they could even be melted and cast into some form or shape that was retained when the object had cooled. It was then that the smith was born, the skilled craftsman who knew the mysterious qualities of these special stones and could transform them into durable metal and forge them into tools and weapons. Metal objects now began to have more specific metal forms and no longer imitated stone or horn tools as they did in earlier times.

This period was followed fairly closely by a second phase in which another important discovery was made. It was observed that the metal nuggets were usually found near some of the well-known, brightly colored stones such as malachite, turquoise, and lapis lazuli, which were not only treasured as beads but also applied in the making of pottery glazes. It was probably a potter who discovered that these stones, when heated with charcoal at high temperatures, would yield a little molten metal that solidified on cooling to form the kind of nugget found in natural deposits. In the case of the three minerals mentioned above, copper nuggets would be produced.

Once this important connection between the brightly colored stones and the metals was grasped, the early smith, still unacquainted with any chemistry, had unconsciously hit on the relation between metals and their ores. We now know, of course, that ores are reduced by coke or charcoal when the carbon monoxide liberated from the hot coke combines with the oxides of the metal and thus frees the latter from the ore. This chemical reaction, discovered quite by accident before the dawn of history, is the basis of modern metallurgy. It made man independent of the scarce deposits of natural metals and delivered into his hands the large deposits of ores, surface veins, and pockets that were still abundant in antiquity though mostly exhausted by the end of the Roman Imperial period. This discovery was made before the beginnings of recorded history, as is proved from prehistoric finds of crucibles for molten metal and various metallurgical tools.

There is little chemistry involved in the production of gold, however. In principle, the metallurgist has only to crush the gold-bearing ore and concentrate the gold particles by washing, leaving the useless gangue or residue to be thrown away. The gold particles would be subjected to melting and cast into rings or bars for trading. This was, in effect, the scheme of gold metallurgy until well into historical times. Apart from a few districts in Asia Minor and other places in the Caucasus, the main supply of gold in antiquity came from the Egyptian deserts of Nubia, where the quarries and mines were worked from earliest times by slaves and captives under the supervision of the army. Often expeditions were sent out to prospect for gold; we even possess a map of such a temporary mining settlement of about 1500 B.C.

Once the principle of the production of metals from ores was known, the fire test was applied quite freely and at about the threshold of the historical period discoveries and advances in metallurgical technique came fairly rapidly. Silver, antimony, and lead were isolated from their ores; a thousand years later tin was added to the list. Silver and lead were usually produced from lead ores; the production of silver was concentrated in Asia Minor before richer mines near Athens and later in Spain were also discovered.

Analysis of early copper objects shows that the smiths apparently found that pure copper was too soft to serve as a substitute for stone. They soon began mixing the metals they obtained and experimented by melting copper with different ores. They learned that antimony or lead bronzes did not give a satisfactory material for tools and weapons, but that good results could be obtained by refining copper with tin ore.

It will be appreciated that ancient man, having no knowledge of chemistry, could recognize and collect ores and other materials only by paying great attention to their physical characteristics—their color, luster, hardness, weight, and resistance to corrosion by acid. (Vinegar was the only acid known in those days.) These properties are mentioned quite often in ancient Sumerian and Assyrian texts. However excellent such observation may have been, it was left the smith in the dark as to the percentage of tin and other metals that the ore contained. Consequently, when producing a bronze from tin ore and copper, he would get a bronze containing from 7 to 12 per cent of tin and be quite satisfied with the result. We know today that the smith should aim more closely at a 10 per cent bronze to get a good alloy suitable for tools and weapons. Now this was not a serious defect in ancient metallurgy, for there was still little specialization of tools calling for accurate dosing of ingredients in alloys. Such varying compositions could be tolerated by the early smith.

The making of alloys spread quickly in early historical times. Bronze Age metallurgy is characterized by tools and weapons fashioned mainly from bronze; casting and forging dominate in this period. The average composition of an alloy, however, was more important than its subsequent treatment, as the composition determined the particular application of the metal produced. As time went on, more alloys became known that were particularly fitted for special applications such as the casting of bells, metallic mirrors, and the like. For example, alloys might be suitable for polished mirrors whereas they might be too brittle for other uses. Gradually the composition of the alloys could be determined more exactly. This was particularly the case when bronze was produced from copper and imported tin after the tin-ore resources of the Near East started to dwindle appreciably (after 2000 B.C.). By the end of the Bronze Age, therefore, the art of alloy production had been perfected and proper composition could be adhered to much more precisely, even though the range of alloys was greatly extended.

These metallurgical discoveries in predynastic times had important social implications. We have good reason to believe that the smith was the earliest professional craftsman in history. All during the Stone Age the different crafts had been practiced by the peasants or hunters in their spare time. Spinning and weaving cloth, making shoes, building houses, and other similar tasks were functions men handled in addition to the normal tending of flocks or plowing of fields. Now the new agriculture produced an excess yield that could feed craftsmen who were not herdsmen or farmers themselves. To be a smith meant that one had to spend one's entire day at this work. The smith, as well as other craftsmen and specialists, had to exchange the result of his highly specialized work for the food that the farmer and husbandman produced.

The early smith dug the ores and produced the metal tools from these ores. But soon the mining of ores became a separate job. Even treating the metal, however, became too intricate a process, and during the Bronze Age three different types of smiths emerged. First there was the metallurgist who produced the crude metal and cast it into bars or cakes to be sold. Then there was the blacksmith, who mass-produced objects of bronze from the crude metal. Finally there were the smiths, who repaired damaged metal objects or who specialized in the art of working gold and silver.

In the field of metallurgy we observe the great impression made on the primitive mind by this mystery of "turning stones into metal." The smith was held in awe both by the peasants and by the pastoral people, the latter treating him also with the distrust they always had for sedentary folk. Because of his mysterious craft the smith was often believed to have magical powers. He was consulted as a wise man who knew more about the hidden forces of nature than the chiefs and rulers did. Curious legends and beliefs grew up around the person of the smith, his tools, and even the metals he forged. His patron was the god of the volcanic fires, typified by such mythological deities as Hephaestus and Vulcan. Stories of supersmiths like Wayland of Teutonic mythology are common in many countries. Perhaps one of the most beautiful is the story of the smith Ilmarinen in the Finnish epic *Kalevala*, which describes the creation of iron and the forging of a magical steel weapon.

The Wheel

PROBABLY the most important single invention of predynastic times was the wheel. In transporting loads man had used sledges and trunks of trees or logs. But technologically it is quite a step from a rolling cylinder to an axle with a wheel attached to either end. In some regions, such as Wales, there are still survivals of early means of transport that combine the idea of a sledge made of two poles with the use of a pair of wheels. However, the actual links between these and the earliest wagon are still a matter of debate. In the first wagons the wheels formed a solid piece with the axle, which turned under the body of the cart. It took a long time for man to discover how to fasten the wheels independently to an axle so that the latter could then remain fixed and only the wheels would turn.

The first wheels were solid disks made of heavy rough-hewn planks fastened together and cut to form approximately a circle. The earliest wagons as we see them on Egyptian and Mesopotamian pictures were clumsy four-wheeled vehicles. Their use was limited, as water transport still prevailed. They served as war chariots to carry warriors to the battlefield, where they were not used in actual combat. These early wagons also served for transporting merchandise, but only to a limited extent, as good roads were not as yet available and donkeys and mules were far easier to handle on such rude tracks and paths as existed. Traveling by cart was never very common in antiquity. Until far into Roman times it must

34

have been rather uncomfortable, inasmuch as the carts had no springs and the roads were pitted with holes and ruts. Moreover, riding in carts was long considered an unmanly form of travel, fit only for women, children, the sick and the old, and scorned by any man who could still ride his horse or mule.

Gradually the spoked wheel was developed, and with the introduction of the horse into the Near East by the nomads of the Northern steppes (about 2000 B.C.) came the more graceful two-wheeled war chariot. These horse-drawn chariots figure largely in the warlike times around 1500 B.C. The Hittites of Asia Minor owed their military successes for the most part to these "tanks of antiquity," which could make a very effective and devastating charge on the enemy. Splendid pictures of these war chariots can still be seen on the walls of the Egyptian and Assyrian temples.

In this period the horse came into use in the Near East, where this strange animal had formerly been referred to as "the ass of the mountains." The camel, though known earlier to the desert nomads and sometimes mentioned by Egyptians and Assyrians, was not used as a riding animal or beast of burden by the latter people before the Persian Empire had been extended to include the greater part of the ancient Near East and thereby had made the crossing of the Syrian desert possible for trade caravans. It is also strange to find that the horse, for centuries after its introduction, was used only to pull chariots, for it was not until much later that the art of horseback riding was developed. But communication and transportation suffered from the lack of good roads, so that the use of the wheel for vehicles was only minor.

The most important application of the wheel was in the manufacture of pottery. The potter's wheel was one of the earliest forms of machinery based on the principle of the wheel.

In irrigation the wheel in the form of the water wheel had begun to play a large part. In these early machines the power to move the wheel could be derived from the flowing river, which could be made to turn the wheel and lift small amounts of water scooped up in pots or wooden buckets built into the rim of the wheel itself. This water would then be emptied at the top of the wheel into a drain leading to the field to be irrigated. A wheel with spikes attached to the rim could be used with advantage in combination with other such wheels to translate a vertical rotation into a horizontal one. This principle is basic to the operation of gears and all geared machinery. It could be applied if water wheels were to be driven by man or animal instead of by water.

Apart from these basic cogwheels and toothed wheels, another important development sprang from the wheel. This was the lathe, which is essentially a wheel with a horizontal axis. The lathe was of great significance in the development of woodworking and metalworking machinery, making it possible for the first of these arts to attain early perfection. However, many centuries had to elapse before metal tools were sufficiently improved so that they could be applied to the lathe. In fact it was not until 1800 that the first good lathes were developed in England for the manufacture of metal machine parts.

Communication

THE ship is another predynastic invention worth discussing, for shipbuilding had a far-reaching effect on the art of woodworking and toolmaking. We know that several basic types of rafts, canoes, and dugouts were invented in different parts of the world. But further progress depended on the materials available to the different regions interested in ships and water traffic.

In Egypt, for example, where primitive types of canoes were developed from bundles of reeds as basic elements, there was a lack of good timber for the construction of larger ships. The local trees, such as acacias, did not produce planks of more than a few feet in length. Accordingly we find that the Egyptians developed trade relations with northern Syria at an early date by coasting close to shore in order to obtain the valuable cedars of Lebanon. Yet the Egyptians failed to become a great seafaring nation.

In Mesopotamia, on the other hand, dugout canoes, rafts, and wickerwork baskets covered with hides or mastic asphalt formed the river craft, and the mountain ranges produced sufficient timber for the construction of seagoing vessels. From prehistoric vases found in Egypt it is clear that these Mesopotamian ships succeeded in rounding Arabia and reaching the Red Sea coast of Egypt. The sail had already been developed, and oars served as rudders.

Both sailing ships and ships moved by oars, for which slaves and prisoners were available, formed the basis of the fleets which from prehistoric times onward visited the shores of the Mediterranean and other waters of importance to antiquity. Most of this shipping was coasting, and even moderate winds and storms constituted a serious hazard for these early sailors, who avoided losing sight of the coast and safe anchorage. Nevertheless even this limited form of navigation meant a great expansion of contacts and a swift means of spreading trade and information.

Writing and writing materials were perhaps the most significant of all the inventions of the predynastic period. The papyri covered with hieroglyphs and the clay tablets inscribed with cuneiform or wedge-shaped characters allow us to penetrate the mind of the ancient world and to study the ideas and inventions of its technologists and engineers. With the development of writing it became possible to teach and to record the growing accumulation of knowledge, particularly in such vital fields as history, mathematics, and civil engineering. The details of the evolution of writing are beyond the scope of this book, but the technique of the production of writing materials is a logical part of our story.

The raw material of clay tablets abounded in the plains of Mesopotamia. The only thing that remained to be done was a preliminary washing of the clay and a final baking of the tablets after the cuneiform had been incised. Such documents were practically indestructible, even when buried in the ruins of ancient towns for thousands of years. Other materials like wooden tablets, parchment, and leather have for the most part perished, except where the climatological conditions have been particularly favorable. These materials did survive in the dry desert sands of Egypt.

The ancient Egyptian, however, wrote mostly on papyrus. He extracted the marrow of the papyrus stalk and cut it into thin strips. These strips were then placed side by side and a second layer was superposed crosswise. These two layers were then glued together, the bond between them being made more permanent by gentle beating with wooden mallets. Sheets of papyrus 10 inches long by 7½ inches wide were made for letters and brief reports, while longer rolls measuring about 32 inches in length were produced for documents and books by joining together a series of sheets. The production of papyrus was the monopoly of Egypt throughout antiquity.

A strong competitor of papyrus was parchment, which was produced from the skins of donkeys, pigs, and even gazelles and deer, by washing, removing the hair, stretching, drying, and smoothing out the surface of the skin with pumice stone and chalk. Better-quality parchment was made from the skins of calves, sheep, and goats. Though much older, this product derives its name from the town of Pergamon in Asia Minor, the center of parchment manufacture in classical times. Parchment was available in sheets and rolls and could be used on both sides, whereas papyrus could properly be used only on the side where the strips of marrow lay horizontally. This was called by the Romans the "recto" side, as distinguished from the "verso." These terms still survive in our modern paper and book trade.

Other materials for short missives and school exercises were shards and wooden tablets with waxed surfaces from which the writing could be erased after the lesson. Two such wooden tablets joined by hinges were called a "diploma" (Greek, "folded paper") and were used for the permits issued to private travelers using the state postal and coach services in Roman times.

I I I

THE GREAT EMPIRES OF THE

ANCIENT NEAR EAST

(3000–600 B.C.)

AFTER 3000 B.C. the papyri and clay tablets, the leather rolls and pottery shards, and the inscriptions on monuments and temples allow us direct contact with ancient civilizations. A wealth of historical and religious documents, contracts, laws, registers, and bookkeeping records are now available, and many more await publication and translation. They show us the great social effects of the discoveries and inventions of predynastic times. They reveal the basic structure of the early empires of Egypt, Mesopotamia, and the Indus valley as they emerge from the mists of prehistory.

These early empires are typical urban civilizations. From the mass of villages of the early peasant civilization in the river valleys, towns crystallized as centers to harbor the new classes of craftsmen, scribes, and merchants, soldiers and sailors, public servants and officials who ran the state. Inroads of nomad warriors during the Late Stone Age not only introduced war as an activity of the state, but in certain cases these warriors conquered the new states and settled in their main cities as permanent rulers. In their wake a new class emerged, that of the slaves, usually war captives bound to the harshest forms of labor in mines, quarries, and fields.

39

The cities harbored the new classes whose food came from the surplus that the great mass of farmers produced. In these cities the crafts and sciences were concentrated. They were based on the advances in the fields of geology, chemistry, natural history, astronomy, agriculture, mechanics, metallurgy, and architecture that had been achieved in earlier periods.

The structures of these new empires differed widely. In Mesopotamia we find an agglomeration of small city-states, each concentrated in a major town. The chief priest of the temple ruled this parcel of the land as the steward of the god who was supposed to be the creator and owner. The organization of the city-state seems to have been a kind of state communism. The products of farms and crafts were brought to the temple where they were registered and stored. The temple issued food and raw materials to the citizens, farmers, and craftsmen.

In Egypt the power was concentrated in the hands of the king, who himself was a god and who administered Upper and Lower Egypt through two separate organizations of officials.

Science and the Craftsmen

As SPECIALIZATION increased, most of the craftsmen of antiquity began to be organized into guilds. The greater part of these guilds were closely associated with the temples or were in some way directed by the state. The "overseers" of the guilds were often of priestly rank. They were scribes who had mastered the mysteries of language and writing. But this does not mean that they were priests in our modern sense of the word, for most officials and noblemen who were believed to have mastered some special field of knowledge had such priestly rank. They might have been educated in the temple schools which, as was later true in the Middle Ages, were then the centers of education. In ancient Assyria the guilds were often headed by an official, usually someone of high rank, who bore a title that meant "one who gives instructions." This and other evidence proves that the crafts through their leaders were in touch with the science of the day.

Science in the period under consideration (3000–600 B.C.)

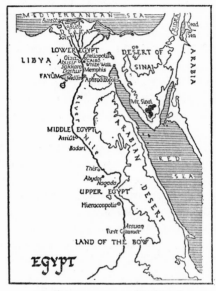

Map of Egypt in ancient times.

had a completely different structure from the science of to-day. We moderns, having collected and analyzed all the relevant data, synthesize these into our scheme of nature. This synthesis then provides us with the means of using nature for our own purposes. Antiquity, especially during the pre-Hellenic period, knew nothing of such procedures. For ancient man there was no clear-cut distinction between the separate fields of religion, philosophy, or science. All these aspects of the world were molded into one encompassing scheme of thought. Ancient man had not yet learned to think in terms of abstract principles and had no concept of the inner meaning of individual phenomena. Such "divine curiosity about the essence of things," as the Greek natural philosophers expressed it, did not yet exist.

41

The educated man of the ancient world had a firm belief that everything in the universe had been created "in the beginning" by the gods. The cosmic order as originally established by the gods existed as a stable scheme from the beginning of time. He had no desire to inquire why or how the observed phenomena of nature worked. He knew that everything had its assigned place in a world that had been molded by the gods on the Day of Creation. He had only to find the place in this cosmic order of anything he was confronted with. Naming a thing meant knowing its place in the cosmos, or putting it in the "net of the world," as the Egyptians expressed it. No further logical reasoning was required. Naming a thing was the same as recognizing its magical links and potencies in the cosmos. Magic, not logic, governed the natural phenomena.

We need not outline these ancient scientific views in detail. The practical result was that though the learned leaders of the guilds did use the observations of the craftsmen, their theories were of no use to the development of the crafts. The ancient scientific leaders were considered an absolute necessity only because they had to put the finishing touches to the work of the craftsmen. For example, when the sculptor, whom the ancient Egyptians picturesquely called "he who makes alive," had finished his stone or wooden statue, it was not fit to serve in the temple or tomb until the priestly overseer of the guild of sculptors had applied the rite of the "opening of the mouth" to it to give it the magical power of housing the soul of the dead man it represented.

Hence the observations of the technologists were embodied in the ancient philosophy of life, but not a single natural phenomenon served to guide scientific theory directly. Today research is considered to be the lifeblood of technology and industry, neither of which can thrive on rules deduced from trial and error alone. This lack of theoretical background explains why, after the astonishing strides made in the latter part of the New Stone Age, so little progress was made in ancient technology. What progress there was emerged very slowly. Technology, unsupported by science, had to go the long way of experience. The very practical technology and engineering of those days seems to have had no connection with the magical philosophy of life which permeated antiquity. The bond is hidden because the connection is one-sided. By imperceptible degrees this magical world became a logical one. Gradually certain aspects of nature became the subject of scientific speculation without interference from philosophical or religious dogmas. Eventually a real natural science arose that could guide and help clever practical engineers and craftsmen.

We know that science was organized even in preclassical times. Both Egypt and Mesopotamia had groupings of learned men—we might call them scientific societies today—that possessed libraries and collected all the scientific observations. These societies advised the kings and priests on problems that were both practical (the construction of temples, for example) and religious or philosophical (the correct date of religious festivals, the calendar, ceremonial, and the interpretation of dreams). As centers of scientific research in the modern sense of the word, however, they remained completely barren.

The Earliest Architects

WE RIGHTLY admire the very practical achievements of the early technologists and engineers. Their huge pyramids and temples still fill us with admiration for the men who planned and carried through these astonishing technical feats. Slave power alone did not account for these structures. Technical skill and organization were required as well. It is certain that structural drawings of the pyramids existed. The stone of these huge graves was quarried on the side of the Nile opposite the building site. The blocks were cut to the correct size and marked with the name of the gang of quarrymen, the date, and the place where they were to be fitted into the pyramid.

No less than 2,300,000 blocks of limestone were used in erecting the Great Pyramid, which was designed as the tomb-monument for King Khufu or Cheops in the 29th century B.C. Many more blocks and slabs of granite and other casing stones were imported from quarries in the south of Egypt by floating them down the Nile on rafts. The pyramid covers an area of thirteen acres, and the sides at the base are 756 feet long. Herodotus, the Father of History, tells us that an army of 100,000 workmen worked on this project for twenty years, and his account is believed to be substantially accurate. The workmen were not all slaves, as is popularly believed, but mostly craftsmen and farmers, the latter working on the job in payment of taxes during the season of the inundation, when agricultural work was impossible anyway. One third of this large number of workers were busy erecting the body of the pyramid, another third quarried and transported the stones and other materials required, and the rest were needed to supply food and to build sheds and sleeping quarters for the laborers. An ancient Egyptian title of those days can be translated only by our modern word "organizer." Surely the organizers of those days knew their job, for even today the handling of such a great mass of people is no simple feat.

This high architectural skill was the achievement of only a few generations; the Great Pyramid was built only about 150 years after the very first stone building had been erected. In predynastic times, natural stone was first employed in lining graves and making floors of important buildings. The art of quarrying was perfected. The old "fire and water" method of disintegrating rocks was superseded by careful drilling of holes and the use of copper wedges and copper saws, aided by emery or sand, to produce blocks and slabs of natural stone. Great stone slabs and obelisks still partly attached to the living rock show how daring the Egyptian engineers were. Egypt was particularly fortunate in having many quarries of all kinds of natural stone suitable for building and decoration.

In Mesopotamia this art was never properly developed. There we find bricks as the principal building material. These bricks, of a type also used in Egypt, were formed from the clay abundantly available in the river valleys. This clay was sometimes reinforced by mixing it with chopped straw and reeds. The shaped bricks were then dried in the heat of the sun. As fuel was scarce in the ancient Near East, and only such inferior fuel as straw, dung, and brushwood was available, the use of burnt bricks was restricted to important buildings like temples, palaces, and graves.

Egyptian stone cutters dressing blocks (above) *and workmen making sun-dried bricks* (below). (*From wall paintings in the tome of Rekhmara at Thebes, XVIIIth Dynasty, 1533–1450 B.C.* Metropolitan Museum of Art.)

Architecture in natural stone was an Egyptian achievement. The oldest surviving building of stone masonry in the world is the "step" pyramid of Sakkarah. During the excavations of the stores and temples within the wall enclosing this pyramid, which was erected for the Pharaoh Zoser (about 2940 B.C.), it was found that his prime minister, Imhotep, was the architect and builder of this first example of natural-stone architecture.

The earlier buildings in this area show a peculiar technique. With the experience gained in building with timber, bundles of reeds, and bricks, Imhotep tried a more permanent material. He had large-size bricks quarried from the natural stone, and after assembling them into crude shapes like walls and pillars, had them cut to look like the older wooden ceilings and pillars of reed bundles, or shaped to give the impression of an opened wooden gate. During these experiments he gradually conceived the idea of assembling smaller stone bricks and slabs so that the resulting architectural forms were no longer an imitation of older structures made of wood or other materials. In some cases he preshaped the stone bricks or slabs to build up stone pillars according to the method that has been used ever since.

We have here a complex of structures which were more or less the experimental field of a builder who was trying to find the proper forms inherent in a new material, natural stone. And so developed the purely Doric columns and other forms which we had always believed to be original Greek inventions. In this complex of buildings we find the experimental series that served to teach the great pyramid builders of generations to follow, who learned to appreciate the forms that were more natural to this new building material. We need not wonder that Imhotep was revered in Egyptian tradition as one of the wisest men of their early days. About 2,000 years after his death he was apotheosized as a god of medicine, a profession that he probably never practiced—at least his original titles do not indicate that he did.

Aqueducts and Canals

IN THE field of engineering this period did not bring many important new inventions except the aqueduct. However, this does not mean that nothing spectacular was done in irrigation and canal building. Irrigation was very much the principal interest of the governments both in Egypt and in

Mesopotamia. But the system used in each country was different.

In Egypt the rise of the Nile occurs in the right season for the farmer, from August until early October. Hence he has time to sow winter or spring crops after working the fields. The system adopted in ancient Egypt was basin irrigation. In each of the irrigation areas built up by cooperative labor, the dikes were cut at the proper moment as determined by the rise of the Nile. The water was conducted over the total area and given time to precipitate its enriching silt. Then the necessary cuts were made in the dikes downstream and the water left to flow back into the river. The Nile has an adequate amount of silt for the fields, but not so much that canals will silt up too quickly. Nature made it easy for the Egyptians. Hapi, the god of the Nile, was a friendly deity.

The situation in Mesopotamia was quite different. Here the sudden, irregular rise of the Euphrates and Tigris rivers came between April and June, and the rivers carried a fivefold amount of silt compared to that of the Nile. The waters came too late for the winter crops and too early for the spring crops. The inhabitants of these plains had to store this water in special basins, but this enabled them, on the other hand, to water their fields at will. This so-called perennial irrigation system required an immense amount of labor, but it allowed the ancient Babylonians to harvest three crops every two years. The gods of the floods were often destructive, and had to be propitiated. The bountiful harvests of Mesopotamia have frequently attracted the attention of classical authors. It is logical therefore to find Mesopotamian city-despots frequently boasting about the canals they dug or put in order again by removing the accumulated silt.

The "steward" of Lagash, Entemanna, built the Shatt-el-Hai, which conducted the waters of the high-level Tigris through the plains to the lower Euphrates at Ur. Another canal took off from the Tigris near Samarra and was led through an aqueduct over the river Diyalah to the regions north of the Tigris. The Hindia barrage or dam restored by

47

Alexander the Great was much older and had impounded the waters of the Euphrates so that they could be distributed through the area around Babylon. The existence of so many small city-states without a strong central government did not promote extreme efficiency of irrigation in these valleys. We also hear of ancient bankers speculating in canal building and in the sale of irrigated fields. But the general scheme remained in good order until the Mongols in their destructive wars of the thirteenth century A.D. depopulated these lands, whereupon the irrigation system fell to ruin through sheer neglect.

The Egyptians were not content with the basin irrigation system they had built up and therefore they extended it considerably. About 2000 B.C. a series of strong kings, the so-called Twelfth Dynasty—notably King Amenemhet III—extended the branch of the Nile called Bahr-el Jusef (Joseph's Canal) until it reached the desert depression called the Fayyum. At the entrance to this oasis Amenemhet built a large dam. Thus he not only led the rich silt of the Nile into this new province, which has flourished ever since, but he also introduced perennial irrigation in a part of Egypt, for the Fayyum could be used as a storage basin and its waters could be led back into the basin system of the valley at will. This system demanded proper and constant care. During subsequent periods of Egyptian history it was neglected and had to be restored by succeeding generations, but it still was widely used until late Roman times, when neglect caused its complete breakdown and the resultant evaporation of Lake Fayyum.

The ancient Egyptians were great builders of canals. At Elephantine, shipping was hindered by the first cataract of the Nile. Here, about 1875 B.C., King Sesostris built a canal 260 feet long, 35 feet wide, and 26 feet deep, to provide his ships with a means of avoiding the dangerous natural course of the Nile. The Greek Ptolemies reigned in Egypt during the last three centuries B.C., and documents on civil engineering jobs dating from this period are quite detailed. We read about

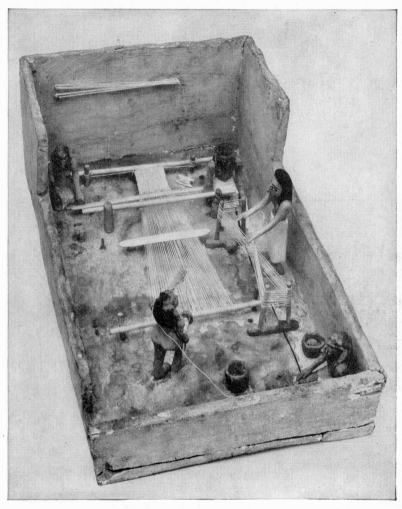

PLATE I   Model of Egyptian spinning and weaving, found in the tomb of Nehen Kwetre at Thebes. (*Metropolitan Museum of Art.*)

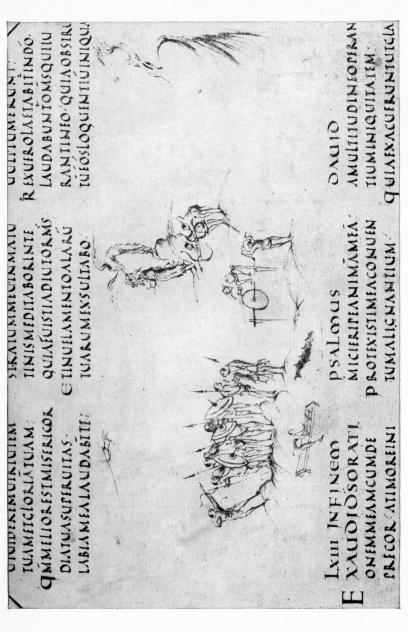

PLATE 2 Part of a page from the Utrecht Psalter, about A.D. 850, showing (*center*) sketch of grinding stone worked by a crank. (*By permission of the Utrecht University*

the construction of dikes and their foundations, and about the use of reeds, mats, and stones to protect them.

It seems that the irrigation units of those days were about 100 acres, which is one tenth of the present unit. On the other hand, we have contracts for the reclamation of 7,000 acres for the state Secretary of Finance, Apollonius (260 B.C.). The architect Cleon had to build 50 miles of dikes! We also hear of the contractors, who in a series of eight contracts had to move over 10 million cubic feet of earth; another contract mentions 1.7 million cubic feet that had to be moved. These contracts show that part of the fee was prepaid and that tools were furnished by the state. Even labor was often put at the disposal of the contractors when there were plenty of state slaves.

Another important engineering feat of the Egyptians was the canal connecting the Mediterranean and the Red Sea. This forerunner of the modern Suez Canal was used for over a thousand years. The Egyptians never were great sailors. Their trade with Arabia and Somaliland consisted of shipping their merchandise along the coast to Myos Hormos, a point about halfway along the Red Sea, where the trade route went overland through the valley of Hammamat to Coptos on the Nile. They avoided the northern part of the Red Sea, where there were many shoals and treacherous winds. The canal that was constructed consisted of two parts. The west-east stretch was a canal running from Bubastis on the eastern branch of the Nile delta through the Tumilat depression to Lake Timsah. It was really an irrigation canal which watered what in ancient times was the valley of Goshen—the region that harbored the Israelites when they lived in Egypt.

The second part of the canal ran north and south from Lake Timsah through the so-called Bitter Lakes to a point just north of the present Suez Canal. The total length was slightly less than 100 miles.

We have sound reasons for believing that this canal was constructed by the same kings who incorporated the Fayyum into their irrigation system. It certainly existed in the later period of Egyptian history when King Necho II (600 B.C.) sent an expedition to circumnavigate Africa. The Persian king, Darius, had the canal desilted so that it would serve his policy of creating sea trade between Egypt, India, and Persia. It was then about 200 feet wide and 40 feet deep. According to the memorial tablets erected by him along this canal, he had a fleet of 24 ships sailing through it to Persia. Alexander the Great and certain Roman emperors are known to have deepened and used it, but it was neglected after the fourth century A.D. and silted up completely.

The aqueduct, so important in water supply, was a Persian invention. From time immemorial the plains of Persia were irrigated by water drawn from the foothills of the mountain ranges. "Qanats" or tunnels were dug into these hills and the tapped water led through drains to the fields. Such tunnels were fairly common in the ancient Near East.

Jerusalem had an important water supply of this kind which played a part in the Old Testament story of the Pool of Shiloah; so had Megiddo. These achievements of mining and architecture set an example for the earliest dated Assyrian aqueduct. It was built about 700 B.C. and led the waters of a mountain river impounded by a barrage at Bavian through a 70-foot drain to Nineveh, 20 miles south. There the waters were used to irrigate the palace gardens and fields of the kings of Assyria. This huge structure in the first of a series of ingenious aqueducts built mainly by Greeks and Romans. The first of these to be constructed at Megara and on the island of Samos date about 100 years later.

It is interesting to note that the great works of the engineers find their expression in early mathematics. The achievements of Egyptians and more particularly Sumerians and Assyrians in mathematics and astronomy were closely linked with practical engineering. We have no theoretical discussion of any mathematical problem but only a series of practical solutions for certain typical problems. They deal with the areas of fields, the slopes of pyramids, the quantity of stone needed for a cylindrical well, masses of earth to be removed in canal building, and similar practical problems. Even astronomy was primarily used to predict the rise of the rivers.

Glass and Textiles

ACCORDING to a widespread but now discredited story, glass-making was discovered by Phoenician merchants who sailed with a cargo of crude soda and were shipwrecked near Mount Carmel. They made a fire on the sandy beach to cook their food, supporting their pots on lumps of soda. Some of the latter, it is alleged, fused with the sand, and the merchants were surprised to find a new material, glass, mixed with the embers of the fire.

This legend is certainly not based on fact. Both the Egyptians and the inhabitants of Mesopotamia knew how to make glazes and types of glass in late prehistoric times. The early glass objects from Egypt were manufactured by modeling clay or earth around a wooden or metal rod whose diameter corresponded with the intended opening of the glass vessel. Powdered glass material mixed with some adhesive medium was then applied to the surface of the clay core with a spatula and the whole was then dipped in molten glass. On being removed from the furnace the glass vessel was cooled, the core removed, and the clay scraped out. This and similar techniques of building up small vessels by arranging threads of colored glass on a clay core were suitable only for the manufacture of small glass jars and vials to hold salves, unguents, and perfumes or for the manufacture of beads and ornaments. Such luxury goods were made in Egypt (Alexandria of Ptolemaic times) and in Syria.

In Mesopotamia most of the glass made was used in the form of beads or glazes for pottery, but here a high degree of specialization was achieved. The oldest glassmaking texts date back to 2200 B.C. In these texts a kind of alchemical language employing symbolic terms is used to cover the trade secrets they transmit. Later Assyrian texts, however, are quite straightforward and prove that the manufacture of glass was well understood. A kind of neutral glass was first produced, then coloring agents were added to the smelt to form the final product. The Assyrians manufactured a large range of colored glasses and were even able to produce a purple glass containing colloidal gold, called "purple of Cassius." They used cobalt salts in their blue glazes, whereas the Egyptians used salts of copper.

Until the invention of glass blowing in Syria in the first century B.C., the technique of manufacturing glass objects was limited to those adaptable to the ancient molding techniques. This barred the general acceptance of glass vessels as receptacles competing with pottery. By the invention of glass blowing, whereby the workman dipped a blowpipe in molten glass and inflated a blob of it at one end of the pipe by blowing, new and larger shapes could be made, ranging from globular to long cylindrical vases. These could be ornamented by engraving, decorated with ductile glass threads or colored blobs of glass, and even shaped with a spatula while hot. The Hellenistic Alexandrians and Syrians also learned to blow glass in molds and were able in this way to achieve glass decoration in relief, though the patterns could not be too intricate. Apart from this amplification of artistic possibilities, the glassmakers were able to anneal glass—that is, to heat it at moderate temperatures after blowing and shaping in order to relieve any strains in the glass and thus render it less brittle.

During the Roman Empire period, Syrian and Jewish glassmakers founded glass factories all over Europe, in Gaul, along the Rhine, and even in Britain. With the fall of the Empire most of the artisans remained concentrated in Syria and Byzantium.

Though the principles of textile manufacture had been discovered in prehistoric times, some minor improvements in the application of mordants, bleaching, and dyeing are of later date. Egypt remained for many centuries the home of the finest linen. Mesopotamia produced famous woolen materials. From India came cotton, which the Assyrians called "tree wool" (compare the German word *Baumwolle*). Here again Syria took over the production of luxury goods made from imported raw materials. This tendency is more or less connected with the seafaring genius of the Phoenicians and with the poor natural resources of their country. Being in contact with the entire civilized world of their day, and living at the terminus of important trade routes, the Phoenicians soon made a flourishing industry of luxury goods such as metal and glass jewelry and trinkets, vessels, ivories, and other products of applied art, though the style was often but a crude imitation of Egyptian and Mesopotamian art. Their coast yielded the mussel "murex" from which the Tyrian purple dye was extracted. This rare and expensive dye was soon imitated but was never equalled.

The Coming of Iron

FAR more important, however, were the new advances in the field of metallurgy, notably the manufacture of iron. Though meteoric iron had long been known and used, this natural alloy of nickel and iron did not lead men directly to the abundant iron ores. Nothing pointed to the fact that the very common red and brown ores contained a metal. Iron metallurgy would not have been easy for a Bronze Age metallurgist. He was accustomed to heating his bright-colored ores with charcoal to obtain a stream of molten red copper from his furnace. Chemically speaking, it is easier to separate iron from iron ore than copper from copper ore. But iron has a considerably higher melting point than copper, so that in the primitive furnaces of the Bronze Age the copper separated from the ore could remain in the molten state, collecting in the lower part of the furnace where it could be tapped off. In the case of iron, however, the little drops of pure metal that were formed from iron ore would solidify at the low temperatures reached in these primitive furnaces and would remain dispersed in a spongy mass of slag.

Accordingly, if the Bronze Age smith had tried to treat

iron ores, he would have obtained only a fusion of the flux (limestone) and charcoal with the impurities of the iron ore and pellets of free metal, and this slag he would in all probability have considered useless. He did sometimes obtain small pieces of iron when refining gold in crucibles, and he fashioned these pellets into amulets and beads. But it took much experimenting to discover that the spongy mass or "bloom," when heated in a fire and hammered, would lose its slag particles and that with continued hammering the particles of metal could be beaten together to form wrought iron. Fairly pure wrought iron, however, has no distinct advantages over bronze; it is more malleable but less hard. The early smiths were unable to cast it and could only shape it by hammering it at red heat. Though man had learned the secret of making wrought iron as early as 2500 B.C., for more than a thousand years it remained a freak metal only, hard to make and of no particular use.

The secret had spread even into prehistoric Europe before a proper solution was found in 1400 B.C., probably in the Armenian mountains and the districts along the southeast corner of the Black Sea. Here dwelt the tribe of the Chalybes who according to Greek tradition gave their name to steel (Greek *chalybs*), and who were celebrated ironsmiths. They had discovered that wrought iron, reheated frequently in a charcoal fire and then hammered, would thereby become much harder than any bronze and would keep its hardness after long use. We now know that the reason for this change is that the iron absorbs charcoal particles on its surface, causing the latter to develop a steel structure. The new metal thus consists of a core of wrought iron enclosed in a shell of steel. This carburization or cementation suddenly transformed the freak metal into a most useful one.

However, the technique of producing this new metal involved an entirely different set of methods, tools, and processes from those used in copper and bronze metallurgy. Slagging the iron ore—that is, adding such ingredients as limestone and the like to liquify as much slag as possible in the furnace—

as well as handling of the bloom (the spongy mass obtained after smelting) were techniques to be learned. Moreover, adjusting the steel surface to the proper hardness required much skill.

Soon after the discovery of the cementation process it was found that very hard steel could be obtained by plunging the hot steel into cold water and thus freezing a structure that was stable only at high temperatures, a process now known as quenching. However, the steel thus formed was often very hard and brittle. In Roman times a further nicety was discovered. When reheated carefully at moderate temperatures, the quenched steel could be tempered or annealed, that is, it lost some of its hardness and brittleness and became tougher. By interplay of these techniques of cementing, quenching, and annealing, quite a variety of steels could be made to suit different applications. It is obvious, however, that slagging ores, handling a bloom, and cementation, quenching, and annealing form an entirely new set of operations.

The ironsmith became a competitor of the Bronze Age smith. He was the pioneer of a new age, the Iron Age. His metallurgy was no longer that of alloys and casting. The proportion of iron and carbon in the metal began to be less important than the treatment of the metal itself.

The spread of iron was hastened by political circumstances. The discoverers of this new metallurgy were subjects of the Hittite Empire of Asia Minor and Syria. The new metal was still scarce as late as 1200 B.C., and a Hittite king often had to wait while a new steel weapon was being forged for him. Among the magnificent treasures found in 1922 in the tomb of the Egyptian king Tutankhamon (1350 B.C.) was a steel dagger, which the king's father had obtained from the Hittites. About 1200 B.C. a number of Balkan tribes invaded Asia Minor and destroyed the Hittite Empire, driving the Hittites out of their homes and strongholds. Among the dispossessed were ironsmiths, who now spread rapidly over the Near East. They were the ancestors of the Kenites of Midian, one of whose daughters married the great Hebrew prophet and lawgiver Moses, and of the groups of smiths that up to the present day forge the weapons of the desert tribes of Arabia. But the technique of the new metal also went West and reached Europe. There it flourished, especially in the present Carinthia, where the iron ores of Noricum produced a natural steel owing to the presence of admixtures like manganese. Here for hundreds of years iron was produced for the smiths of Italy. Another center of iron metallurgy was started in northern Spain, in the country of the Basques.

The consequences of these discoveries were far-reaching. The Iron Age denotes a period in which metal really became common. Copper, and especially bronze for which tin was needed, always remained somewhat rare. These metals were never able to take the place of stone completely. Iron, however, was abundant. The ores were plentiful in practically every region, and iron could be produced in large quantities now that the intricacies of its special techniques were appreciated. In the older armies only the noblemen and the guards had good bronze weapons. The bowmen still used arrows with stone tips, or stone clubs. Now steel replaced all this. Steel was also much better material for plowshares than bronze, for it cut deeper into the soil and wore longer. Again we see the extension of farmed lands and the increase of Iron Age population. Steel axes, incidentally, were instrumental in the destruction of many forests, principally those in the Near East.

Money and Communications

THE improvement in the refining of precious metals had an unexpected result. Natural gold as collected by concentration of crushed ores had for many centuries a varying silver content, which often made it white and silverlike. The ancients called it "electrum" and hence we had the same word for amber and natural gold because they happened to have about the same yellowish color. Since payments were then usually made in kind, the precious metals helped to make trade easier. The Latin word for money (*pecunia*) is related to *pecus*, meaning cattle, reminding us that cattle and hides were once forms of money. Silver and gold were much easier to handle, of course, even when simple forms of trade like barter left only a small fraction of the price to be paid in cash. A long-standing custom required that silver and gold be weighed when used for payments. Silver, which was always produced in a very pure state, was used in weights of 14 grams called shekels, a larger unit being the talent. Bronze and copper were sometimes used in the form of bars and cakes.

The varying composition of natural gold made these trans-actions difficult. Then, somewhere around 1500 B.C., jewellers began attempting to refine gold. They soon found that when gold was heated with salt and straw in crucibles of bone meal or some other absorbent material, the silver impurities would be slagged and absorbed by the walls of the crucible, leaving the pure gold untouched. Similar processes were developed and the art of refining became highly perfected about 700 B.C. These ancient methods are still used by jewellers and mineralo-gists today.

At the same time an important discovery was made in Asia Minor, where it was found that when certain stones were polished their surfaces could be marked with gold. The color of such gold streaks varied according to the quality or purity of the gold. Gold of uncertain purity could thus be tested by comparing the streaks it made with those of a standard grade of gold, and the gold content of the sample estimated within reasonable limits. This type of stone was known as a touchstone or Lydian stone, so named from the district where it was first found.

The refining of gold and the possibility of testing it with the touchstone led to the manufacture of the first coins, which were pieces of gold of a certain constant weight stamped with an official seal or device to make them legal tender. The kings of Lydia in western Asia were the first to produce real coins soon after 700 B.C. Precursors lacking some of the characteristics of coins—constant weight or standard purity—are known to have existed before that time.

Both the Greeks and Persians quickly adopted this brilliant idea to assist trade. They soon reaped the benefits of a good stable coinage. Within a few generations the debasing of coins was practiced, too, but its inflationary effects were soon evident. The Persian king Darius was the first to establish a gold standard in his huge empire and to fix the "normal" ratio of silver and gold that is still current.

In fact, the establishment of a good currency with fixed values for gold and silver was just one of the ways in which the Persians sought to weld their empire into a unified whole. The Persians also tried to establish good communication between distant parts of their empire and created a postal service.

Road building was still in its infancy. The civilizations of the river valleys, such as those of Egypt and Mesopotamia, had always favored water transport. Their countries were not suitable for the development of roads and we find only occasional instances of road building in all of the period from 3000 B.C. to 600 B.C. In a few instances, so-called ceremonial roads were built in large cities like Thebes and Babylon, or in temple compounds and enclosures for the many religious processions of carts bearing huge statues of the gods. Some of these roads were enclosed by high walls built of beautiful glazed brick. Their surfaces were well drained and sometimes contained artificial ruts to guide the carts of the gods. Bricks, mortar, and asphalt were applied on stone foundations.

But there were no roads worth mentioning between the towns and the countries, only tracks that travelers had followed from time immemorial. Sometimes defiles were cut into the rocks, or passages over the rivers were improved by building bridges, but in most cases fords were used. Water transport even over the sea was far better developed. The Persian kings, quick to grasp the importance of communication for furthering a strong central power, arranged for the clearing of the tracks. They built posthouses every 15 miles—one day's march apart—where the traveler would find a bed and fresh horses.

The posthouses were also used to garrison troops, who could ensure the safety of the travelers and of the official messengers who used this imperial postal service. They may have also been used to transmit messages with torches, a system used for centuries as a kind of primitive telegraph. The routes thus covered were very long, considering the size of the then known world. The most famous route was that from the capital Susa to Sardis on the west coast of Asia Minor, a distance of 1,585 miles! The royal messengers, as the Book of Esther tells us, rode mules, horses, or camels. The speed attained was about 100 miles a day, provided conditions were favorable.

Impressive as these results may seem, the centralizing tendencies of the Persian kings came to nought because of a succession of weak rulers, under whose ineffectual leadership the empire gradually lost its strength and eventually succumbed to the Macedonians and Greeks under Alexander the Great (330 B.C.)

I V

GREEKS AND ROMANS

(600 B.C.—A.D. 400)

THE period lasting from about 600 B.C. to A.D. 400 is dominated by classical civilization—the culture of the Greeks and Romans. The Greek scientists contributed an invaluable new approach to science: they were the first to study natural objects and phenomena for the sake of these things themselves rather than as problems primarily connected with philosophy and religion. The earliest group of Greek natural philosophers was known as the Ionian school, for its members lived in the cities on the west coast of Asia Minor, which according to tradition had been colonized by the Ionian tribes. These cities were important centers of trade where the worlds of the East and West came in close contact. The older science and technology of the East had more influence on Greek science than was admitted a generation ago. At any rate the Greeks transformed these foreign elements into something peculiarly their own.

The early philosophers like Thales, Heraclitus, and Anaxagoras tried to explain the physical world in terms of its own phenomena without having recourse to philosophy or religion. Of course their final concept of nature was deeply imbued with both. They lacked the proper instruments for accurate observations, and often they were satisfied with only a few experiments or observations. Hence their conclusions may seem childish to us now. Nevertheless they introduced a new concept of science that is still valid today. Their systems did not survive long, for the Italian school of Pythagoras and other schools in Greece attacked their materialism and reintroduced philosophy and religion into every mode of speculation on nature. Philosophical reasonings and mystical interpretations soon overwhelmed the younger physical theories.

The influence of Pythagoras on Socrates and Plato is clearly demonstrated in Greek scientific theory. Plato held that the world of the senses was only a very crude picture of the real world of "ideas," which according to him represented the real essence of things. Therefore there was little to be gained by experimenting and studying the world of the senses. A few obvious truths and logical thinking would lead men to this real world which was behind the phenomena of everyday life. Clearly this great philosopher, who held such abstract ideas, would not have cared for concrete scientific observations and experimenting. Too few facts and too much theory led to philosophical speculations on natural science, speculations that could have been disproved merely by repeating the experiments from which they started.

Science fared no better in the hands of Aristotle, the teacher of Alexander the Great. But in the later period of his life Aristotle turned away from his master Plato and wrote several treatises which again breathe the scientific spirit of the older Ionian writings. There he collected the facts of biology and other scientific subjects, based his conclusions on many observations of his own, and sought to explain the laws that govern these aspects of nature.

Machinery in Classical Society

THE lack of adequate instruments, the tendency to build theories on only a handful of facts, and the severance of the bonds with technology and engineering blocked the path of classical science. The Greeks and Romans were fully convinced that science had arisen from practical needs. Eudemus the mathematician (fourth century B.C.) was the first to tell us that the Egyptians had developed their mathematics because the floods destroyed the boundaries of their farmlands. The great Roman architect Vitruvius (first century B.C.) was convinced that "only those who have mastered theory and practice are fully equipped to achieve their task with honor."

But generally speaking Greek scientists had a horror of manual work and despised those who had to engage in it. They loved theory, but when discussing how to use this knowledge Aristotle and Plato are definite in their rejection of practical applied science as a proper task for the scientist. There is even no such word as "scientist" in any classical writings; the term *philosopher* is used instead. Applied science was the domain of that large class of anonymous slaves and craftsmen that belonged to the structure of ancient society. Only a few names of real scientists working in the fields of technology and engineering are known. There was no urge whatever to develop power resources. It looked as if the slaves were a sufficiently plentiful source of energy. There seem to have been no problems to push the Greek intellect toward the development of machines save in the field of warfare.

Alexandrian science produced several men like Heron and Ctesibius who had great capacity for developing machinery. But their genius was doomed to spend its energy on mechanisms for show and amusement only. The Greeks did not have the wisdom to see that only by conquering nature with its own weapons can we wrest its secrets, and that little is to be gained from barren reasoning based on a few unverified observations. The ancient craftsmen always seem to have produced enough to satisfy the limited demands for manufactured products in antiquity, and so there was no strong urge to industrialize society.

The engineers of the classical period played with the forces of steam and wind. They were able to construct machinery that worked by moving weights or by air pressure, sometimes even by heat. But they never harnessed the winds. Even the common sailor would resort to rowing when he encountered the treacherous winds blowing round the many capes of Greece. The windmill was not a Greek invention, but was adopted from Persia. Air pressure was developed in ancient machinery by heat or by forcing a piston down a cylinder

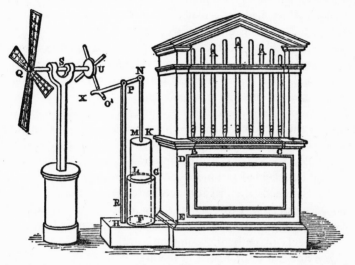

Greek altar organ (after Heron) blown by the agency of a windmill. Rods MN and XN translate rotary motion of wheel U to reciprocating motion, thus pumping organ intermittently. (The New York Public Library.)

mechanically. Nor did the Greeks develop the use of water power; the few Greek and Roman rivers did not have sufficient water all the year round. The water wheels imported from the East were mainly driven by man or animal power.

It is clear that the ancient engineers designed and developed labor-saving machinery, but they never tackled the problem of substituting machinery for human labor. When they used the principle of the lever and hung a pail on a balance arm that carried a counterweight on the other end, they merely eased the manual work without mechanizing it. There was no urge toward mechanization at all. Science in antiquity never conceived of a "picture of the mechanism behind nature," such as we find in Western Europe from the sixteenth century onward, and which can come only from a generation that is familiar with machinery. The ancients never dreamed of a conquest of nature to better the conditions of life. They studied nature to achieve peaceful harmony of thought and greater wisdom. They had little concern for the great mass of slaves who provided them with the necessities of life.

The degrading effect of slavery prevented ancient society from reaping the harvest of the inventions and discoveries that could have been obtained with a little cooperation between science and the arts and crafts. Neither Athens nor Rome were true democracies in our modern sense, whatever theories their leading men may have propounded. Although it is true that, relatively speaking, most of the slaves led a fairly untroubled life, society was composed of a small group of citizens led by a landed and moneyed oligarchy.

The citizen of the classical age had a great sense of beauty and harmony. He expressed this not only in his monuments but also in the products that his workshops turned out, for even objects of daily use combined utility with beauty. But he was not really interested in methods of mass production or in the craftsmen who made things. The slave was simply a form of energy to be bought and sold on the market—not a human being needing help and encouragement to make his labors more productive and less burdensome. The Greeks did not bother to use the new science they had acquired to open up the resources of their country. Science was used as an entry to philosophy and the philosophical tenets of the ideal state could even decree that the pursuit of a certain kind of knowledge was inimical to the general welfare.

Turning to the arts and crafts of the Greeks, we cannot help noting, if only from the examples displayed in our museums, how beautiful the products of the Greek craftsman could be. From the various contemporary accounts, which have not yet been completely studied from our point of view, we know that the crafts of the East were adopted in Greece. However, the products turned out there were not imitations but typical Greek creations.

The Greeks had developed their own forms of economy in which wine and olive oil had a leading role, being the main products to be exported and traded for grain. Incidentally this olive-oil industry shows that the Greeks were capable of developing machinery if the demands were sufficiently strong. The oil was extracted from the olives by first crushing them and then extracting the oil from the crushed mass. The crushing was achieved either in mills like those built for grinding corn or in edge rollers or vertical mills called *trapetum*, many examples of which have been found. The oil was then separated from the kernel-free crushed fruit by means of an olive press. In this press layers of the mass separated by wooden boards were compressed by a long lever beam loaded with large stones. Gradually a better press was developed, consisting of two fixed uprights and a heavy horizontal top beam below which the crushed fruit and the wooden boards were stacked in alternate layers. Wedges were then driven into the stack to exert pressure on the crushed fruit.

A third and more sophisticated type of press used screws to press down the mass of wooden boards and layers of fruit. This shows that the Greeks and Romans not only understood the principle of the lever and wedge, but could also use the screw to exert pressure. Murals from Pompeii show the use of endless screws in a linen press in which the screws bear down on wooden boards that in turn press the household linen. The same principle was also used in primitive pumps, whereby an endless screw or wormless gear was turned in a tightly fitting cylinder and thus raised water from one level to another. This pump, commonly used in Egypt, is generally known as the Archimedean screw, as Archimedes is said to have been its inventor.

Both olive oil and wine were transported in pottery vessels which excel in design and decoration. Pottery and bronze casting belonged to the important crafts of ancient Greece.

We have information on leather working, spinning, and weaving, and on the very important silver mines of Laurion on which the wealth of Athens depended. But there were no new

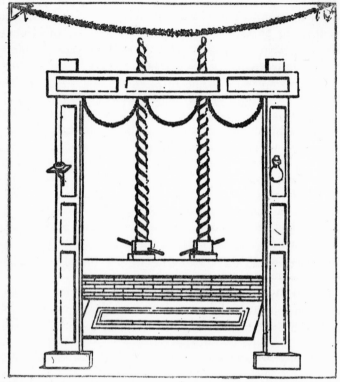

Fuller's screw press, after mural painting at Pompeii. (*From H. H. Tanzer*, The Common People of Pompeii, *Johns Hopkins Press, Baltimore, 1939, p. 11.*)

developments, for Greece was a poor country and had to rely more on commerce than on manufactured products for general consumption.

Greek Engineering

THE Greeks were no mean engineers. As early as 600 B.C., Eupalinus of Megara constructed the aqueduct on the island of Samos. The water was drawn from an inland lake and had to pass through a tunnel eight feet in diameter and nearly a mile long, under a hill nine hundred feet high, in order to reach the coastal plain and the city. Within the tunnel a channel three feet wide contained the pipes for the water. Water pipes of this type were often hollow tree trunks, the conical ends being joined and sealed with lead. Such "pressure lines" were applied by the civil engineers of the town of Pergamum.

Another important engineering feat was the drainage tunnel of Lake Copais in Boetia, which received the waters of the Cephissus and other small rivers. The natural subterranean passages for this water often got choked and then the land along the lake was swamped. In the days of Alexander the Great (356–323 B.C.), the engineer Crates undertook to construct two tunnels through the limestone hills surrounding the lake. He was prevented from completing this work through political pressure. Modern excavation, however, has not only proved the existence of these tunnels, each of which is nearly 2,000 feet long, but also has shown that an older system of canals and dikes existed to harness the waters of the lake.

The Greeks were builders of breakwaters and harbors, too, and the army of the Persian king Xerxes dug a canal through the Isthmus of Mount Athos and laid a pontoon bridge over the Hellespont. The Greeks tried in vain to dig a canal through the Isthmus of Corinth. They had to content themselves finally with a system that hauled the ships over a causeway of logs to the other side of the isthmus, a distance of about four miles.

The heyday of originality in Greek engineering began about 600 B.C. It was over when Alexander the Great achieved his conquest of the Persian Empire in 330 B.C. This conquest had immediate results, for it spread Greek civilization over the entire Near East far into Afghanistan and India and up to the confines of Abyssinia. It inaugurated what is called Hellenistic civilization, which is characterized by the foundation of Greek cities with Greek colonists over this entire area. It brought the ancient Orient into close contact with Greek science and philosophy.

One of the most important results was the foundation of Alexandria and its Museon or Temple of the Muses, an academy of sciences and arts where the Egyptian state concentrated some of the most brilliant minds of the day. It also put at the disposal of the academy a huge library, study rooms, and laboratories, an observatory, a zoo, a botanical garden, and hospitals. Other centers of scientific research were Pergamum in Asia Minor and Antioch in Syria. Some scientists, like the famous Archimedes, worked in close contact with these academies through regular correspondence.

In Alexandria flourished great inventors like Heron and Ctesibius, who had a genius for the mechanical. Heron constructed many mechanical devices, such as a penny-in-the-slot machine for holy water, temple doors that opened when a fire was lit on the altar, and even an automatic theater that could perform several acts of a play. He was also famous for his aeolipile, an instrument also known to Vitruvius. It was a primitive steam turbine in which the blades of a wheel were turned by a jet of steam; in some models a hollow sphere is made to rotate about its axis. The fact that it performed no useful work did not lessen its value in the eyes of the Greek inventor.

Heron was also the inventor of the hodometer, an instrument that registered the length of the route covered by a vehicle and was the primitive ancestor of our modern taximeters and pedometers. Heron gave the correct theory for the geometrical construction and planning of tunnels, while both Philon and Ctesibius studied water clocks that operated on the principle of the flow of water into or out of a calibrated vessel.

The Hellenistic age, at least the early part of it, was one of recurrent wars. The mechanical genius of the Greeks in this field will be discussed in its proper place. Engineers like Athenaeus excelled in siege engines and left us several books on this art. Civil engineering in general flourished. Hermodorus was the designer and builder of dry docks that were famous in antiquity. Temples devoted to Neptune, the god of the sea, had been constructed on promontories and had served as beacons for the sailors, but now a special lighthouse, the Pharos, was built in Alexandria to show the way to the harbor. This building had eight stories and was said to have been 500 feet high. Sostratus of Knidos was its architect and according to tradition he constructed a mirror to project the light of the burning fire in the brazier on its top 30 miles across the Mediterranean. The tower was finally destroyed in an earthquake in A.D. 1375. The later Roman lighthouses—for example, the famous ones at Carthage and Ostia—were copies of this Hellenistic original.

The Roman Engineer

THE best engineers of antiquity, however, were the Romans. The confederation of the Latin tribes on the banks of the Tiber had gradually extended its sway over the whole of Italy. After three ferocious wars against Carthage it had achieved the conquest of the shores of the western Mediterranean. Hardly a century after Alexander's death it had conquered Greece, Macedonia, and a part of Asia Minor, had penetrated into the Near East and had achieved considerable influence in Egypt. Another two centuries were needed for it to become master of what was then considered to be the civilized world, but the Roman Empire lasted until well into the fourth century A.D. The first two and a half centuries of this era formed a period of international peace.

The Roman always remained a farmer at heart. He was not scientifically minded and most of his science is either Greek or Greek inspired. Even imperial Rome shows the ruggedness and practical common sense of the farmer. The Roman despised and feared pure science. It seemed a waste of time to him. Because of his realistic and practical views he is often called the "American of antiquity." However, like most historical parallels this is only a part-truth, for the Roman cared only for applied science. He observed nature but was a poor biologist; he was a good engineer but a mediocre mathematician; he reformed the calendar but made no significant contribution to astronomy. Even in warfare the Roman made no significant contributions. Science was valued only so far as it had practical and useful results for the State. The Roman did not have the patience of the Hellenistic scientist, who sought to discover the laws of nature. He was a great lawyer and an able statesman who furthered science only to the extent that it was helpful in carrying out his public works. So-called scientific authors like Cato, Varro, and Pliny were not scientists but compilers of miscellaneous useful information. Even a practical engineer like Vitruvius published a book that made many wonder whether the author was really the great architect of the Emperor Augustus.

But the Roman adapted the results of Greek science and engineering and he had a natural feeling for these practical arts. His astonishing public works, more particularly his roads, are often said to have been the solid foundations of his rule over so many and widely diverse countries. They outlasted the empire itself and even the Dark Ages that followed. They stand out among the many links that connect our modern civilization with that of the classical world.

The Pax Romana clearly furthered the arts and crafts and their development. Mining, metallurgy, glass and glazes, dyes and textiles, fats and waxes, salt, soda, sal ammoniac, potash alum, perfumes, leather goods, and many other crafts, products, and trades are mentioned in Latin texts. We know that guilds of craftsmen existed in all the principal towns of the empire. In some cases the Roman bankers furnished capital to craftsmen. Sometimes they even provided buildings for them to work in, as well as tools and materials. Such seems to have been the case with the metallurgical factories of Capua, south of Rome, where bronze utensils and art products were turned out in large quantities. But these beginnings of our modern factories did not destroy the guilds of individual craftsmen.

In many cases industry was a state monopoly, because the state was the only source of money and manpower. State-sponsored enterprises were engaged in the mining of copper, iron, gold, and silver in southern and northwestern Spain and Carinthia, and perhaps also worked the tin mines of Cornwall. Nevertheless in none of these cases did major inventions improve the old techniques developed in the Near East. The Romans had the means for mass production and used them intelligently. But their lack of interest in scientific research blocked the way for improvement of technical resources. Their public works have justly drawn most of the attention of later ages. It is contended with some measure of truth that the Roman legions and their roads created the Empire.

It is interesting to observe with what simple instruments these results were obtained. The water level, plummet, surveying instruments equipped with sights (such as the dioptra and groma) measuring rods, ropes, chains, and hand labor were the sum total of their equipment. For drainage they used water wheels and bronze pumps as described by Heron and Vitruvius, very much like those used in the 1800's by our own fire brigades. These bronze pumps did not exist only in the minds of historians; several of them have actually been excavated from Roman remains. With these instruments and the application of Greek geometry and mathematics, the Roman engineers achieved their astounding work. It should be recalled here that most of these public works were executed by state slaves or by the army in peacetime. In many cases the job was left to contractors who owned gangs of slaves.

The Roman Road

TURNING first to road building, we must admit that the Romans were good observers of local conditions and that they were very apt in using local developments. When they conquered the Low Countries they found many ancient log roads that had been constructed by the local tribes for traveling through the fens and bogs of their country. The Romans were quick to note the efficiency of these constructions. Standard methods of construction soon appeared in the handbooks of the army engineer corps.

Here is what Statius, one of their poets, tells us of the building of a great highway under the emperor Domitian (about A.D. 90):

Now the first stage of the work was to dig ditches and to run a trench in the soil between them. Then this empty ditch was filled up with the foundation courses and a watertight layer or binder and a foundation was prepared to carry the pavement. For the surface should not vibrate, otherwise the base is unreliable or the bed in which the stones are rammed is too loose. Finally the pavement should be fastened by pointed blocks and held at regular distances by wedges. Many hands work outside the road itself. Here trees are cut down and the slopes of hills are bared; there the pickaxe levels the rock or creates a log from a tree; there clamps are driven into the rocks and walls are woven from slaked lime and grey tufa. Hand-driven pumps drain the pools formed by underground water and brooks are turned from their courses.

Indeed these Roman roads were thick blocks of masonry usually consisting of four layers, like those Roman floors about which Vitruvius tells us in his *Ten Books of Architecture:*

First I will begin with rubble paving, which is the first stage in finishing, so that account may be taken with special care and great foresight, of a solid foundation (*statumen*). If we must carry our paving on level ground we must inquire whether the soil is throughout; it is then to be leveled, and rubble must be spread over the surface. But if there is a made site, in whole or in part, it must be rammed carefully with piles.

The architect then goes on to say:

A layer of stones (*rudus*) is to be spread each of which is not less than a handful. After spreading the stones, the rubble, if fresh, is to be mixed, three parts to one of lime; if it is of old materials five parts of rubble are to be mixed with two of lime. Let it then be laid on, and rammed down with repeated blows by gangs of men using wooden stamps. When the stamping is finished it must be no less than nine inches thick, that is, three quarters of its initial height. On top of this (the *rudus*) another layer is laid (*nucleus*) consisting of a hard coat of powdered pottery, three parts to one of lime, forming a layer of six inches. On the finishing coat a surface layer (*pavimentum*) is laid.

Though this is the description of a floor, we know from excavations that it also applies to Roman roads. The "statumen" and "rudus" together can be compared with our hand-laid foundations in which the rudus is a damp course shutting out water from the statumen. The nucleus is a kind of binder course for the pavimentum proper. In road building, stone rollers such as Virgil describes were used.

The Roman road engineer had very good materials at his disposal. He was always careful to adopt local materials as far as possible, locating quarries near the place where he built his road, with the result that the materials used differ widely in the Empire, as do the types of construction. Lime mortar was adopted from Hellenistic practice about 300 B.C. The Romans used it very cleverly in combination with rubble, potsherds, and crushed bricks to prepare a grout which could penetrate between the handlaid stones of the foundation layers and thus give them the solidity of a wall. A modern engineer has truly characterized the Roman roads as "walls on the flat." Their thickness varies for the main highways from three to five feet—more than four times the thickness of our best concrete roads today. Their average life, which we can determine from the inscriptions and milestones, was about 70 to 100 years. This is high when we remember that traffic consisted mainly of iron-tired vehicles and unshod animals, both fairly hard on a road surface.

The grouting of gravel surfaces was also used, and the result was actually a concrete road. The invention of concrete and its application in architecture and civil engineering was the only great discovery that can be ascribed to the Romans. About 150 B.C. they discovered the natural strata of trass (a porous volcanic rock) near Puzzeoli, a valuable substitute for lime which came to be known as puzzolana. This material enabled the Romans to make a mortar that would set under water and when shut off from air. It was usually mixed with lime but when applied under water it was used in the pure state. Later other deposits of such natural cements were found, notably those in the Eiffel region of Germany.

This natural mortar enabled the engineer to mix a concrete consisting of three parts gravel and one part mortar, or other mixes containing sand and similar materials which he called *caementum* and applied to buildings as well as to roads. When the Emperor Augustus prided himself on having found Rome a city of bricks and leaving it a city of marble, he meant that he had constructed huge concrete buildings that were finished off with marble slabs.

Road constructions varied considerably. The example described above refers to a normal type of road. We know of Roman roads in England built on a pile foundation, of others in Italy carried through a concrete trough because of corrosive volcanic subsoil water in the neighborhood. There are cunning Alpine roads hacked in the slopes of steep mountains and provided with artificial wheel ruts or tracks to guide the vehicles to the safety of the valleys. To avoid steep inclines, the Roman engineers frequently built embankments. These were strengthened by retaining walls with strong buttresses and carried the road straight over deep valleys. The choice of the track showed great practical knowledge. In the mountains the sunny side of the slope was chosen to avoid avalanches. The road was carried as directly as the lay of the land permitted. Detours were avoided whenever humanly possible. A defile between Hungary and Rumania carried a road along the banks of the Danube. Here the road was partly cut into the cliffs that rise sharply out of the river, and partly carried on a wooden scaffolding built into the rock, thus giving it the normal width of 12 feet.

The width of these roads varied according to their importance and use. In the Imperial period it was common to find main highways 80 feet wide, having a main road surface of 40 feet with two sidewalks of 20 feet each, separated from the middle course by low stone walls or strips of grass. The sidewalks were used by pedestrians or horsemen, the latter finding the low walls and stepping stones a great convenience in mounting their steeds. Sometimes these sidewalks were used to enforce one-way traffic, while the middle of the road served for the movement of troops. Secondary and tertiary roads were, of course, considerably narrower.

Communications and the Empire

ROAD building was not, however, a Roman invention. The Romans adopted it because they had learned from history how important a good system of communication was for a strong central power in controlling the affairs of a great empire. In fact, they had learned much from the Persians and the Egyptians, who in Ptolemaic times imitated the Persian postal service in their smaller country. The Romans had also seen roads built in the region of Carthage, and nearer home in the country of the Etruscans whom they had conquered. Greek cities had good roads when they could afford them and most of the later Hellenistic cities were well paved.

The Romans started to organize and reconstruct the older track systems of Italy about 300 B.C. They extended it as their conquest of the world proceeded. When a district was subdued and pacified, the roads would penetrate it and make it accessible to the Roman legion at any time. Trade would follow quickly. This usually caused the road system to be extended to mining districts or to other important centers of trade and industry. Roads were also needed because an ever-increasing percentage of Italian land was now under cultivation and the institution of property holding was gaining strength. The ancient undefined track now had to be delimited and protected from encroaching farmers. The introduction of lime mortar and later of concrete limited the road to a narrow band of communication that proved to be the backbone of the Empire.

This road system developed from a nucleus of gravel and

earth roads which radiated from Rome; the saying, "All roads lead to Rome" had literal significance in those days. The first man to have a paved road constructed was the blind censor Appius Claudius, who was in charge of the public works of the Roman Republic. He had the Via Appia, an old track, paved as far as Capua (312 B.C.) and later the pavement was extended all the way to Brindisi. The Appian Way, named after its builder, was the first great Roman road and it opened up the rich country of Campania to Roman trade. Gradually all the roads leading from Rome were paved. Under the Empire there were 180,000 miles of paved roads, 53,500 miles of which were main highways, the rest secondary and tertiary roads.

Traveling from Britain to the Euphrates, the Roman citizen could ride along 2,500 miles of excellent highways. Travel was relatively swift, the average speed of the Roman State Post being five to six miles per hour, and under favorable circumstances much higher speeds were obtained. We know of special messengers or couriers who averaged six to ten miles per hour over a period of several days. Though this is a snail's pace compared with the speed of modern travel, one must realize that never again until the days of Napoleon was travel as rapid as in the days of the Roman Empire.

The Roman postal service was a very much improved version of the older Persian system. Every 10 to 12 miles the traveler would find a relay station (*mutationes*) where fresh horses were available. Every 30 or 40 miles the larger *mansiones* would lodge him overnight and provide him with the necessary supplies. These *mansiones* were situated at very important stopping places and in big cities. Originally the service was strictly confined to government servants and officials, who received a "diploma" from the Emperor authorizing their use of these facilities, sometimes hiring conveyances or messengers. Guilds of persons acting as travel agencies were soon organized. After the second century A.D., private companies also forwarded letters and parcels. The *stationes* not only catered to the traveler but provided a blacksmith, a doctor, and practically everything else one might need. These stations were also used as barracks for the military police who patroled the roads.

We even possess timetables of postal services from different parts of the Empire. Milestones were erected along the roads. Apart from indicating the distance from the Golden Milestone erected in Rome, they often conveyed news about conditions along the road. Maps were well known. Special pocket editions in the form of rolls on which a distorted and abbreviated map showed the stations and distances along the roads were called *itineraria*. Traveling 30 to 40 miles along these roads was a comfortable day's journey. We know that the great author Pliny took along a little library when he rode in his coach. Cicero while traveling dictated his letters to his secretary, Tullius Tiro, who was the inventor of stenography.

Sea traffic also profited immensely by the Pax Romana. The main type of warship was still the galley rowed by slaves and prisoners and only partially dependent on its sails. But all merchant ships were usually sailing vessels of about 500 to 1,000 tons burden. Occasionally large ships up to 3,000 tons were built. One of these served to transport an Egyptian obelisk, among other goods, to the city of Rome, where it still stands in front of St. Peter's basilica. The ship was then filled with sand and concrete and sunk to form the foundation for part of the breakwater built for the new harbor of Ostia at the mouth of the Tiber near Rome.

The Tiber in its torrential seasonal floods carried a great deal of silt to the sea and shifted its delta. Constant dredging was therefore imperative until the emperors decided to build a harbor connected with the river by a canal to keep the Tiber from getting choked up with sand. The breakwater built on the ship that had transported the obelisk was crowned by a two-hundred-foot lighthouse. The Emperor Trajan built a new harbor because the old Claudian harbor had become too small. The new port covered 90 acres and was hexagonal in shape, with quay walls nearly a mile and a quarter in length.

The depth of the harbor was 18 feet. Another famous harbor was that of Alexandria, and large lighthouses were erected at Boulogne and Fréjus in Gaul as well as in many other locations.

Aqueducts and Bridges

THE achievements of the Roman civil engineers were of great importance. One of the fields in which they were most successful was that of water supply. Here again the blind censor Appius Claudius was the pioneer. In 312 B.C. he started building the Aqua Appia, which brought water to Rome from a source in the hills ten miles south of the town by way of an open canal that crossed the valleys into the towns in a series of splendid arches. It was the beginning of many such aqueducts, the longest of which for a time was the Aqua Marcia (56 miles). The Emperor Hadrian then constructed an aqueduct for the town of Carthage which was no less than 80 miles long.

The water supply of Rome was originally part of the responsibility of the town authorities. Augustus formed a special board that after 9 B.C. was entrusted with the task of supplying water. We know a great deal about the presidents of this board from a book written by one of them named Frontinus, who was in charge from A.D. 97 to 104. He describes the water supply in great detail. Its personnel of 700 consisted of surveyors, inspectors, masons, pavers, and general workmen or laborers, a few architects and plumbers, and a small administrative staff. A group of technicians calibrated the bronze nozzles through which the water was introduced into the private houses, so that the amount of water used could be calculated for assessment purposes. The *libratores* checked this important nozzle and then gave it to the *vilicus*, who stamped it with the calculated rate of flow.

We may obtain from Frontinus's book the exact details on all the water sources, their output and the capacity of the aqueducts as well as their actual dimensions. He took great care to have the volume of water measured at different points along the aqueduct and supply lines. Thus he tells us that upon finding a source delivering only 12,700 units he would check and correct the deliveries from this aqueduct, which his records indicated should be over 14,000 units! No less than 35 per cent of the water was lost between source and house through leakage and faulty nozzles. The unit-delivery nozzle gave a supply of about 1,465 cubic feet a day. The total water supply of Rome in his day was no less than 36 million cubic feet a day, or close to 270 million gallons—about three times the amount used in present-day Rome.

This huge amount of water flowed constantly and as the offtake was not constant it had to be dispersed intelligently. The water as tapped at the source usually flowed through two basins to settle the clay. Then it entered the *specus* or aqueduct channel which was closed with slabs that could be removed for inspection. In the city of Rome the water flowed into reservoirs located in the surrounding hills. Each of these *castellae* had three main drains, one to each of the important groups of clients, the fountains, the public baths, and the public buildings. Drains taken off at a higher level led to private houses or blocks and industrial buildings. When the offtake of the latter group was less, for example during the night, the surplus water was either led to the fountains or used to swish the drains. In private houses or blocks of apartments the water was usually stored in tanks on the highest floor, sometimes pumped up by water wheels or bronze pumps. One paid for the maximum amount one's house nozzle would admit, whether the water was actually used or not.

If we take Frontinus's figures, 17 per cent of the water was used for industrial purposes, 39 per cent for private purposes, and the remaining 44 per cent on 19 barracks, 95 public buildings, 39 public baths, and 591 fountains. Water was led into the houses in lead pipes; we are led to wonder what the effect was on public health. It was already known in those days that earthenware pipes were healthier, but they could not withstand pressure so well as the lead pipes. We also read in Frontinus's book that the quality of the water was tested by evaporation tests in bronze or copper vessels, by a sedimentation test, and by the practical test of cooking vegetables and noting any peculiarities of taste or color.

Many details are known of the water supply in other Roman towns where it was carefully adjusted to local conditions. These towns were not always so well supplied with water as the capital. For instance, the householders in Pompeii had a regulated water supply that gave them less water during the day than users in other towns. This did not matter very much, as life was spent more in public buildings and in baths than at home.

Nor was the Roman engineer satisfied with a water supply in channels that drained by gravity. In certain cases, as in the water system of Pergamum, water was led from the mountains through an ingenious closed system of syphons over hills and valleys into the coastal plains. This meant that the water mains had to be capable of withstanding a pressure of twenty atmospheres. (When this line was excavated in modern times, the German Academy withdrew its support of the expedition, because it believed that the Romans could not have known the syphon and that therefore the excavator was cheating by digging up modern installations.)

The money for these public works was first obtained from war booty and from the munificence of public-spirited officials. However, during the Empire it was obtained from the charges levied on the water supply to industry and private consumers. The Emperor Nero had a special line installed in his palace that delivered water from the sea. Hot-water lines heated by the usual Roman central-heating systems were quite frequent. Central heating was achieved when fuel was burned in furnaces installed in the cellars and the resulting hot gases were conducted through the space between the double walls and ceilings of the house. It was developed especially in Gaul, Germany, and Britain, where the Romans were exposed to a harsher climate.

Water supply also entailed the disposal of sewage and garbage, a problem as old as urban civilization itself. The old towns of the Indus Valley (Mohenjo Daro), Mesopotamia and

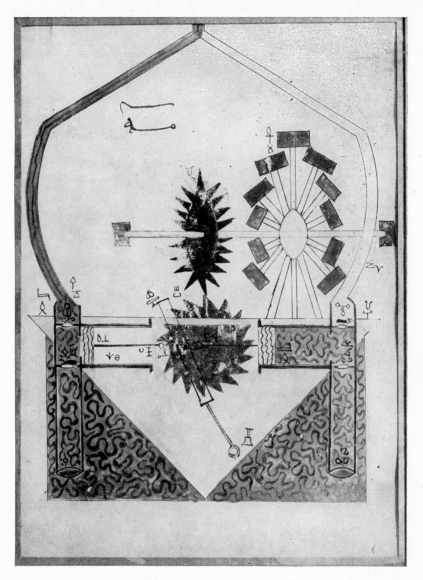

PLATE 3 Original illustration to 12th century Arabic manuscript by Al-Jazarī, showing his apparatus for raising water from a flowing stream to a height of about 65 feet. (From A. K. Coomaraswamy, *The Treatise of Al-Jazarī on Automata*, Courtesy of the Fogg Museum of Art, Paul J. Sachs Collection, Harvard University.)

PLATE 4 Building the highway at Bavai-Tournai, circa 1300. (From Jacques de Guise, *Le Chronique de Hainault*.)

ancient Crete had excellent provisions for sewers and sanitation. In Rome itself the first large public work was the building of the Cloaca Maxima, which drained the Forum in the center of town. Its construction was so good that it is still in operation today. Most other Roman towns had elaborate sewerage facilities; these, however, have broken down through neglect following the fall of the Empire. Other great drainage works were executed near Lake Fucinus, a lake in a depression between high mountains. The Emperor Claudius had a tunnel built in A.D. 52 to carry off its waters to the River Liris and thus regulate its level.

A similar drainage tunnel at Lake Albano was constructed four hundred years earlier. A canal system to drain the marshes south of Rome worked for many centuries until neglect again reduced this region to one of the worst malaria-stricken parts of Italy. Other big canals were those built by the Roman army between the Rhine and the Ijssel in Holland and between the Rhine and the Meuse, providing additional outlets of flood water and navigation facilities. Embankments and dikes to prevent the heavy floods caused by the torrential rivers were constructed throughout Italy. The old embankment of the Tiber, which was stepped back in three stages, was superior to the modern one built in 1870.

The older bridges of Rome and other parts of Italy were wooden structures erected on piles. After the fourth century B.C., however, stone bridges were built. Though the Romans knew how to construct coffer dams and subaqueous foundations, they very often lacked the proper facilities for draining the huge pits excavated for the heavy masonry piers. These, therefore, were weak points. They resorted to narrowing the waterway with excessively thick piers, or they built huge spans to avoid the construction of piers in midstream.

Military engineers were very clever in constructing bridges of wooden piles across large streams. Julius Caesar is said to have built one across the Saône in one day. Another bridge across the Rhine was 1,400 feet long. A most remarkable bridge was erected by Trajan across the Danube in A.D. 106 using twenty piers, each 150 feet high and spaced 170 feet apart. This bridge was probably of the Burr type used during the nineteenth century.

Many of these magnificent stone bridges still stand. There is the five-arch bridge near Rimini whose roadway is 50 feet above the river bed. A 600-foot bridge with six arches (two of which are over 110 feet long) crossed the Tagus near Alcantara. Finally there is the famous Pont du Gard near Nîmes, 150 feet high and 900 feet long, which carries both the roadway and an aqueduct.

War Engines

THE only field in which mechanical inventions played a great part was that of siege and warfare. The urge to make science the handmaid of Mars arose during the Golden Age of Greece (fifth and fourth centuries B.C.). Athens, ambitious of creating an empire, flung its navies and armies west and east. During its wars in Sicily and those of the Sicilian tyrant Dionysios of Syracuse, war engines were frequently used. We hear of batteries of mechanized bows or catapults covering attacks and retreats. Camouflage, smoke screens, and gas attacks were used by the warring Greek states. King Philip of Macedonia and his famous son Alexander organized their army trains and the transport and assembly of war engines, consisting of easily transportable parts. Names of specialists in this field, such as the engineers Artemon, Philistos, and Diades, now appear in the war annals.

In the period after the death of Alexander the Great (323 B.C.), science was relied upon to help the Hellenistic generals. The fact that standing armies now gradually replaced the levy of citizen-volunteers had a profound influence on the relation between warfare and science. The effect of the changes wrought by the new military tactics can be traced in the evolution of communications and signaling apparatus, of cartography and civil engineering. In peacetime the army was often employed in building aqueducts, bridges, and roads. Pliny mentions that the army was even used for the layout of vineyards and for combatting swarms of locusts. But the great demand of the new army was for mechanized arms.

Most of these machines were built of wood. If we did not have at hand elaborate treatises on the construction of these machines, little would be available to prove their existence beyond a multitude of stone cannonballs. These stones were flung with machines that worked on the principle of the ancient sling. They hurled stones of from three to ten pounds into towns and fortifications. The mechanical sling was called an *onager*, or mule, because its action recalled the kicking of that animal. A wooden arm, to which a sling was attached holding the stone ball, was bent back under pressure of catgut strings and held by a catch. When released, the arm struck a cushion and the stone ball was flung from the sling. Reconstructions have proved that a four-pound stone could be thrown a distance of 1,000 feet. The strings used to pull back the arm were made from animal entrails or strands of hair and could easily develop a force of 135,000 pounds.

The so-called catapults developed from the bow. They had two bundles of strings to force the bowstring back, were fitted with sights, and could make all the movements of a modern antiaircraft gun. The little sledge moved by the bowstring could contain arrows or stones. A modern reconstruction of the catapult in the Saalburg Museum in Germany shot an arrow 950 feet against the wind. Three-foot arrows went about 1,100 feet, and lead balls weighing one pound each traveled 900 feet. When hitting a shield one and one-quarter inches thick and covered with thin iron plate, these arrows would penetrate at least one and one-half feet, and must therefore have wounded the shield-bearer.

Since animal tendons weather, Philon had already hit on the idea of using bronze springs, and Ctesibius had suggested the use of air pressure, developed by heating enclosed volumes of air. Neither of these ideas, however, had much practical result. Dionysius of Alexandria constructed an ancient equivalent of the modern machine gun, in which the bow was bent by turning a wheel and was released by an endless chain which at the same time reloaded the bow from a till of arrows. Reconstructions of this reloading bow at Saalburg proved that ancient boasts of its accuracy were quite justified. Other large machinery like rams and towers or platforms moving on wheels were, of course, well known, since they had been invented in Trojan times or even earlier.

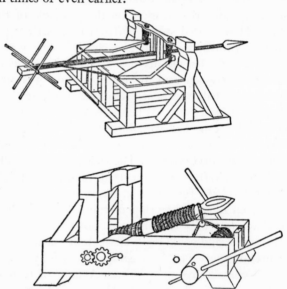

Hellenistic ballista (above) *and catapult* (below). (*From Lynn Montross,* War Through the Ages, *Harper & Brothers, New York, 1946, pp. 20–21.*)

It should be clearly understood that these new machines were developed not only by practical experiment, but also by accurate design calculations. It is well known that the famous mathematician and physicist, Archimedes, designed and constructed war engines to help defend his home town of Syracuse against the assaults of the Roman army. Again, Philon's treatise *Belopoiika* (on catapults) contained formulas to correlate the caliber of the engine with the weight of the projectile. Separate formulas were developed to express this caliber in terms of the length of the arrow or the weight of the missile. Only a small part of the ancient handbooks on war engines and tactics have survived, yet from these we know that hosts of others existed.

Nor were these war engines just expensive freaks. When Carthage fell, the Roman army captured over 2,000 catapults. Vegetius, an ancient tactician, recommends the employment of three of these ancient weapons to every hundred men, three times the number of field pieces used by Napoleon, famous for his artillery duels. The Romans themselves contributed little to the art of constructing war engines, though they made full use of the older Greek inventions in equipping their armies. In fact, the Romans' only contributions may have been the horse-drawn, wheeled "guns" called *carroballistae*, and the onager or mule already mentioned. Both are depicted only on Roman monuments.

Thus even in antiquity war had a few beneficial effects. Money to assist the growth of applied science and engineering was supplied in order to defeat the enemy, and these developments, impossible then as now in peacetime for lack of funds, had applications not limited to the field of warfare alone.

It is clear that all the engineering feats mentioned above served the state in peace and war and not the individual. Industry relied on slave labor or on the power of water wheels fed by rivers or aqueducts, as in Rome itself. Since they were without the stimulating effect of scientific research, the Romans contributed no inventions worth noting.

Even in Roman times, scientific work remained concentrated in the academies of the eastern Mediterranean. Though less pioneering work was done, the detailed task of compilation was important, and served to codify what earlier generations had uncovered. But here again the forces that had motivated science in earlier days—its contact with arts and crafts, and the spirit of inquiry that had pervaded early Greek science— were spent a few hundred years after the death of Alexander the Great. Scientific speculation became barren and men turned once again to magical and religious fantasies. It is true that the conquests of classical science were spread over the entire Near East and went even further. But the contact with Indian, Persian, and Near Eastern systems of thought turned it from its original path and led it into syncretic speculation.

Alchemy and Metallurgy

IN ONE field, however, a happy development took place. In the first century of our era, certain Christian Egyptians (Copts) turned to the study of matter. Alchemy had its roots in ancient Mesopotamia; in Egypt as early as 300 B.C., the scientist Bolos of Mendes wrote the first book on the chemical structure of matter. For centuries craftsmen had tried to imitate jewels and precious stones by artificially coloring less precious metals and such absorbent materials as the nodes of silica in bamboo stalks. Two parts of a papyrus now in the Leyden and Stockholm libraries contain recipes going back to originals from Thebes and Alexandria. Written down by craftsmen when there was much demand for imitation jewelry, they are much earlier than copies that date from the third century A.D. This work comprised observations of what we now call chemical reactions.

The first Alexandrian chemists also drew on the experience of the technologists who used such instruments as the water bath when preparing fats, and who made perfumes by the digestion or maceration of flowers and spices with oils and fats. Then there were the many cooking utensils manufactured in quantity in such factories as that at Capua. All these instruments were used by the earlier chemists who now pried into the structure of matter and studied the reactions of salts and metals. This required considerable skill in handling of fires, the construction of furnaces, the manufacture of all kinds of earthenware and fireproof material, and the production of glass and glazed vessels.

But the harvest was rich, and improvements in old apparatus made possible the first qualitative studies of fusion, sublimation, and distillation processes. It must be realized that the lack of such instruments as thermometers and the fact that no solvents and no stronger acids than vinegar were known limited the field of study. The ancient chemists worked mainly on reactions of liquid and molten compounds and the high temperatures they used in their early distillation apparatus did not allow them to recover the low-boiling compounds. Hence such a chemical as alcohol remained undiscovered, though alcoholic beverages like wine and beer had been known for centuries. The discovery of such important processes as distillation was to bear fruit in later centuries.

Unfortunately, later generations of chemists working in Syria introduced Persian and Chinese speculations. The practical chemical art was then tempted by such mirages as the "philosopher's stone" and the "elixir of life." These speculations kept chemistry from having practical results for centuries and made scientists look down on the art of the alchemist. Its processes, however, proved useful to the practical technologist. It was he who was going to develop the use of distillation, sublimation, and other processes in chemical technology.

Hellenistic metallurgy introduced a few interesting novelties. In the period when the new iron metallurgy was born, certain tribes in the Armenian mountains had smelted copper with a kind of earth which we know to be the zinc ore calamine. This cementation of copper produced brass. Brass manufacture spread slowly through the Near East and to the West. It became popular only in the early Roman Empire, where the process was used to produce cheap mass-produced articles and even brass coins for currency. Local Italian and German ores began to be exploited. Cyprus was another important center; the Persian product was exported to India, whence the secret of its manufacture passed to China.

The discovery of cast iron is often wrongly ascribed to the ancients. Cast iron is an alloy of iron and carbon that is formed at high furnace temperatures and runs from the furnace in liquid form, as copper does in copper smelting. But such a phenomenon would have been highly puzzling to an early smelter. Early furnaces did not allow such high temperatures except accidentally. We have ample proof that cast iron was produced in certain cases but was thrown away because nobody could handle it. The many statues said to have been made of cast iron were actually of wrought iron. Some passages speak of chased or molded iron, not of cast iron. It was to take many more centuries of furnace development before the conditions were obtained that made possible the regular industrial production of cast iron.

There was one important gain in the spread of Hellenism over the Near East. The old contacts with such distant countries as India and China grew closer. The contact of ideas existed but remained rather vague though noticeable. Nevertheless material contacts were expressed in the exchange of many commodities. Thus in the second century B.C., alfa-alfa grass and the vine went east to China. The first news of silk manufacture came back with the silk for which Rome had spent its gold reserves, beginning in the first century A.D., although it took five centuries to smuggle silkworms in bamboo staves from Turkestan to Byzantium (the modern Constantinople) and to bring this craft to the West.

The art of making good glass with borax arrived from China in the fifth century. However, the West was still unaware at that time of the existence of tea (first described in a Chinese book of the third century), and the important invention of paper by Tsai Lun in the year 105 still remained a secret. On the other hand, block printing, which had been used in China much earlier, was applied in the Near East, where the process was used to print decorative designs on textiles.

The importance of these new trade routes can hardly be overestimated, for contact with India and China was never broken afterward. However difficult the contact might be, theories and inventions or discoveries continued to travel east and west after Hellenistic times. Ideas would travel to the other end of the world to return in some unexpected form. Developments would be anticipated in the other part of the world, but they were often jealously guarded as trade secrets.

V

Wardens of the Classical

Heritage

(A.D. 600–1200)

W HEN the prophet Mohammed and his successors the Caliphs raised the banners of Islam in the seventh century, the grip of the Roman Empire no longer held the known world together. The influx of barbarian tribes from beyond the Rhine and the Danube, together with the decay of government through decentralization and civil wars, had brought about the disintegration of the Roman Imperium. In the West from the fourth century onward, barbarian kingdoms squabbled over the heritage of the Emperors.

The Byzantine Empire, centered around its capital at Byzantium (later Constantinople) defended this new phase of the Eastern Roman Empire a little more successfully, maintaining a wavering control over the eastern coasts of the Mediterranean. The armies from the desert, however, met little resistance. Misrule and exhaustion of the spirit had defeated the peoples under Byzantine sway long before these armies arrived. Within a hundred years Islam had established its rule from the Pyrenees to the Indus Valley and Central Asia. Though separate kingdoms and sultanates were soon set up, this whole region for many centuries may be regarded as a unit.

This world of Islam was a melting pot of peoples. When we speak of Arabian science in the course of this story we include the Persian, Syrian, Egyptian, Moorish, and Spanish scientists and technologists who contributed to Arabian technology. However, the world of Islam was also a great civilization that formed the pivot of the world in its day. Theories and practical inventions poured in from East and West and were diffused over the world in both directions. Apart from this important role as a link between the East and West, the world of Islam, together with Byzantium, was the warden of the classical heritage.

The young civilization of Islam had great religious fervor and a crusading spirit, but possessed none of the scientific and technical achievements of antiquity, although it had the spirit of inquiry that fired the mind to learn and to investigate. Hence the period up to about A.D. 750 is one of orientation. After the decline of Hellenistic civilization early in the Christian era, Alexandria was no longer the seat of knowledge. The leadership, so far as there was any inquiry of a scientific kind, had passed into the hands of the Syrians, from whom the first Arab scientists received a somewhat garbled impression of ancient science and technology. But as soon as the period of conquest was over and the Caliphs of Damascus and Baghdad settled down to organize the empire, they started to collect ancient manuscripts from the libraries of Alexandria and other large cities. They sent embassies to Byzantium to copy as many of the Greek manuscripts as they could lay their hands on.

When religious troubles started in the Byzantine Empire, many nonorthodox scientists fled to the country of the Caliphs, where they were liberally and hospitably entertained. Christians, Syrians, Jews and heathens settled in famous centers such as Harran, Baghdad, and Jundashipur, where they taught the Arabs the science and technology of the Greeks. New universities arose in Basra, Kufa, Cairo, Toledo, and Cordoba. The library of Cordoba in 900 contained no less than 600,000 books; its catalog was published in 44 volumes. This is astonishing in view of the fact that the library of the French king in 1300 consisted of slightly more than 400 titles.

The Arabs, quite unlike the Hellenistic scientists, approved

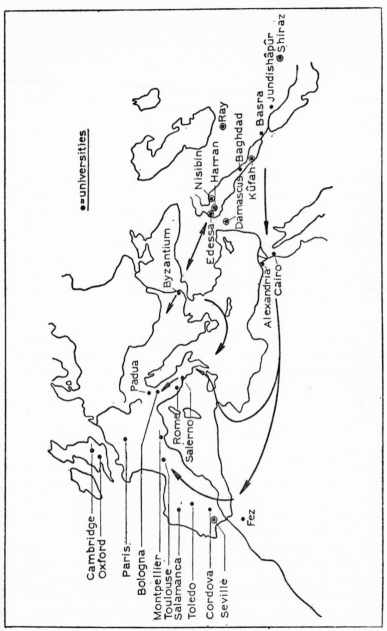

Map showing the diffusion of classical science from East to West.

of experiments in the laboratory and workshop. Though some of these may seem extremely elementary to us now, we must not forget that their civilization was the mirror in which the West first saw the reflections of the classical heritage. The Arabs were interested not only in Aristotle's philosophy but also in his systematic biological observations. Most important of all was the fact that they salvaged mathematics and mechanical science from the wreck of the Roman Empire. From India they borrowed the so-called Arabic notation and the typical algebraic form of thought. These two inheritances were welded into an impressive whole. It was this body of mathematics that the West discovered in the twelfth century and that enabled it to erect the foundations of modern science. But the Arabs themselves did not confine science to the laboratory. In the tenth century it was widely applied to the practical arts and crafts in the brilliant Arab states then flourishing in Spain, Iraq, and Iran.

The period 750 to 900 was one of translations. Apart from the many scientific works translated into Arabic, we read of books being translated or written on theoretical mechanics, the elevation of water, water wheels, balances, and water clocks. The three sons of Mūsāibn Shākir composed a *Book of the Artifices*, which contains much material similar to the automatons detailed by Heron and other Hellenistic authors, but also describes vessels for hot and cold water, and water wells with a fixed level. Many agricultural treatises were based on the old *Geoponicæ* written by classical authors. This is also true of the lapidaries or mineralogical treatises composed in this period. Al-Kindī was the author of an original series of small treatises on producing iron and steel for weapons. They were important, for the Arabs had learned the art of making crucible steel from the Indian smiths and had founded such metallurgical centers as Damascus and Toledo. Here "damascened" blades were made according to a technique very like that of "wootz steel" in India, and these blades remained famous up to the present day.

The Arabs had a great interest in civil engineering as applied to agriculture. They repaired the dikes and dredged the canals of the ancient irrigation systems, which had been neglected in the last few centuries before Islam, and made great efforts to restore those ancient systems when the power of Islam was at its height (900–1100). Still, the largest canal of the period was built in China, where the Grand Canal, 1,200 miles long, was started early in the twelfth century.

The Arabs were also responsible for many artesian wells constructed in North Africa and in other semiarid regions, though curiously enough the earliest well of this type was dug in France (Pas de Calais, 1215). But as in many cases where the Arabs were not the pioneers or original inventors, they had a keen eye for important inventions and did not hesitate to adopt them, often even before their importance was realized in the country of their conception. This was also true of the compass, gunpowder, and many other useful inventions born beyond the realms of Islam.

Power Sources of the Arabs

THE Arabs were the first to start a more systematic development of the water wheel and windmill. Whereas in the classical world the water wheel never played a major part, the Arabs were really interested in its development as one of their primary sources of power. In Mesopotamia they adopted a floating undershot wheel on barges in the Tigris to supply power to millstones, paper factories, and other machinery in which they made liberal use of wooden cogwheels and other means of transferring power.

The windmill was another source of power that was adopted and diffused by the Arabs. The idea of making the wind do work was an old one. Heron proposed a kind of windmill to move bellows. Use of the wind to rotate a vertical axis was already made for religious purposes in Central Asia, where the Chinese travelers found the well-known prayer wheel in common use about A.D. 400. And so we need not wonder when an Arab legend tells us that the first windmill was constructed for the Caliph Omar by his slave Abū Lulūa. An early description says: "They have eight wings and stand behind two pillars between which the wind has to drive a wedge. The wings are mounted vertically on a vertical pole, the lower end of which moves a millstone turning over a lower millstone."

A later historian tells us that "in Afghanistan all windmills and water wheels are driven by the north wind and hence they are oriented that way. This wind is very constant in that country, blowing more constantly and harder in summer. Attached to the windmills there are series of shutters which are closed or opened to shut out or to admit the wind. For if the wind is too strong the flour burns and becomes black, even the millstone itself may grow hot and disintegrate." Construction with sails and shutters is certainly an Arabic achievement that finally turned the windmill into an efficient source of power.

Up to the tenth century the windmill was used mainly in Persia and Afghanistan. Thence its use spread slowly westward and grew common in the Arab world two centuries later. It was adopted by the Chinese and Indians who used it like the Arabs to extract the juice from sugar cane. It is interesting to note that the earliest windmills of the West Indian sugar plantations were hardly different from the older Persian ones.

The Crusaders noticed these windmills in the East and brought the idea to Europe. There they became a common feature of the landscape of Flanders, the Low Countries, northwestern Germany, and England, though their number has been reduced lately by the introduction of steam and electricity. It is also curious to observe that the windmill has now practically disappeared from the Near East and Egypt. This may be due to the inroads of the Turks and the Mongols, who destroyed much of the magnificent irrigation works of Mesopotamia, especially in the region north of the Tigris, which is at present a barren waste.

In the Golden Age of Islam (900–1100), realistic scientists like Jābir and other famous men succeeded in promoting chemical technology by their close study of many chemicals and natural products. The development of scientific instruments made this possible. Al-Bīrūni used his pycnometer to determine the specific gravity of many minerals and precious stones, and other scientific tools were designed. The university town of Harrān was the center of the manufacture of scientific instruments, mostly mathematical and astronomical types. It was also famous for its accurate balances.

One of the most universal instruments propagated by the Arab world was the astrolabe. This instrument certainly goes back to Ptolemy and other Hellenistic astronomers, but the Arabs perfected it into a useful and universal instrument for measuring angles and calculating positions of heavenly bodies. In its simplest form the astrolabe consisted of a disk graduated along the rim and provided with an alidade or calibrated rule with sights. It could thus be used in vertical and horizontal positions to measure declinations and ascensions. Several hundred practical applications of this instrument are described in the ancient handbooks; beautifully ornamented examples made of bronze and silver have been preserved.

The chemical knowledge of the Arabs was considerable. Though they did not improve theoretical chemistry, their applied chemistry was much more advanced than that of the Hellenistic chemists. A large group of chemists was drawn into the abstruse theories and discussions on alchemy, while several great chemists despised the "devotees of al-kīmīyā who know three hundred ways of fooling their dupes." A genius like Jābir described improved evaporation, filtration, sublimation, melting, distillation, and crystallization methods. Others, like ibn-Sīna, better known to us as Avicenna, classified minerals and chemicals and described their manufacture in great detail. Through the efforts of these chemists the difference between soda and potash (sodium and potassium) was established. The purification of vitriols, alums, saltpeter, and sal ammoniac was no longer a mystery. Most of this work was made possible by improvements in chemical apparatus and in the quality of glass and glazes.

Arabian Technology

THE Arabs were, of course, famous for the art of pottery and especially for the lustered and colored glazes applied to earthenware. These glazed vessels, many of which were fireproof, were well designed for technological processes. Though the import of Chinese pottery and porcelain dates back to the eighth century, the secret of porcelain manufacture was not

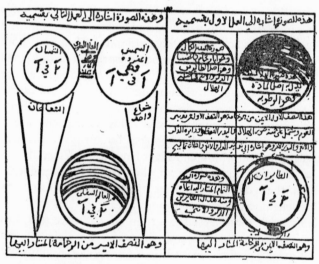

Alchemical diagram from Arabic treatise.

known in Persia before the twelfth century. Curiously enough, even by that time this important art had not spread to the West, where it was not discovered experimentally until the eighteenth century.

The improved quality of this pottery greatly helped the Arab chemists to attempt something like mass production of certain chemicals. They invented cylindrical or conical furnaces in which rows of alembics were arranged to produce rose water or "naphtha" (gasoline) by the heat of combustion gases. A fire in the citadel of Cairo in 1085 destroyed no less than 300 tons of gasoline stored there. The "gallery-furnace" method just described was the only way in which such large quantities could be produced. The ancient texts mention towns like Damascus as manufacturing and distilling centers.

The Arabs were interested in the production of textiles, too. During the eighth century they had introduced cotton into China. The production of silk, on the other hand, had been kept a trade secret by the Chinese. Silkworms were smuggled out of Turkestan in the sixth century and this art spread into Persia and Byzantium. The manufacture of woolen rugs and carpets was a typical art of this civilization and Turkish carpets are still highly valued today.

Just as certain names of chemicals and apparatus (such as "alkali," "antimony," and "alembic") passed from the Arab language into our own, so have many Arabic names of textiles been adopted by us. Thus damasks originally hailed from Damascus, and muslins from Mosul, while the word *taffeta* is derived from the Persian "taftah" and *fustian* (a cloth famous in the Middle Age) comes from Fostat, a suburb of Cairo. Egypt still produced the finest linen, Upper Egypt and Mesopotamia were renowned for their beautiful woolen goods, and Persia produced both linen and cotton. Cloth was largely the product of home industry; the women did the spinning, while weaving was a man's job.

The rise of an Arab paper industry was due to contacts with China. There in A.D. 105 an imperial official, Tsai Lun, had discovered the secret of papermaking at his home in Leiyang. He found that a pulp made of fibers produced from rags, mulberry bark, hemp and grass could be ladled onto a sieve, where it would lose a great deal of water and form a kind of fleece. When this fleece was carefully separated from the sieve and dried, a sheet was obtained which could be smoothed with alum or other sizing to produce a good writing surface. This new material—we call it paper although it is quite unlike the papyrus from which the word itself is derived—soon displaced bamboo and wood, which had been used in China previous to this time. By the ninth century paper napkins were already being produced in that country.

The art of papermaking spread quickly to the frontiers of the Chinese Empire. Nestorian Christians in Turkestan copied their Bibles and wrote their letters on good rag paper beginning with the third century A.D. The famous excavator, Aurel Stein, found many samples in these regions, where the paper remained in perfect condition in the sand-covered ruins of old towns. But the Chinese strove to keep their manufacturing process a secret from foreigners.

Here, as in the case of silk manufacture, the secret could not be kept long. When the Arabs took Samarkand, they captured several Chinese workmen who only a year before (752) had come to that town to work in the newly erected paper factory. Through them the secret became known and as early as 793 the first paper mill was built in Baghdad. Paper soon became so popular that about 800 we find writers of letters excusing themselves when they still had to resort to papyrus. About the year 900 standard formats of paper were introduced in Baghdad and some qualities were made extra-thin so that they could be used for "air mail" by pigeon post.

The paper trade was, of course, closely connected with bookbinding, an art in which the Arabs excelled. They made hand-tooled leather covers of great beauty, and the practice of using gold to decorate these bindings spread to the West. The form of book cover with overlapping edges such as is still used on some types of leather-bound Bibles is an original Arabic invention, as is the marbled paper used for the end papers of many modern books.

Around the year 1000, seven standard sizes of paper were used in the East, and Egypt already had wrapping paper. Paper money was introduced in Tabriz in 1024. Then in the eleventh and twelfth centuries the art spread to the coasts of North Africa and thence to Sicily and Spain. In Sicily, paper disappeared temporarily when the Normans conquered the island, but in Morocco and Spain many new paper mills were built in Fez, Cadiz, Cordoba, and Seville. From these towns the art spread to Europe in the thirteenth century, and paper slowly began to displace the older and more costly parchment, though the latter continued to be widely used. Because parchment was expensive and scarce, the medieval monks often resorted to erasing the text of old documents so that they could reuse the parchment for new epistles and records. A parchment treated in this way is called a *palimpsest* (Greek, "scraped again"). The original writing on many of these palimpsests can now be read by means of ultra-

Gallery-oven drawing from ancient Arabic manuscript.

violet and x-ray photography, and a number of lost texts have thus been recovered.

The older writing material, papyrus, had practically disappeared by the eighth century. Its manufacture had already declined during the fourth century, when it was mainly produced for the fabrication of ropes. Books were then no longer made of papyrus but of parchment. This shift contributed heavily to the decline of the papyrus industry, which now survives only in Sicily.

Sugar refining was an Arabian discovery. When sugar cane was imported into southern Persia from India about the year

500, the juice was produced by crushing the cane, but the Arabs were the first to devise a method of refining it. At first this was done by mixing the juice with milk and decanting the mixture, the impurities remaining with the milk in the form of a sediment. But in the eleventh century, Egyptian chemists discovered that the juice could be treated more efficiently and profitably with lime and ashes. After filtration, the greater part of the sugar could then be obtained by evaporation and crystallization.

Egypt then was a leading producer of sugar cane, and the new process of sugar refining spread all the way back to India and China. Marco Polo tells us that even the most skilled refiners in China were Egyptian workmen. Cane sugar could not be grown in Western Europe. When its production was undertaken in the European colonies in the West Indies, Egyptian methods and even Egyptian apparatus like mills were copied by the New World planters. Here again we find Arabic words that have crept into the English language, such as *julep* (Persian gulāb), meaning rose water, which was originally an aromatic medicinal drink; and *syrup*, which is derived from the Arabic word *sharāb*.

The method of distilling alcohol and of producing strong acids like sulfuric acid and nitric acid were introduced from Italy in the twelfth and thirteenth centuries respectively. They greatly affected many techniques. The production of perfumes, for instance, changed completely. The older chemists had produced their perfumes by "enfleurage," that is, the mixing of flowers and herbs with oils and molten waxes, which were then separated by filtration. The essential oils that carried the perfume were thus absorbed in the oil or fat. But the Arabs now began mixing the flowers and herbs with alcohol or water and distilling this mixture to produce a liquid perfume. When water was used the essential oils formed a thin layer on top of the mixture and could be removed in a concentrated form. In this way rose water was produced from rose leaves.

Apart from the production of perfumes, which was mainly

concentrated in Mesopotamia and Persia, there was the important manufacture of olive oil, which accounted for most of the consumption of fats in the Arabic world. Here classical methods remained unchanged.

Strong acids were also used in the beautiful metal inlay work that the Arab craftsmen were famous for. Through them the art of refining and testing metals was greatly improved and many good Arabic treatises on refining gold and silver were written in Egypt.

The Arabs were quick to recognize the value of new inventions. Thus while the compass was probably invented in Amalfi (Italy), the Arabs were using it in navigating the Mediterranean and the Indian Ocean before Petrus Peregrinus described the instrument as a curious phenomenon in 1268. The compass card appears on early Arabic maps, which were a distinct improvement on earlier Hellenistic charts. In the same way the Arabs adopted and improved the early European church-tower clocks that were moved by falling weights. They did not, however, succeed in making watches and spring-driven clocks. Neither did they improve on the hourglasses and water clocks that had been invented by the Greeks. This improvement had to wait for Henlein of Nuremberg, who made the first spring-driven watch about the year 1500, a timepiece called *Nuremberg egg,* as the Bavarians pronounced "Uhrlein" (little watch), "Eierlein" (little egg).

The Arabs were constantly at war with the Byzantines and other "heathens," so that the development of war engines progressed steadily. We need not describe here the host of storm rams, moving towers, and catapults used in those days. The introduction of chemical weapons on a large scale dates from these times. Thus one of the great state secrets of the Byzantines was "Greek fire." Tradition names a Syrian, Kallinikos, as the inventor, who escaped from his native country and settled down in Byzantium about the year 650. The few and sketchy descriptions of this Greek fire show that the word "fire" really denotes a series of inflammable mixtures that either were fired before being thrown as bombs or hand grenades, or exploded upon contact with water. Quicklime, gasoline or naphtha, saltpeter, and similar compounds made up these mixtures, which were also used in liquid form and were squirted from pumps upon the enemy ship or fortification.

The Byzantines used these arms effectively to beat back both Arab and Mongol attacks by land and sea. The Arabs learned the secret and the Crusaders tell us of the awe that the Greek fire instilled in them when they saw it used in Palestine and Egypt. European books such as Marcus the Greek's *On Fires to Burn the Enemy* mention these chemical weapons. The Second Lateran Council forbade the use of these inhuman weapons of war in 1139, and this code was kept by most civilized nations until the First World War.

The Arabs and the Mongols who learned from them had special engineering corps in the army that repaired and laid bridges, conducted sieges, and handled siege engines. We hear that Hulagu Khan formed a group of 1,000 *naffatyn* (or naphtha throwers) who were clad in asbestos uniforms in accordance with Arab practice. Thus they could enter a burning city in the wake of their own incendiary bombs.

After the year 1100 Arab civilization declined. The Arab states fought constantly among themselves and some were conquered by the Christians and other peoples. The inroads of Turks and Mongols shook the world of Islam to its foundations, but these invaders did not succeed in destroying it. Nevertheless the decline that set in around 1100 was certainly partly due to these destructive forces. Though much remains to be learned about Arab technology and engineering through continued study of the available manuscripts and other records in the East itself, there is little doubt that after 1100 the spirit of inquiry and research was broken. After that date Arab scientists wasted their energies in squabbles over theoretical and mystical problems and showed little interest in the improvement of their material culture. Arab technology and engineering came to a standstill. The torch of civilization had passed out of the hands of the Arabs into those of the Western world.

V I

Technology and Theology

(A.D. 400–1500)

WHEN in the fourth century A.D. the Roman authority in the West finally crumbled under the attacks of
tribes crossing the Rhine and Danube rivers, which for three
centuries had been the frontier of the Empire, the so-called
Dark Ages are said to have begun. Popular opinion still mis-
takenly holds that the invaders laid waste city and country
and thus contributed to the stagnation of civilization. Actually during the last days of the Empire the decentralization
of government had already been carried to dangerous extremes
in the hands of emperors like Honorius and Arcadius, whose
father, the emperor Theodosius, had divided the Empire between them at his death in A.D. 395.

The invading tribes, which were not very numerous, settled
mostly in the larger cities and ruled largely by collecting
tribute. They were absorbed fairly quickly and after a few
generations had been almost completely assimilated with the
conquered. What broke down was the old Roman system of
central government. The Empire was dissolved into a great
many self-sufficient units. The countryside, little touched
by the invasions, was thrown back on its own. The despair of a
few late-classical authors should not blind us to the fact that
the Roman Empire had really corroded from within and died
of old age.

This disintegration of central authority had profound effects on the development of engineering, for only a central authority is strong enough to organize and finance expensive public works like road building, canals, and bridges. And so it was that the world that survived the invasions was broken up into small villages and farms, monasteries and manors, all self-centered and producing for their own immediate needs. This economic scheme was overlaid by an ancient network of roads and highways, bridges and aqueducts, which had been built for a huge empire. Old army encampments had formed the nucleus of most towns. These often weathered the storms, for they had long been the centers of trade, and trade was still being carried on, though on a far smaller scale than before. Syrian and Italian traders still brought their wares up the rivers and mountain passes to the northern and western parts of Europe. Trade still focused on the Mediterranean world that had begotten Roman civilization.

Gradually the towns and villages of Europe were consolidated into countries, duchies, kingdoms, and empires. More than once this process of consolidation and reorientation was seriously interrupted during this long period of growth. The greatest dangers in those days were the inroads of the Vikings (850–950). Then the future of the Western world seemed once more to be in mortal peril despite the promising recovery made in the Carolingian Age (800–850). Both Vikings and Arabs were at the height of their offensive power. But their invasions were stemmed, and the Vikings settled down to become part of the scheme of things in Europe.

From then on Europe began to flourish, at first slowly and then with accelerated speed. Countries like Germany, France, and England began to emerge, so that by the twelfth century the danger was past and the culture of the Middle Ages was approaching its highest point.

Medieval Science

THE philosophy underlying medieval civilization was based exclusively on Christian theology and morality. It had as its goal the Kingdom of Heaven rather than the conquest of nature. The effect of this philosophy on science and technology was indeed profound: in the field of science the modern scholar is inclined to think "disastrous" would be the better word.

Science in the Middle Ages was totally different from modern science in concept as well as in method. Science was no longer the handmaid of philosophy; instead, both were made to serve religion. This can be clearly seen from a consideration of the syllabus of an early medieval university. The basis of medieval education was the *trivium*, consisting of grammar, rhetoric, and logic. Then the student enrolled for the *quadrivium*, which comprised arithmetic, geometry, music, and astronomy. Apparently astronomy involved some instruction in natural science as well, but the arithmetic taught was of the simplest kind. Geometry did not even fully embrace the books of Euclid. Music was hardly more than a mystical philosophy of numbers. The instruction in astronomy was aimed at little more than enabling the student to calculate the date of Easter. These seven liberal arts were then rounded off by the study of natural and moral philosophy, metaphysics, and theology; thereafter the student might turn to the study of law, medicine, or perhaps church architecture. But generally speaking his education was mainly along ecclesiastical lines. The universities of the Middle Ages never intended to turn out anything but doctors of divinity, law, or medicine. There was no place in the curriculum for natural science as a separate field of study.

The Bible and the Church Fathers reigned supreme until well into the thirteenth century. Then conditions changed, though not because of the Crusades, as is still commonly believed. A set of scholars, mostly English, were not satisfied with the state of learning and attempted to introduce some improvements. They took the trouble to study at Spanish universities and began to translate Arabic, Jewish, and Hebrew works. Greek originals or their Arabic translations were discovered and imported from Byzantium, Toledo, and other great universities outside the pale of Christendom. Above all, the works of Aristotle were recovered in more complete form, free from the distortions introduced by the various Latin copyists. The latter part of the Middle Ages saw the incorporation of Aristotle's philosophy into the theology based on the Christian Bible. All of this commendable scholarship reached its apex in the work of Albertus Magnus and St. Thomas Aquinas. Through the efforts of Robert Grosseteste and Roger Bacon natural science became a separate field of study at Oxford University.

Classical Greece and Rome had known nothing like a university, which was wholly a product of the Middle Ages. It was born in Italy about the year 1000 in such early schools as Salerno, Bologna, and Padua. Famous universities like Paris, Oxford, and Cambridge were founded in the course of the twelfth century. And though natural science as such was rarely a separate field of study, the recovery of the scientific works of Aristotle and other Hellenistic and Arabic authors sowed the seed for a new approach to the "shape of things in nature." This study was to flourish and bear fruit in the sixteenth century. More and more scientific discussions occur in medieval manuscripts. The famous English friar, Roger Bacon, could dream in 1269 of "the making of instruments of marvelous excellence and utility, as instruments of flying, and moving in chariots without animals at an incomparable velocity, and of navigating without oars more swiftly than can be supposed possible by the hands of men. . . . Flying machines can be made, and a man sitting in the middle revolving an engine by which skillfully made wings beat the air like a flying bird."

But contemporary scientific studies had no effect on applied science and engineering, though they forecast the revolution to come. Medieval science in general did not consider man *per se* a fit subject for study, and turned its attention to astrology and magic instead. The first man to declare that it was the duty of natural science to harness the forces of nature for the benefit of mankind was Roger Bacon's name-sake, Francis Bacon (1561-1626).

The Medieval Engineer

THE engineers and technologists of the Middle Ages were therefore left on their own by the university scientists. No theoretical background or encouragement helped their progress, which perforce had to proceed by trial and error. But there were other factors that tended to support their efforts. One of these was the heritage of technical achievement of the Graeco-Roman world, which, contrary to common belief, was never lost during the Dark Ages. Thus, for example, the Roman roads continued to survive for many centuries even though the peasants in some regions used them as quarries when the long-distance traffic for which they had been built no longer existed. While there had remained a widespread trade in salt, metals, timber, wine, spices, and textiles, river and sea traffic now absorbed most of it. On the other hand, the Roman roads, in the long run, were less suited to the harsher climate of the northwest. The rains and frost often broke up the slab pavement and disintegrated the foundations. Taught by this experience, the engineers of the Middle Ages actually invented a more suitable form of road construction by laying stone cobbles in a thick cushion of sand, a type of pavement that is still in common use in Europe and the United States.

Secondly, the "barbarians" of the Dark Ages were not such low brutes as was once commonly believed. They had a civilization of their own and brought to the West such widely divergent gifts as furs and trousers, the art of building houses that were more suited to the climate than the Roman patio type, feltmaking, cloisonné jewelry, the ski, the use of soap and butter, the making of barrels and tubs, new grains like oats, rye, spelt, and hops, and the art of falconry.

Through the trade routes of the steppes commerce was

established with Central Asia and the Far East. The Arabs traded directly through Russia with Sweden and the north. Byzantine and Arab influences also passed through the Mediterranean. It has been established that the compass, gunpowder, and printing with movable type were riginally Western inventions. Several of them were passed on to the East by various routes, some of which led directly from Europe eastward through the steppes of Central Asia. The origin of many other inventions is still shrouded in mystery, for the history of ancient and medieval technology has not yet been fully explored.

A third powerful factor was derived from the tenets of Christianity. According to Genesis 1:27, God had created man in His own image. Hence however degraded the status of man might be, he remained in God's image. Slavery lost its grip on mankind in these Christian ages, for whatever certain classes in Europe may have said and thought of it, Christianity forced mankind to regard their fellows as men, not as chattels. There was now a constant urge to better the earthly lot of mankind. Along with the new social and economic trends toward reform we find the first development of machinery to replace hand labor for heavy tasks. Men began to dream of machines that would take over their more arduous duties. What the Romans had never tackled was now attempted.

The creation of automatic machines and the mechanization of labor go back to the beginning of the medieval period, when the quest for sources of power derived from nature first originated—a quest that still continues to stimulate the inventor's mind at the present time. It is typical of European technology that patents which sometimes occur in the form of privileges in antiquity after a long struggle find their modern form in Florence in the fifteenth century. Venice had its first patent law in 1474. In England, a system of grants existed and after 1561 a regular stream of English patents appeared. This means that individual rights to inventions were recognized in Europe, a great stimulus both to inventors and to the development of power machinery.

The Middle Ages, then, contained the beginnings of modern European and American inventiveness. There is no doubt that the Middle Ages mean much more in the history of technology than is usually admitted. Medieval technology was, of course, very much in the service of the Church, a fact that is clear in such early technological works as Heraclius's *On the Colors and Arts of the Romans*, or Theophilus's *On the Various Arts*. The latter, for instance, is a description of all the arts that go into the embellishment of churches and chapels. It details the tenth century's achievements in lead glass windows, the construction of organs and their pipes, the casting of bells, the manufacture of inlaid caskets and cloisonné jewelry, the art of making chalices and other metal objects encrusted with precious stones, and so on. The metallurgical processes are discussed extensively, even the smelting of the ores, the selection of wood for charcoal manufacture, the building of glass furnaces, and many other interesting techniques.

But all of this information is directed toward applied art and does not describe technology in the strict sense of the word. Technological information is hard to get in medieval manuscripts and has to be collected from scraps of information. So we should really say that the Middle Ages to a certain extent developed the resourcefulness of numerous smaller groups of humanity and that during this period new technological patterns were evolved.

Horse, Water Wheel, and Windmill

WE HAVE had occasion to remark that animal power was inefficiently used by antiquity. The main trouble lay in the yoke system of harnessing. Though it was adequate for slow-moving oxen, it was completely unsatisfactory for the faster horse. The yoke rested on the withers of a team. From each end of the yoke ran two flexible straps: one a girth behind the foreleg, the other circling the animal's neck. The front strap pressed on the moving animal's windpipe and prevented the animal from pulling hard. Calculations show that no greater force than 70 pounds could be exerted by one horse under this arrangement, and the ancients possessed no means of harnessing two horses in tandem.

Great improvements came during the later ninth and early tenth centuries. First of all, the modern horse collar, a rigid structure resting on the shoulders of the horse, was introduced. This permitted the animal to throw its full weight into pulling and greatly improved its efficiency. Secondly, the tandem harness was invented, which allowed an indefinite number of animals to be combined in pulling. The first invention alone increased the pull of one animal to three or four times what the ancients got out of it. Third, the horseshoe was introduced. Ancient horses were all unshod, though a kind of attachable shoe had been used for slippery surface and snow at an early date. But ancient horses had no nailed shoes, so that broken hooves very often rendered the animals useless. It will be clear that these three inventions meant another enormous stride toward the liberation of the slaves. Formerly all heavy loads had to be moved by manpower. Now animals could be used more effectively. Incidentally, the more efficient use of the horse also helped in building up better agricultural methods.

This agricultural revolution is closely connected with the introduction of the northern wheeled plow equipped with colter (or knife) to cut the grassy surface, horizontal plowshare for cutting the furrow itself, and a moldboard for turning over and pulverizing the soil. Its exact origin is still obscure, though it certainly came from north of the Mediterranean area. It is obvious that this new plow greatly increased production by making possible the tillage of rich, heavy, river-bottom soils that were badly drained. By making deeper furrows, it also eliminated the need for cross plowing —that is, plowing a field twice so that the second set of furrows cross the first at right angles. Thus the new plow initiated the typical northern system of strip farming, whereby the total available land was divided into long strips for allotment to each farmer, the idea being that one man would not get all the good land at the expense of the other farmers.

Sixteenth-century woodcut of late medieval agriculture, illustrating use of the horse-drawn plow. (From the Grüninger edition of Virgil's Georgics *published at Strassburg in 1502.)*

The ancients with their much lighter plow had always resorted to a block system that derived from their habit of cross plowing. The new system of plowing long strips with parallel lengthwise furrows was a much more efficient method of cultivation.

However, the new plow taxed the pulling strength of one animal because it cut so much deeper. The peasants, accordingly, began to cooperate in pooling their oxen and thus laid the basis for the medieval cooperative agricultural community, the manor, although the introduction of this plow may actually have been much earlier. Its effects were stimulated by the introduction of the three-field system in the latter part of the eighth century. The improved rotation of crops and fallows definitely increased the efficiency of agricultural labor. There was less plowing combined with more surface in crop than with the older two-field system, in which one field lay fallow while the other was cultivated. But while it worked very well in the north of Europe, it would have failed in the south for lack of summer rains.

The improved harness, which may have been introduced from Central Asia, allowed the use of the horse in this new agricultural scheme. Oxen were slow, though they consumed only the cheap hay and thus saved the more valuable grain that was an important item in the peasant's diet. The introduction of the horse in plowing meant a saving of labor, despite the consequent consumption of grain as fodder. By the end of the tenth century the horse was well established in northern European agriculture, and was gradually displacing the ox.

A smaller but no less important invention connected with the horse was the stirrup, also introduced into Europe during the Dark Ages, presumably from the steppes. It made horsemanship and cavalry more efficient. Incidentally, it also contributed to the rise of frontal cavalry attacks in medieval warfare. Shock tactics became possible through the use of the stirrup, which allowed the cavalryman to brace himself for the charge.

The second important source of power was the undershot or overshot water wheel moved by the force of rivers and streams. Though this was an ancient invention, probably dating back to the first century B.C. (then mentioned in Asia Minor), it was not employed by the Romans on any appreciable scale for reasons already discussed. During the Dark Ages, however, its use spread to the north, where it became rapidly established as it had in the world of Islam. In the north it was more at home. There the rivers did not dry up in summertime but supplied a constant stream of water to move the wheels.

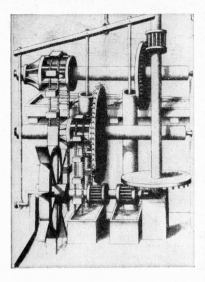

PLATE 5 Gearing system combining a water wheel and several machines, devised by Jacopo da Strada about 1580.

PLATE 6 Old medieval power loom. (From the *Mendelsche Brüderbuch*, circa 1450.)

PLATE 7 Water wheel and mine hoist, from Agricola's *De Re Metallica*, 1550.

PLATE 8 Drawing by Leonardo da Vinci showing his design of a new type of spinning wheel. (*Codex Atlantico*, Fol. 393, verso *a*.)

PLATE 9 Early Dutch dredger, drawn by Pieter Breughel the Elder, c. 1569. (*Courtesy of the State Museum, Amsterdam.*)

The water-driven mill was the typical power plant of the Middle Ages. It could grind corn, move the carpenter's saw, and—above all—the smith's bellows. This greater supply of blast air was most important to medieval metallurgy and was one of the causes of the development of cast-iron production. Incidentally, it also meant the evolution of gears and cams and the practical study of mechanics, a science that was to flourish in the later Middle Ages. A stream of manuals on mechanics, engineering, and metallurgy began to flow in the thirteenth century.

The crank, developed at this time, was one of the most important inventions in the history of mankind. This method of translating reciprocal motion into rotary motion is probably as important as the wheel itself. We know that it was already known in the Utrecht Psalter (circa A.D. 850), and was used in hand mills, later on rotary grindstones.

A third medieval source of power was the windmill, introduced from the East, though in what way is still unknown. The earliest example of European windmills were built in Normandy about 1180, whence its use spread to England and the Low Countries. It quickly became the typical power plant of the flat wind-blown regions on the Atlantic seacoast. The Persian windmill had a vertical windshaft with sails, whereas the typical European windmills have a horizontal one.

In the mountainous districts of Europe and in the south with its rapid streams, the water wheel remained the principal source of power. But the windmill was soon turned to efficient use in grinding corn, drainage (fifteenth century), and in all the multiple uses to which such power machinery could be turned. It avoided the building of costly dikes and mill ponds necessary to drive water wheels. Until the advent of the steam engine it remained the chief source of power in Holland. That country has not yet completely relinquished this cheap form of power, as it still fulfills its task of draining the lowlands reclaimed from the sea.

Rise of the Textile Industry

ONE of the first medieval crafts to profit by machinery, especially in the case of tilt hammers and pounders moved by water wheels, was the textile industry. With the exception of metallurgy and mining, clothmaking was one of the few medieval crafts that developed into something like an industry.

Medieval woolweaver and his tools. (*From Stephanus,* Boek von den Schakspiel, *Lübeck.*)

For the medieval guilds, however high a level their craftsmanship may have attained, were always seriously hampered by lack of capital. This state of affairs retarded the introduction and development of more expensive tools and machinery, and it also gave rise to the curious forms of financing peculiar to those times.

The cloth industry was really a complex of several handicrafts, each of which was the exclusive business of a separate guild. Thus every operation in clothmaking was decentralized and dealt with by a separate group of craftsmen. The wool was first carded or combed by hand, then spun on the rock or distaff; next the yarn was woven on a loom worked by hand or foot, and finally the loose web thus made was fulled by hand (or foot) and the cloth was ready for dyeing and finishing.

The process of fulling consisted of beating or compressing the woven cloth in water. It served first of all to shrink the cloth. This increased the density and weight per unit length, giving it much greater resistance to weather and wear. Secondly, it served to "felt" the cloth, entangling the fibers so closely that the pattern of weaving was often invisible. It gave the cloth greater strength and a smoother and softer finish. This was essential to the later finishing processes like raising and shearing. The fulling process also scoured and cleaned the cloth, removing, with the aid of detergents like fuller's earth, the oil with which the wool had been impregnated before spinning.

In the early Middle Ages fulling meant beating with the feet, with the hands, or with clubs. The first method was used for long, heavy broadcloth. The latter two, both usually called hand fulling, were applied to smaller articles. Fulling by foot was mechanized in the Middle Ages by a twofold invention. In the first place the action of the two feet was replaced by that of wooden hammers, alternately raised and dropped on the cloth as it lay in the trough and controlled by a revolving drum on the tilt- or lift-hammer system. This revolving drum was attached to the shaft of a water wheel, which supplied the motive power. A series of hammers could now be worked by one man alone, whose job was to stand by and watch the cloth to see that it kept moving properly through the trough.

The spinning wheel was introduced in the thirteenth century, mechanizing the second phase of clothmaking. It is now clear that it was a Western invention, certainly not introduced from India. The medieval spinning wheel was actually the first step on the road to fully mechanized spinning. It consisted in providing mechanical means for rotating the spindle while spinning. The whorl or wharve of the spindle was grooved and was moved by a band connecting it with a large wheel turned by the left hand. Thus the process of winding up the yarn was mechanized. The twist was still given by the right hand of the spinner. This primitive "bobbing wheel" remained in use for coarse yarns up to the nineteenth century. During the sixteenth century a treadle was developed to move the bobbing wheel by foot, thus leaving the spinner's hands free.

The next step was the semimechanization of the twisting operation by the application of the flyer to the spinning wheel. This was the so-called Saxony wheel of the sixteenth century.

The complete mechanization of spinning with a series of spools was achieved in the course of the eighteenth century when Paul, Wyatt, and Arkwright invented fully mechanized twisting.

This mechanical development was possible only because the cloth industry was financed by big bankers and merchants who supplied the different guilds involved with the necessary raw materials and capital. Apart from their function as bankers, they had to receive the raw wool, pass it on to be carded, collect it, pass it on to the spinner, and so on until the finished cloth was returned, thus supervising and coordinating the different phases of the cloth industry. This is typical, too, of other crafts like mining and metallurgy which grew up in the Middle Ages, protected and sponsored by the rising capitalism.

The cloth industry, then, concentrated in such rich countries as Italy, Flanders, and England, where large amounts of capital were accumulating. Because the craftsmen belonging to these guilds grew more and more apart from those in other guilds who could still finance their own shops, they gradually acquired the characteristics of skilled labor and became wage earners of the modern type. The contrast between them and the banker-employer began to take forms differing greatly from that between men with money and, say, weavers some centuries earlier. All the forms of class warfare begin to appear:

sweating, lockouts, strikes, and other features of modern industrial systems. Destruction of machinery or attempts to prevent its introduction were also reported.

Cast Iron and New Arms

THE greatest technical achievement of the Middle Ages was the production of cast iron. Actually it was the result of a slow development of the smelting furnace. Antiquity, as we have seen, had known cast iron only as a freak; it was never used when it was accidentally produced but was simply thrown away. The production of a type of iron capable of being cast into molds meant a great advantage and a chance to use some of the techniques of the bronze smith in iron metallurgy.

To produce cast iron it was necessary to have a hotter furnace than any used up to that time. The Roman metallurgists had already experimented with different types of smelting furnaces. Later generations improved their efficiency as well as their output. Furnaces were now capable of operating at higher temperatures and their size was considerably increased. At the same time water power had to be harnessed and used to move the larger bellows that were now required. This meant that a larger amount of blast air was introduced into the larger furnace per unit of time, resulting in higher temperatures. As the iron remained longer in the larger furnace at higher temperatures, a larger percentage of carbon was absorbed so that a good grade of cast iron resulted.

By 1300 the use of water wheels to move larger bellows improved conditions in the blast furnaces of the iron industry along the Rhine so much that regular production of cast iron became possible. The new art was soon widely mastered. In contrast to the older processes of producing wrought iron and steel, a liquid product could now be released from the bottom of the furnace by opening the clay-sealed holes, and the cast iron could be made to flow in the molds previously prepared from mixtures of sand and clay. This did not, however, displace the older techniques. Wrought iron continued to be produced as well as crucible steel, which was smithed into strips and often welded together into weapons and tools of a peculiar structure. The days of cast steel were still a long way off.

Cast iron soon had an important influence on the construction of war engines, for the invention of gunpowder came about the same time. Cast iron was used very effectively in

Armorer in his shop. (*From Rodericus Zamorensis*, Spiegel des menschlichen Lebens, *Mämler, Augsburg, 1479.*)

the manufacture of cannon and other ordnance. The smaller arms and tools were still produced from the older wrought iron. The water wheel also meant the introduction of water-driven hammers, which could handle large lumps of wrought iron. But most metal tools and weapons were still made by hand. In fact, the spread of the production of cast iron and the introduction of the blast furnace was very slow. Older kinds of furnaces incapable of producing cast iron remained in use for the production of wrought iron for many centuries. When the great changes in metallurgical techniques came in the nineteenth century, scores of different furnaces of widely varying age were in use all over Europe, very often producing only for local consumption.

Many earlier writers have claimed that gunpowder, like the compass, was invented in China in India. It is now clear that both were originally Western inventions dating from about the end of the thirteenth or beginning of the fourteenth century. Here again the Arabs quickly introduced the new invention of gunpowder into their realm. It is also well known that the Chinese prepared pyrotechnical devices with saltpeter in 1175 and that the Mongols reported an "arrow of flying fire" said to have been invented by Wei-Ching in 1282.

True gunpowder as an inflammable mixture of finely divided carbon and saltpeter (to which flowers of sulfur were later added) was invented along the lower course of the Rhine between 1320 and 1330. As early as 1331 firearms were used during the siege of Cividale, Italy, by German soldiers. During the siege of Terni in 1340 the first cast-iron "bombards" or mortars were used. Early experimenting with bronze guns and mortars in such battles as those of Cahors and Tournai (1345) was fairly successful. It led to the concentration of the production of guns in famous centers like Augsburg after 1370. The inventor of the cast-iron mortar was Merklin Gast, who also produced the first good hand firearm, which helped to make Augsburg and other centers renowned for the quality of their gunmaking.

These early firearms raised scores of new problems. One of the most important of these was that of loading the gun. The earliest mortars and handguns had incorporated the principle of breech loading—that is, introducing the bullet and gunpowder at the rear of the bore instead of at the muzzle. But this system had to be abandoned fairly soon, as no gastight breech block could yet be constructed due to the insufficient accuracy of the existing tools. The gunmakers therefore returned to the principle of muzzle loading, which had been in use for many centuries. In fact, it was only when an abundance of steel and accurate machine tools made gastight breech blocks available cheaply around 1840 that the muzzle-loading system was finally doomed.

The earliest handguns made after 1398 had separate chambers for powder and bullet. It was not until well into the sixteenth century that these two chambers were combined in one loading unit, although Leonardo da Vinci had conceived the idea of a cartridge perhaps 60 years earlier. The Swedish king Gustavus Adolphus provided his soldiers with primitive cartridges during the Thirty Years' War. The cartridge was a brilliant idea which eventually solved most of the breech-loading troubles, but its general introduction dates back only a hundred years, for accurately machined mass-produced articles were not available until about the middle of the nineteenth century.

The poor fit of the medieval cannon ball and bullet with reference to the gun barrel prevented an efficient use of the full force of the exploding gunpowder, so that gunmakers were always looking for better explosives. The use of gunpowder in power form was superseded by the more efficient granular gunpowder toward the end of the fifteenth century. After 1525 gunpowder was judged and priced according to grain size. The gun barrel was extended to make more efficient use of the energy developed by the exploding charge, and the stock was bent to make it rest more easily against the shoulder. In 1540 August Kuttner discovered that a spirally grooved or "rifled" barrel would impart a spinning motion to the bullet and give it a more accurate trajectory. This method of constructing gun barrels gave the rifle its name.

The search for new explosives was on, but it was not successful until the nineteenth century when chemical knowledge was much more advanced. No substitute for gunpowder was found. In 1495 Leonardo da Vinci invented a gun fired by compressed steam, but this invention remained barren. However, a much less dangerous way was found to put the spark to the tinder. In 1378 the first fuse was invented. The fuse solved the problem of the firing of weapons like mortars but brought no solution for handguns. Here the powder on the pan connected with the powder in the barrel had to be fired by sparks which in turn were ignited by striking a piece of pyrites or flint. This led to the evolution of the matchlock gun, followed by the improved wheel-lock gun (1517, Nuremberg), and other types until the nineteenth century again brought the solution to the problem with the introduction of the percussion cap (1807).

But the fuse led to the invention of a new arm, the hand grenade. The first hand grenades were used in 1435, but they were not very safe for the grenadier to handle and did not become dependable until about 1600, when they had been sufficiently improved so that Prince Maurice of Orange could introduce them in his army.

Medieval bombard. (From Lynn Montross, War Through the Ages, *Harper & Brothers, New York, 1946.)*

The idea of making bullets or other projectiles that exploded in air occurs frequently in the notebooks of Leonardo da Vinci. Its first practical realization came in 1573, and in 1596 models appeared with an adjustable firing gear. The first efficient exploding projectile was invented by Renaud Ville in 1602, but its development remained at a standstill until 1803, when General Henry Shrapnel (1761–1842), who gave it its modern name, perfected an improved type of bursting charge for the British Army.

The main problem of the medieval gunsmith was to find materials that could withstand the high pressure of the explosion gases. The earlier bronze and cast-iron guns and mortars were very unreliable, and not infrequently the gun crew was hoist with its own petard. Some of the earlier mortars were made of strips of metal held together by iron rings. Wrought iron had often to be resorted to. The handling of large castings and the construction of the proper molds, as well as the melting and handling of the large quantities of molten metal with which to cast the barrels, were beyond the medieval gunsmith's capacities. On the other hand, the demand for the new arms was pressing and many ordnance engineers turned to the improvement of casting methods. Still it was not until 1720 that Keller of Cassel, Germany, succeeded in casting the first complete gun in a single mold, the rough casting being then drilled to form the barrel. Only when cast steel was available in the nineteenth century could guns be produced more cheaply.

Army officials were naturally unwilling to accept inaccurately made guns or guns of unique design whose parts (and bullets) were not interchangeable with those of other guns. Hence the army was one of the first groups to insist on interchangeable standardized parts. This made artillery into something that could only be handled on a large scale. The earlier "bombardiers" had been craftsmen, and had been treated on the battlefield as specialists or technicians, not common soldiers. As guns and rifles became standardized, however, this privileged position changed rapidly. The fifteenth century was the period in which some of the earliest handbooks on gunmaking were published, such as Konrad Kyeser's *Bellefortis*, in which the methods of constructing standard guns and handguns are clearly described. These methods paralleled the evolution of better ways of aiming, the application of sights to hand arms, and the adjustment of the elevation and traverse of artillery by means of worm gears and screws.

About 1500, artillery had become a better and safer arm, just as the more scientific forms of guns, developed some seventy years earlier in Como, Italy, had been improved and generally adopted. The famous artillery school of Venice was established in 1506, only a few years before the equally famous one at Burgos, Spain. Both profited by the system of standard artillery introduced by the emperor Maximilian I and based on the weight of the cannon ball that the gun fired. From this system came the well-known terms "ten-pounder," "twenty-pounder," and so forth. A system assessing guns according to standard bores was developed in 1540 by George Hartmann of Nuremberg. For hand arms Prince Maurice of Orange introduced the system of standardization based on the number of bullets contained in a pound.

Standardization was not limited to guns and cannon balls, but spread to other features of the military. In fact the coming of firearms meant the mechanization of warfare. Standardization of guns was soon followed by organized drill, standard uniforms, and finally by conscription. It spread to the arsenals of Venice and Holland, where it was applied with great profit to the merchant marine and the royal fleet. Indeed, armies and navies from the time of the fifteenth century belonged to the strongest forces behind the movement for mass production of interchangeable machine parts and tools, a development that was to reach its full flowering in the first half of the twentieth century.

It should be remembered that firearms were far from perfect in the first two centuries of their use, so that their influence on medieval warfare should not be overestimated. In fact it was not until about 1500 that they began to play a really important part in European warfare. Thus, for instance, the end of the typical medieval tactic, the charge of the mounted knights in armor, was not due to the coming of firearms, but partly to the famous English longbow and partly to the stubborness of the trained Swiss foot soldier. Only long after the Swiss had caused the downfall of the once invincible cavalry did guns and firearms become real dangers in warfare. Guns did not become a serious menace to the medieval fortress until about 1500. Then they began to change the whole system of warfare and started a new cycle of scientific design and construction of fortresses. Nonetheless the early guns and mortars were still greatly admired and imitated by the Arabs and Mongols, who drew European experts to their courts.

The introduction of artillery also had a profound influence on science, for it raised many problems that were discussed for generations at the Italian academies, the Royal Society in London, and other learned bodies and universities. The whole problem of the path of a projectile was subjected to much study and experimentation. The calculation of trajectories involved the laws of falling bodies, the effect of gravitation and wind resistance, and many related physical phenomena which together make up the modern science of ballistics. The solution of these problems was of greater importance to pure science than to warfare alone. Thus the "bestial frenzy" (as Leonardo characterized it) had a few effects that were of lasting value to mankind, though they did not outweigh the sorrows and devastation of war.

Chemical Technology

MECHANICAL and industrial developments were accompanied by some notable discoveries made in the field of chemical technology. These were closely connected with the development of distillation apparatus. The older chemists had always cooled the alembic, or heart-shaped condensing head built on top of the still. Gradually the practice of cooling the spout of the alembic was introduced, and after the fourteenth century the spout was enclosed in a condensing coil, from which the modern condenser is derived. With this improvement it now became possible to recover by condensation those liquids or substances having low boiling points.

The earliest descriptions of alcohol date from about the year 1100. They can be found in manuscripts from that great medical center, Salerno. A hundred years later alcohol obtained by distilling wine was already a well-known substance. Strong alcohol was usually prepared in two stages during the Middle Ages. The primary distillation produced a 60 per cent alcohol which was called *aqua ardens* or burning water. A redistillation brought the percentage up to 96 per cent (or 192 proof in modern terminology), the final product being known as *aqua vitae* or water of life. In 1320 alcohol was produced on a larger scale in Modena, Italy, and knowledge of it spread to France and Germany. Monasteries and apothecaries used this alcohol in preparing concoctions of herbs, which were sold as medicines at first. The Black Death which ravaged the population of Europe was one of the causes of the spread of strong alcoholic beverages. After this holocaust had passed, the habit of drinking brandy, liqueurs, and aquavit or gin remained firmly entrenched as a social custom.

These strong drinks now slowly became more popular than the older light wines and beers. Already in the fifteenth century we find several towns in France and Germany forbidding the use of strong liquor and enacting laws to punish public intoxication, which had been fairly rare up until then. The use of bear yeast to turn grain into alcohol also began at about this time, but met with the resistance from all classes, for the use of grain to make alcohol was considered to be a sinful waste of a valuable food. Several centers famous for their herb gardens and flowers were now producing alcoholic extracts and distillates of the type still used as liqueurs. The Benedictine monastery gave its name to a famous brandy, and towns like Naples, Modena, Würzburg, and many regions in France also produced liqueurs.

The improved distillation technique made possible another significant advance in chemistry. From 1150 Italian chemists distilled nitric acid from a mixture of saltpeter and alum. Venice and certain towns in France and Germany were the manufacturing centers of this acid, which was the principal reagent used in the refining of gold containing silver. Sulfuric acid was produced in the thirteenth century either by dry distillation of alum or by burning sulfur under a glass bell jar over water. The first method produced a much stronger acid than the latter, and not until the sixteenth century did Libavius prove that they were identical. Muriatic acid was distilled in the fifteenth century from a mixture of alum and common salt. The knowledge of these strong acids quickly spread east and west. They could be used for the solution of salts, in metallurgy and metalworking, and as mordants and bleaching agents.

The knowledge of the acids and of low-boiling solvents like alcohol was of major importance to the development of both theoretical and practical chemistry. The older chemists had generally been limited to the study of solids or liquids; now these could be studied in solution with other compounds. The chemical industry became the domain of the distiller's guild, which in the fifteenth century embraced not only the gin manufacturers but also the apothecaries and acid manufacturers. The distillation of acids opened the door to the production of a variety of new chemicals.

The character of many products changed completely. Medicines in the early Middle Ages usually took the form of powders or syrups. These were now generally replaced by tinctures—solutions or distillates of the drug or specific in alcohol. Perfumes had always been prepared in the classical way by mixing herbs and flowers with oil or molten fat. This ancient method of enfleurage was now partly superseded by the distillation of the raw materials with alcohol or water.

The chemical industry was greatly assisted by the improved quality of glass and glazes, and Italy had become an important center of pottery. Many techniques were introduced from the Arabic world, and therefore indirectly from China. Faience and majolica techniques were born in this way. The improvement of glazes enabled the practical chemists to obtain good materials for handling such corrosives as strong acids. At the same time the mass production of better and more beautiful household pottery led to a gradual displacement of tin or pewter vessels and plates. Even in the Middle Ages certain towns in Italy and Germany specializied in the manufacture of good laboratory ware.

The production of glass also made great strides. Glass windowpanes were known in antiquity, but their use did not become common until civilization had spread to the colder northern and western lands along the Atlantic coast. In churches and dwellings these windows became a necessity. Panes made of mica, as used by the Romans, were too expensive and impractical. After the fifth century we find increasing evidence of the use of glass windows in churches. By the tenth century stained glass windows had become one of the chief glories of the medieval cathedral.

Stained glass windows were not only highly decorative but a practical necessity, for it was impossible to produce glass sheets large enough for the huge windows of the lofty cathedrals, some windows being over 40 feet high—those at Beauvais reach a height of 55 feet. Small panes not more than a foot square could be made either by the crown method (blowing a hollow sphere of glass and rotating it until it flattened) used by the ancient Romans, or by casting. It was not until after 1800 that the hand-cylinder method of making window glass came into use, whereby the workman blew a long glass cylinder about a foot and a half in diameter and about five feet long, cut it open lengthwise, and rolled it flat to form a windowpane. But in the Middle Ages such techniques were impossible because of the limited size of the glass furnaces and the absence of rolling mills capable of producing a flat glass; moreover, glass could not be properly refined and decolorized without better knowledge of chemistry.

Hence the medieval glazier's art consisted of building up windows from small pieces of colored glass held and strengthened by lead ribs, which also formed part of the design. As the windowpanes grew larger the functional meaning of the leading grew more and more to be that of merely reinforcing the window against wind pressure. The leaded glass windows of the sixteenth century consist of fairly large panes on which the design is engraved by etching and painting with special ingredients.

The gradual development of the size of windowpanes can still be seen in any ancient European town, where the very old houses have windows consisting of a checkerboard of smaller panes. Thus we find a continuous development from the older leaded glass made up of a mosaic of small colored bits of glass to the modern form in which the techniques of etching and painting are prominent.

The greatest center of glassmaking in the medieval world was Murano, a small island in the lagoon of Venice. Its traditions go back to classical times, and as a result of the skill developed there glass became one of the most important of Venetian exports. The art of glass blowing spread from Murano to France and Germany, but the quality of Venetian glass always remained superior, being more transparent, stable, and decorative than Roman or other types of glass. Murano had introduced the Hellenistic invention of heating finished glass articles in sand to eliminate all strains due to blowing and bending. This was a decided improvement, especially in the case of chemical glassware that was now increasingly used after the thirteenth century.

Soap was another Western innovation developed by chemical technology. Though the ancients knew ointments and medicinal preparations that contained the ingredients for soapmaking and also knew how to prepare alkaline lyes from the ashes of plants, the Gauls seem to have been the inventors of soap. Pliny mentions that it was "an invention of the Gauls for giving a reddish tint to the hair. It was prepared from tallow and the ashes of the beech and yoke-elm, both as liquid or solid soap." In the second century A.D., the Gauls seem to have already used it for the washing of clothes. Aretaeus, who brings us this news, himself recommends it for the baths. There is no evidence that the Romans made soap, despite certain references to a soapmaking factory at Pompeii. By the seventh century, however, the manufacture of soap in Italy had become so important that the soapmakers were organized into a craft guild. Craftsmen of this type also appear in documents related to the times of Charlemagne.

By the thirteenth century the trade was well established in towns like London, Bristol, Coventry, and many continental towns. The demand seems to have exceeded the supply and the former was continually increasing. Spanish soap was already produced from olive oil. Black soaps were made from the remains of burnt oil, notably in Amiens and Abbeville.

The main problem of the soapmaker was to obtain the supply of ashes from which he made his crude lye, for it was also in great demand for glass manufacture, and charcoal was an important raw material for medieval metallurgy. The large-scale destruction of woodlands began seriously to impede the growth of these industries. White soap was made by mixing fern ash and unslaked lime, allowing the lye to stand for several days and running it off into a kettle. There it was mixed with oil and tallow and heated. Sometimes bean flower was added, and when very thick it was molded by hand. The manufacture of perfumed soaps dates from the sixteenth century and was disseminated from Naples and Bologna. Not until better supplies of alkali were found in the later eighteenth century, however, could the soap trade prosper.

The tide of experimental chemistry that swept over Western Europe in the twelfth century had an immense effect on all of the arts that could be put to the service of the Church. One of the most important of these was the art of painting. The walls of the churches were covered with frescoes illustrating scenes from the Bible, thus serving to familiarize the faithful with the Scriptures in the absence of vernacular Bibles, for the only Bibles available at the time were in Latin and could be read only by the clergy and the scholars. These wall paintings were executed on plaster grounds or on gessoed panels, gesso being a mixture of chalk, gypsum, or plaster combined with glue or gelatine. It served as a ground for the egg-white tempera then used as a vehicle for pigment. In the thirteenth century the art of true fresco painting—that is, applying pigments on wet plaster—began to be understood and practiced. The gessoed walls or panels gradually disappeared. Tempera paints (pigments mixed with glair or gum) were also in frequent use.

The great stimulus to the modern art of oil painting came from experiments with drying oils. These had been known for a long time and are mentioned in classical writings. But linseed, hempseed, or walnut oils, boiled and cooked with resins used as a medium, are medieval inventions. As oil varnishes they occur in the eighth-century Lucca manuscript and in such early books as the *Mappae Clavicula*. Then by the tenth century, Theophilus reports, they had come to be used for the glazing of metals and to color them red. The evolution of the technique of oil painting began in Italy and then spread northward.

There probably never was any "secret of the brothers van Eyck," the famous Flemish painters who flourished about 1400. The truth is that by 1400 the art of oil painting had reached Flanders and began to be used on a wider scale. Many new pigments were available to the painters of the Middle Ages. The ancients had resorted to the use of natural pigments like wood, madder, brazil wood, kermes, and Tyrian purple. But in the twelfth century the art of making white-lead paints from lead and vinegar was discovered. Vermillion was introduced from the Arabic world. Then the medieval alchemist discovered many pigments now commonly prepared by the chemical industry. The "illuminated" manuscripts were still produced on parchment, which came from Bologna.

Sailing the Ocean

THE industrial and technological developments of medieval Europe were possible only because of stable economic and political conditions evolving at the end of the Dark Ages. But this evolution had also opened windows facing to the West. Europe no longer looked to the Mediterranean but to the Atlantic and the unknown lands that lay beyond. However, the fears of the classical sailor had to be overcome and ships and navigation had to be recast. The development of the seagoing sailing vessel is a major technical achievement of the Middle Ages. The Mediterranean sailors stuck to the galleys, relying on their oars, though their merchant ships adopted the lateen sails. The inhabitants of the Atlantic coast never confined themselves to coasting. They had dared the storms and seas, and long before the days of the Vikings they had sailed out into the ocean, discovering such far-off lands as Iceland. It is well known that the Vikings reached Greenland and the North American continent.

The earliest ships in this region were the dugout canoe and the wickerwork coracle, but before the Christian era larger ships were built and propelled by oarsmen. Such ships, in which chieftains were sometimes buried under great mounds, as the Gokestad ship and the Oseberg ship, were some 60 feet long and 15 feet wide. They were rowed by 32 men and steered with a lateral steering oar, like the Mediterranean ships. Whenever the wind was favorable they used a simple type of sail. This was the type of ship from which the Vikings terrorized the lands along the sea.

But already in the time of Charlemagne other types such as the Frisian ship, had been developed, in which the inhabitants of the Low Countries sailed south to buy salt and wine which they traded in the north and in the Baltic for corn and timber. This remained for centuries the mainstay of the Dutch trade. Though these "cockboats" could use oars, they depended mainly on their sails. Their owners knew and regularly employed the art of tacking against the wind. These broad, deep ships soon displaced the older types and were also introduced into the Mediterranean.

One of the effects of this new type of ship was that the older merchant towns, often built far up the river as a protection against the inroads of pirates, now slowly moved toward the mouths of the rivers. The new cockboats served both the merchants and the navy. In the latter case two towers or "castles" were erected front and aft, from which arrows and other missiles were poured on the enemy. These castles gradually became part of the ship, hence the term "forecastle." Gradually the size of ships increased and more masts and sails appeared. The oars disappeared completely and the seagoing sailing ship came to stay. But the larger types still had to be strengthened with wales to withstand the impact of the ocean waves.

These ships were still clinker-built, that is, the rows of planks that formed the hull overlapped. Thus we can see that they originated in the dugout canoe, the sides of which were simply made higher. In this way they resembled the Mediterranean ships. But by the fourteenth century a new carvel-built type of ship became more common. The hulls of these ships consisted of planks fitted together like a plank floor and held by a system of ribs and timbers. The size of ships quickly increased to about 500 tons and the English and French navies of the year 1400 had ships up to 1,000 tons burden.

Apart from the design of the hull, a very important innovation was the rudder. The introduction of the hinged sternpost or median rudder certainly contributed to the efficiency and size of the ship. The lateral steering oar quickly disappeared from the Atlantic coast and later from the Mediterranean as well. We do not yet know where the hinged rudder was conceived. It occurs in the twelfth century and models of Saxon boats of the tenth century now in the Leyden Museum have vertical sterns. By the thirteenth century it was also known in the Arabic world, which, however, may have quickly seized and adapted this important innovation as they had done with many other Western inventions.

The fore-and-aft rig was developed in the West from the older Mediterranean lateen sail, which appears in Greek miniatures of the ninth century. How this development took place is still unknown, but it certainly contributed to the greater efficiency and increased speed of Western shipping. It reduced the size of the crews and invited ocean exploration.

The introduction of the compass, though a Western invention, was much delayed by popular superstitious belief. The story (which occurs in the *Arabian Nights*) of the magnetic mountain toward which all ships having a compass and iron nails would be drawn to destruction impeded its adoption. Though the Arabs were quicker to use this valuable navigational instrument, it also slowly found its way into Western shipping. With the new and stronger hull design, rig, and rudder, it formed the basis of European world trade. Without these, the American continent would never have been reached, explored, and settled. These innovations would bear fruit when the new discoveries of the fifteenth century led to more and larger ships built in Western Europe.

The fifteenth century is rightly called the Age of Discovery. The Portuguese were the pioneers; the Spaniards, Dutch, and English followed only in the sixteenth century. However, tradition and technical limitations still imposed severe penalties on ocean sailing. The discoverers of this century hardly dared risk the open sea; most of their voyages were coasting expeditions, yet even then great losses were suffered on these voyages, 50 to 80 per cent of the ships being lost. It is probable that even Columbus would never have ventured out into the uncharted Atlantic to discover what proved to be a New World had he not underestimated the length of the voyage. The story of the crossing with three tiny ships of 40, 50, and 100 tons shows that neither the sailors nor Columbus were expecting the trip to last as long as it did.

In the beginning of the sixteenth century the experience gathered by the discoverers led to strengthened constructions of the hull to make ocean sailing safer. There was, however, another grave difficulty associated with the instruments then used on board the ships. With the compass, astrolabe, cross staff, and other simple nautical instruments used in those days, it was comparatively easy to determine one's latitude when at sea. Yet whenever a ship was sailing out of sight of the coast the determination of the longitude could be made only with appreciable but unavoidable error in the result. This made cruising in the open a risky business. Hence there was a strong urge to increase the precision of longitude measurements, for the maps of harbors and atlases of the day were already fairly satisfactory. Now the scientists applied themselves to the correction of astronomical tables so as to provide more precise data on eclipses and conjunctions of planets to be used in reckoning longitude. Gemma Frisius suggested the use of clocks for the same purpose in 1532, and this suggestion started the quest for an accurate ship's chronometer, an instrument that was not to be perfected for some two hundred years. The experience of the discoverers prompted new maps and new instruments and provided data for checking the efforts of the instrument makers.

Paper and Printing

NEW methods of communicating the written word were introduced in the fifteenth century. The art of papermaking had slowly penetrated into Europe from the Arab world, and by the middle of the fifteenth century it was definitely established and driving parchment and vellum from the market. We do not yet know to what extent China and its technique of block printing influenced the West by way of the steppes and through contact with the Arabs. The oldest Chinese books printed from blocks date from A.D. 868; movable type of baked clay seems to have been invented by Pi Sheng about 1045. But the links between the printing art of the Far East and that of the later Middle Ages are still missing.

Stamps for monograms were used in charters of the eleventh century. Pictures engraved on wood blocks were used in making the hundreds of "pietàs" or religious pictures collected and treasured by pilgrims. We know of stamps used by medieval bookbinders to decorate book covers, and textiles had been decorated with clay stamps or woodcuts since Hellenistic days.

And so the idea of printing was in the air. It is certain that we have to do with two separate movements, one being the invention of printing with movable types by Gutenberg or Coster, who produced the first printed books around 1454, and the other being the invention of printing books from blocks, the oldest examples of which date from 1470. Holland, Germany, France, and Italy still debate the question of who was the inventor of movable type, though it would seem that Coster has slightly better claims than Gutenberg. But the latter produced the beautiful "Mazarin" Bible in his workshop at Mainz, and soon printers were established in Rome, Venice, Valencia, London, Antwerp, and Leyden.

Though the block printing of books is the logical development of the earlier type of seals and stamps which we have already mentioned, it is often wrongly claimed to be an original invention. But printing with interchangeable, replaceable type where each character is separately cut and movable was a highly revolutionary development. It was the first step on the long road toward the interchangeable, standardized parts which are mass-produced and used to build up all kinds of machinery. The mass production of single characters or letters meant that they could be arranged in any combination or pattern, and that they could be used over and over again to print other books, whereas the engraved blocks were intended only for a specific book or page. The reproduction of a text even in an unknown language now became a perfectly mechanical operation, being merely a question of casting and setting the necessary type. Along with the invention of firearms, printing from movable type belongs to the most enduring and influential of medieval inventions.

The oldest books were Latin Bibles and Greek or Latin classics, but soon the printers began to turn out vernacular Bibles and other books on medicine, alchemy, and technology, which spread the knowledge of the few to the literate students in all parts of the world. The grip of the Middle Ages was broken. Though we cannot draw a sharp dividing line between one period of history and the next, we may well consider the invention and development of paper and printing to have ended the technical phase of the Middle Ages.

VII

New Wine into Old Bottles

(1500–1750)

Toward the end of the Middle Ages there arose a strong reaction against the great theologicophilosophical structure built by the churchmen upon the Bible and the works of
Aristotle as foundations. The tidal wave that burst the bonds
of medieval thought started in Italy as early as the fifteenth
century and reached the coast of the Atlantic toward the
end of the sixteenth. The Renaissance was a rebirth of individual thought and expression, a new humanism. It was mainly a
movement in the field of fine arts, literature, ethics, and philosophy. "Let us go and wake the dead," was the cry of those
who wanted to absorb not only Plato and Aristotle, but all
classical authors, whose writings were now diligently un-
earthed and studied. Dante, Petrarch, Boccaccio, and Villani
can be considered the pioneers of this movement. Rabelais
wanted to "restore the good literature," Lorenzo Valla spoke
of a "rebirth of the noble civilization," Vasari of a "renaissance
of the fine arts." Education took completely new forms. The
discovery of America and of other new lands brought new
products and new impressions to an awakened Europe where
men were now seeking to explore every field of human activity.

The small self-centered world of medieval man changed
rapidly. It is true that the "mask of paganism" which the Ren-

136

aissance wore was hardly more than the pose of an intellectual minority, for civilization and the culture of the masses remained essentially Christian. Man was still the center of the universe as in the Middle Ages. Neither Galileo nor Copernicus would have met such violent resistance had this not been so. The leading classes were no longer satisfied with medieval thought, however. They dreamed of the return of a Golden Age, of a rebirth of a better world, a renaissance of that richer civilization of the ancients. The ancient classical standards of virtue, truth, beauty, and social justice regained their former values. But the Christian background of Western civilization was still so firmly rooted in men's minds that much of the existing culture was left intact, though it was dressed up in what was believed to be Roman and Greek forms.

The Birth of the New Science

GRADUALLY the new concept of science and education gained momentum. The school of Robert Grosseteste and Roger Bacon at Oxford, and later the followers of William of Ockham at the University of Paris—John Buridan and Nicolas Oresme among others—had stressed the necessity for observing facts and their relations in order to penetrate into the secrets of nature. Experience, they said, was the only test of physical truth. These men built up a positive science of physics, coining many fundamental terms and concepts which served to construct the new dynamics and astronomy of later generations. This new wine burst the old bottles.

The Black Death, together with the disastrous Hundred Years' War between England and France, called a temporary halt to economic and technical development in the West. For a century or so the center of scientific and technical activities shifted again to the prosperous merchant towns of fifteenth-century Italy. Then in the sixteenth century the scene shifted definitely to the Atlantic coast.

Gradually the Renaissance revealed itself as a period of change and amalgamation, of preparation and trial. The earlier

Renaissance scientists studied nature because it was part of the classical concept of education. If they drew bold philosophical conclusions from new facts of nature they risked persecution, as did Galileo and Giordano Bruno, the latter being burned at the stake in 1600 for his unorthodox views about the universe. But little by little the break between philosophy and theology widened. The scientist first tried to hide his bold conclusions in a cloak of metaphysics. Then in the seventeenth century the scientists began to speak less equivocally, using a scientific language that we have no difficulty in understanding today. Science was now no longer limited to a few special fields. From the seventeenth century onward the whole domain of nature was its province.

That early scientific genius, Leonardo da Vinci, was convinced that the laws of nature could be discovered by experiment, measurement, and calculation. His ideas are symptomatic of many philosophers and scientists of the day. The statesman and scientist, Francis Bacon, stated in his book *The Advancement of Learning* that nature itself would yield the tools with which its secrets could be understood, and that the study of nature would not only provide useful facts but would also make mankind richer and happier. Natural philosophers like Descartes believed that nature could be studied to yield simple and clear rules and laws.

Science thus had ceased to be the handmaid of religion. Natural philosophy would explain the world and disclose its laws to the scientist. This did not mean that on the whole these new scientists and humanists were irreligious. On the contrary, many of them, like Boyle and Newton, believed that the study of nature would reveal and confirm the purpose of creation and the intentions of the Creator. The study of nature was to many the "glorification of God."

The new science that burst forth in fifteenth-century Italy remained fettered to medieval concepts for quite some time. Its youthful enthusiasm led to experiments and adventures in all fields, but its earliest efforts were marked by breadth of vision rather than by depth of understanding.

Mathematics, mechanics, physics, and astronomy profited most from this revolution. Later generations had to explain many knotty problems which the pioneers had either accepted as already solved or passed over without question in the absence of proper tools and instruments. The exuberance of the first generations was halted by the religious struggles at the end of the sixteenth century, but the new science had come to stay.

The individual centers at the beginning of the sixteenth century were still located in Italy and Germany, but as a result of disastrous religious wars and local hostilities the centers of trade and industry began to shift to the Atlantic coast. The discovery of the New World drew the attention of Europe to the West. European civilization in the seventeenth and early eighteenth centuries was no longer Mediterranean in character, having become definitely a Western culture.

Progress in science was not achieved by the universities, which remained in the grip of Aristotelian logic up to the age of Newton, but by practical engineers and by the learned societies that grew out of the association of enlightened individuals. The earlier Italian societies like the Accademia del Cimento and the Accademia dei Lincei, of which Galileo was a member, were the examples for the "House of Solomon" proposed by Francis Bacon in his *New Atlantis* as the ideal center of scientific studies and "palace of invention." The work of these societies and the publications they issued had a distinct influence on the founding of the Royal Society (chartered July 15, 1662) and the state-sponsored French Academie des Sciences (1666). In 1700 Leibnitz helped to found the Berlin Academy of Sciences. He was also instrumental in founding the Academy of St. Petersburg. Here, in these scientific societies, the best minds of the seventeenth and eighteenth centuries met and discussed the leading scientific theories and experiments of the day. This atmosphere had a profound influence on the science and technology of the age.

In these circles many new instruments were born, tested, developed and improved. The members of these societies gave the world the telescope, the microscope, the thermometer, the barometer, the air pump, the new clocks moved by escapement and pendulum, and also the scientific tools such as mathematical symbols, logarithms, and the calculus. The human eye, aided by the microscope and telescope, was now able to penetrate new worlds; the kingdom of nature was revealed to be at once larger and smaller than mankind had believed. Science now definitely became the art of measuring, weighing, and calculating, combined with the application of inductive and deductive reasoning to establish physical laws or to test hypotheses. Its subject matter ranged from the infinitely small to the infinitely great, from microscopic infusoria to stars and galaxies. It was no longer interested primarily in quality, but in quantity. It was no longer satisfied with medieval scholasticism but required rigorous proof in the form of mathematical equations.

Technology and the New Science

FROM the very beginning of this period the contacts between science, technology, and engineering began to increase and multiply, because the new scientific societies were definitely engaged in the pursuit of applied as well as pure science. The Royal Society studied "all things mathematical, philosophical, and mechanical," and its charter expressly mentions "the recovering of all such allowable arts and manufactures as are lost," and "the improvement of all useful arts, manufactures, mechanical practices, engines, and inventions." From October, 1622 onward, its members helped to judge applications for patents. The same service was rendered by other academies.

The seventeenth century has often been called the Age of Projects, and it is true that applied science came into its own only in the eighteenth century with the Industrial Revolution. Yet even before that time not a few projects were the result of cooperation between the new science on the one hand and either engineering or technology on the other. The artisans and craftsmen were definitely interested in the new mathematics and mechanics. Sailing the ocean created a demand for better star tables and stimulated the new astronomy, being also an important factor in the development of better clocks. At the same time the navigators profited from every forward stride of the new science and from the evolution of new instruments.

Not only were theoretical mechanics developed by such men as Leonardo da Vinci, Simon Stevin, and many others, but the sixteenth century also started a boom in applied mechanics. This was partly due to the thriving metallurgical and mining industries and partly to the growth of nationalism and strong centralized power in different countries, a trend that implied greater interest in public and military works. The national armies profited greatly from the new science. The new mathematics and mechanics were soon applied to new problems in the field of ballistics.

Great names now famous as artists, such as those of Michelangelo and Bramante, were then closely connected with the new science of constructing fortifications, which in turn was dependent on the new mechanics. Famous mechanical and civil engineers like Alberghetti, Jacopo Mariano, Valturio, Orsini, and Carafa served a great part of their lives as military engineers to local Italian potentates. When Leonardo offered his services to the Duke of Milan, he professed wide knowledge of fifteen branches of military engineering and mentioned only secondarily his achievements in the art of painting and sculpture. Great scientists like Stevin and Descartes were proud to serve Prince Maurice of Orange as military engineers and advisers.

Strangely enough, this awakening of nationalism did not prevent science from being as international as ever. The leading scientists corresponded freely with one another and certain of them, like Oldenburg (secretary to the Royal Society), Mersenne, and Isaac Beekman, served as clearing houses of information in the days when periodicals were not yet published regularly. The increasingly accurate tools and instruments also stimulated technology and engineering, regardless of political boundaries.

Applied mechanics profited from the invention of printing. The sixteenth and seventeenth centuries produced a series of manuals, illustrated with handsome engravings and woodcuts, which give us a lively picture of the ingenuity of the inventors of this period. Among the important books were Jacques Besson's *Theater of Instruments* (1578), Ramelli's *The Various and Ingenious Machines*, and Jacopo da Strada's *Survey of All Kinds of Water-, Wind-, Animal-Driven and Hand-Driven Mills and Beautiful and Useful Pumps* (1616). There are also Verantio's *New Machines* (1617), and such early scientific dictionaries as Conrad Dasypodius's *Mathematical Lexicon* (1599) and Jacques Ozanam's *Mathematical Dictionary* (1691). These beautifully executed volumes are among the best reference sources on the mechanical designs of this period.

One is impressed by the increase in size, power, and complexity of the machines built at this time. The principles of the wedge, screw, lever, pulley, rollers, and sledges had of course been fully understood by the practical engineers of Greek and Roman days, and the scientists of antiquity had partly unraveled the laws underlying these tools. The remaining problems were solved by the Renaissance scientists when they created the new mechanics. Italian engineers could now apply these principles in their practical applications and did so with great ingenuity.

The variety of each type of machinery is astonishing. We find, for example, a wide assortment of different types of pumps, some of which sucked up liquids by creating a vacuum under the plunger, others that squirted the liquid from the cylinder by pressure of the plunger; there were even pumps of the centrifugal type that moved the liquid by means of a fan or blade. The first two types were sometimes single-acting, that is, had only one cylinder; but to make them yield a continuous stream of liquid two cylinders were often combined to form a double-acting pump. Flap and ball valves were used and the principle of the sliding valve was known, though some times applied in a primitive fashion.

This was indeed the Age of the Pump. Ramelli's book cited above describes no fewer than 100 examples of pumps and 24 mills, together with a number of jacks, bridges, and derricks. The difficulty in constructing these pumps was the fact that timber had to be used, for it was still impossible to cast accurate metal cylinders of large diameter. Parts had to be designed and machined by hand, and no two pumps were exactly alike. This was a great disadvantage in the spread of the universal use of screws, gear wheels, and the like. The use of internationally adaptable parts such as characterizes our machine-age industry was then unknown.

The practical experience gained with pumps in mines, drainage projects, and water-supply systems had a profound influence on the development of theoretical science even in fields that were quite remote. The observation that water cannot be raised higher than 34 feet by suction led to the conception of the barometer and to the investigations of the "spring of the air," of the various degrees of vacuum, and atmospheric pressure. This in turn led to the construction of air pumps and vacuum pumps. Other sciences made use of this new knowledge of pump action. William Harvey, when he described the circulation of the blood in the body, clearly conceived the heart as a pump that distributed the vital fluid to all parts of the body.

The evolution of many new types of pumps had other interesting ramifications. Among these was the development of the fire engine, so important in the days of wooden houses and frequent, devastating fires. Adequate pumps and efficient fire engines or force pumps to squirt the water onto the blaze were impossible so long as they leaked. It was still difficult to achieve a proper fit between cylinder and piston, or to make the valves seat tightly. Morland was the first to make a pump in which leather rings suitably attached to the piston prevented leakage from the cylinder (1674), though several other inventors had already suggested packing materials.

Early attempts to construct good fire engines had been made in the sixteenth century, probably in imitation of the earlier Roman squirting pumps previously described.

In 1614 Auleander designed a fire engine producing a jet "as thick as an arm and as high as a house," to be followed by the heavier engine invented by Hans Hautsch of Nuremberg in 1655. It is remarkable that he designed an engine with a wind-chamber giving a continuous jet, for early Dutch engines of this type did not. First to produce a continuous jet by using an air chamber and two cylinders combined were the brothers van der Heyden. Their invention, coming as it did in 1671, was too late to be used in combating the Great Fire of London (1666), a conflagration that proved how helpless man was against the devastation wrought by fire.

Leonardo the Pioneer

WE HAVE mentioned engineers several times in the course of this chapter—especially Leonardo da Vinci. The title "engineer" as distinguished from "architect" was first adopted by Salomon de Caus (1576–1636). Its use spread from France to Germany and England. "Engineer" then still meant "military engineer," while "architect" was equivalent to "civil engineer." But in the course of the seventeenth century the first title was also applied to mechanical and civil engineering.

During the early part of the Renaissance, engineering and technology had not yet received any appreciable support from the new scientific movement. They were left on their own and, though supported by the powerful young capitalism, had to struggle along by trial and error. It is amazing to find that a genius like Leonardo did not affect this period so widely as one might be led to expect, for this man, who is known to most of us today as a great artist, was actually an even greater architect, engineer, and inventor.

Born in a village near Florence in 1452, he was educated by his father, patrician and notary. In 1480 he offered his services to Ludovico Sforza il Moro, Duke of Milan, in a letter in

PLATE 10   Sectional model of a reverberatory furnace constructed after the designs of Leonardo da Vinci. (*Codex Atlantico*, Fol. 396, recto *a*.)

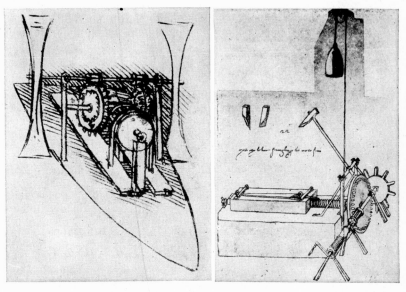

PLATE 11   Leonardo's sketch showing the mechanism of a paddle-wheeler invented by him, to be propelled by two treadles. (*Codex Atlantico*.)
PLATE 12   Leonardo's sketch of a file-making machine invented by him. (*Codex Atlantico*, Fol. 6, recto *b*.)

PLATE 13 "The Engineer," print from Weigel, *Abbildung der gemeinützlicher Hauptstande*, 1698.

PLATE 14 Furnace for crucibles, designed by Leonardo da Vinci. (*Codex Atlantico*, Fol. 32, recto *a*.)

PLATE 15 *a* and *b* Cleaning and repairing streets in the Middle Ages—two pictures of members of the Nüremberg guilds from the *Mendelsche Brüderbuch*, about 1450.

PLATE 16 Small portable blast furnace devised by Reaumur to produce better castings. (From *L'Art de Forger le Fer*, 1722.)

MOLA ALATA.
Alata quæ ventis agi nunc vult mola   Ignota Romanis fuiſſe dicitur.

PLATE 17   Early post and tower windmills for grinding wheat.

MOLA AQVARIA.
Aquarias quiſquis molas antiquitus   Putat repertas, tota aberrat is via.

PLATE 18   Water-driven wheat mill. (Both illustrations are from early prints by Phillipp Galle, 1537-1612, courtesy of Spillers, Ltd., London.)

which he details his proficiency as a military and civil engineer. One is astounded at the catalog of his skills in so many different fields. He remained in the Duke's service until 1499, when he returned to Florence to enter the service of Cesar Borgia as his chief military engineer (1502–1506). At the end of his life he was called to France by Francis I to help in the latter's canal-building projects (1516). He died there three years later.

It is doubtful whether any man has been more proficient in every field in which he tried his hand. Leonardo seems to have painted with the same ease with which he constructed fortresses, cannon, canals, bridges, irrigation works, harbors, water wheels, and locks. He tried to use steam to fire a gun, invented a camera obscura, and designed helicopters and airplanes with movable wings. He dissected at least thirty human bodies and was a master of anatomy. He studied fossils and had surprisingly modern geological ideas. His extensive notebooks contain pithy observations like "the sun does not move" and "a weight falls toward the center of the earth by the shortest path," which are tantalizing to the modern reader. All through these notes runs the definite opinion that all scientific work should start with experiments and end with conclusions.

But the huge mass of observations and experiments which Leonardo buried in the many volumes of cryptic notes did not touch his generation. Apart from notes on anatomy and painting which were published in 1651, the greater part of these notebooks was dispersed after his death and their publication was deferred until the nineteenth century. Even at the present writing much of it remains in manuscript form. Hence this great genius had little influence on his own times except through the few works he executed himself, and through the work of his pupils. The body of his scientific thoughts, which would have caused a furore in his day and would unquestionably have led their author to the stake had they been known, remained unproductive in these notebooks.

Reading these notes makes one wonder what could have happened, for they touch not only on the principles and philosophy of science, but also on calculations and actual applications of science. In the field of military engineering, we find projects and drawings of moat protection, masonry cupolas and bastions, slings and catapults, scaling ladders, rapid-fire catapults, breech loaders, machine guns, conical shells, shrapnel, gas, submarines, projects for barrage protection, and rolling mills to manufacture iron bars for the construction of gun barrels.

As a civil engineer Leonardo studied the theory of stresses and determined the breaking strength of materials. In his studies of flight he also experimented with balloons of thin waxed paper. Apart from several models and trials with heavier-than-air machines, we find Leonardo as the inventor of the parachute which is first pictured in Verantius's *Machinae Novae* (1617). His work on hydraulics was probably intended for publication in book form. The notes are very complete and his views on hydrostatic pressure anticipate those of Pascal (1623–1662). Leonardo was also interested in city planning and drew plans of double-decked streets for big cities. Apart from the completed project for the sewerage system of Urbino, Leonardo thought much about the subject and grasped the relation between proper sewerage and health. We have no need here to discuss Leonardo's consummate skill as a painter and sculptor.

The Power Sources of the New Europe

THOUGH the contacts between science and technology became closer in this period, there was little change in the sources of power. Essentially the water wheel and the windmill remained the only possibilities, discounting for the moment the first attempts at steam engines that fall in this period.

The use of the windmill as a source of mechanical power spread slowly after the thirteenth century. A deed recording the oldest mill in the Netherlands is dated 1197. Probably these earliest mills were fixed structures with their front facing the prevailing winds, e.g., to the southwest in the Low Countries. But the oldest example recovered is a post mill, in which the body of the mill as a whole can rotate on a vertical post or shaft to face the wind at all times. This post is mounted on heavy oak crosstrees and propped with double stays, the crosstrees being supported on heavy brick foundations. Later when such mills were used to drive tools fixed on the ground, the solid post was replaced by a tubular one that contained the standing post which moved the pumps and other tools. These earlier mills were always in danger of being blown over in heavy gales.

The sixteenth century saw a decided improvement in windmill construction. The cap and the almost horizontal wind shaft carrying the sweeps were made to turn and catch the wind, the rest of the windmill then being of fixed construction. This new tower mill (*bovenkruier*) also provided much better accommodation for the miller. It is often described as the Dutch mill, in contrast to the old post mill or German mill. There is, however, no historical basis for these names.

Another innovation of the sixteenth century was the use of sails with doubly curved surfaces, which provided a favorable angle of incidence to the wind at any radial distance. This was probably a Dutch invention, as the German mills of that date still show the flat sweep. In order to reduce the resistance of the wind, the Dutch millwrights also adopted the slender wooden construction, usually with an octagonal or hexagonal cross section. It is not known where these improvements were first conceived, for here again Leonardo has sketched them in his notes.

One of the earliest applications of the windmill was for cleaning and grinding corn and bolting flour. Towards the end of the fourteenth century it was also used for drainage purposes. A special type of marsh mill was developed called *wip-molen* in the Netherlands. In this type the sweeps and shaft drive a vertical axle that carries a bucket wheel on its lower end. The whole construction could move freely to catch the breeze and proved a practical solution to the problem of raising water by wind power. This was most important in the Low Countries, where rain water and seepage water have to be drained continually from lands that are for the most part below sea level. Simon Stevin was the first to calculate the efficiency of these drainage mills in his essay dated 1634.

As Holland lacked water power, windmills were also of great help in sawing timber, which was in great demand for shipbuilding and other types of construction. The earliest instance of a sawmill is mentioned in 1592. Most of these were of the Dutch-mill type described above. But another type of mill was developed that permitted the entire structure to be turned on rollers so as to catch the most favorable wind. This type was called the smock mill (*paltrokmolen*).

The development of the sawmill also led to the invention of the disk saw in Holland in the sixteenth or seventeenth century. Unfortunately the earliest Dutch patent of 1644 that possibly describes a circular disk saw is too vaguely worded, else we could be certain that this was one of the earliest attempts to replace the reciprocating to-and-fro motion of a tool by a continuous rotary movement. Such rotating tools and parts could be more easily fixed and required less space; the transmission of power by means of belts or gears was also easier. Hence this point can be traced right through the history of mechanical engineering.

Windmills remained the most important source of power in Holland and neighboring countries until well into the nineteenth century. They were turned to any imaginable technical use, such as the grinding of pigments, stamping, oil-seed pressing, paper manufacture, and mechanical power. Such districts as the banks of the Zaan just north of Amsterdam teemed with windmills and formed the industrial district of Holland in the seventeenth and eighteenth centuries. The introduction of mechanical power was often resisted by the guilds. Thus the sawmill met considerable opposition in England, and even in 1768 the workmen there went so far as to demolish a mill for fear of unemployment in their ranks.

In other countries the water wheel, either undershot or overshot, was the main source of power. Larger and more powerful constructions were attempted as mechanical skill improved and more practical knowledge of the properties of materials was gained. Some of the designs (examples of which again occur in Leonardo's notebooks) have cup-shaped extremities on their arms that made them resemble the later Pelton wheels. Gears and cranks are widely used to transmit the rotational power of the wheel. These toothed wheels were either cast solid or built of wood with metal teeth. Gearing principles were well understood and most of the terms we use in this field today go back to ancient French or Italian nomenclature. Rocker shafts or eccentrics were also used to translate rotary movement into reciprocating movement.

However, these old and well-established sources of power were limited by nature. And so beginning with the sixteenth century, the search for other prime movers began. We have mentioned Leonardo's steam gun. The famous Dutch scientist Christian Huygens, experimenting with Denis Papin, devised a kind of internal-combustion engine in which the piston was moved by the explosion of gunpowder (1673), but such attempts remained unfruitful. Porta is said to have attempted a steam turbine to raise water, an illustration of which is found in his works. Even back in the Middle Ages the mathematician Gerbert of Rheims (975), later Pope Sylvester II, is credited with an organ in which air for the pipes was compressed by steam power, but this story is purely legendary.

The earliest steam engine can be said to have been the one described in the 1663 patent granted to the Marquess of Worcester. He used a cylinder into which steam was blown and then condensed. The resulting vacuum, after opening a valve, would suck the cylinder full of water. This water could then be blown out of the cylinder by steam pressure and the cycle restarted. By combining two cylinders and a suitable valve system a continuous stream of water could be pumped away by this engine. Essentially this was not yet a real steam engine, but a steam pump that was to serve the pressing need for a mechanical means of draining mines—a need that became increasingly urgent as the higher strata of the ores became exhausted.

The next step was taken by Denis Papin, the French inventor who is better known for his pressure cooker (1680) designed to extract glue from bones, the principle of which is still applied in our modern pressure cookers. In 1687 Papin designed a steam engine that worked on the same principle as the earlier Worcester engine, except that the vacuum obtained by condensing steam in a cylinder drew down a piston, which could thus be made to move engine parts—for instance, to hoist up loads. His book on steam engines was published in 1707 during his stay at Cassel, Germany. Papin constructed a little paddle-wheel boat moved by such an engine, in which he intended to travel from Cassel to London. Unfortunately he had attracted the envy and wrath of the Cassel guild of river boatmen who, during the night of September 25, 1707, had Papin arrested and destroyed his ship, which was large enough to carry 4,000 pounds of cargo. Papin died soon afterward in London without having been able to rebuild his ship, but his ideas on steam engines were taken up by Newcomen, the builder of the first real engine.

Apart from Morland, the inventor of the efficient packing material for pistons, others tried their hand at steam pumps. The first to achieve a really practical success was Savery. Using the same principle as Worcester, he obtained a patent in 1698 and constructed several of his machines, one of which was for Campdan House, Kensington, where it pumped water from a well at the rate of 15 tons per hour (about 60 gallons per minute). It cost £50 and developed energy equivalent to about one horsepower. These steam engines were water pumps and were used mainly for the drainage of mines. Savery designed a better and more efficient engine known as the "Miner's Friend," which he used in the mines of Cornwall.

Unfortunately they were not a practical success. They remained expensive and dangerous to handle, for the knowledge of the strength of materials used in building these engines was still very meager and explosions were frequent. Hence the mine owners stuck to their hand- or animal-driven drainage pumps. The steam engine had no future until it was recognized and designed as a new source of power that could move all types of machinery—not just drainage pumps.

The Road Regains Its Importance

THE consolidation of Europe and its different nations, together with growing technology and trade, demanded better communications. The Middle Ages had failed in this respect. The stronger governments of this period could at last start adequate public works such as had not been undertaken for many centuries after the fall of the Roman Empire. Charlemagne in 800 had tried to reshape the old road system and to extend it into new domains beyond the Rhine, but he had not had time to complete the project.

Little road building was done in the Middle Ages. Though the law distinguished between royal roads, crossroads, and private roads, it made no distinction as to their maintenance, and the old Roman roads often served as quarries for the peasants. The new long trails through Central Europe into Russia were little more than tracks. The fundamental difficulty was the lack of central governments that could afford to undertake these extensive works. The local landlords and farmers either were too poor to pay for the repair and upkeep of these roads or else profited from the sale of tools and the operation of inns, all of which made traveling a slow and costly business.

The first problem tackled was that of reestablishing efficient postal service. In France Louis XI took things in hand, repaired some main roads and reinstituted a postal system of couriers (1464). In the Holy Roman Empire Franz von Taxis organized postal systems for the Emperor about 1500. In both cases these state couriers made journeys of up to 50 miles a day, but the ordinary traveler hardly did more than 15 miles. With the rise of scientific cartography in the sixteenth century the first road maps and travelers' handbooks began to appear, like Robert Étienne's *Guide to the French Highways* (1553). The only way to collect sufficient funds was still by establishing more tolls, which in turn actually hindered land traffic considerably.

In England, Queen Mary appointed road inspectors (1555), each of whom was responsible for the upkeep of a designated stretch of road. In 1663 the Turnpike Act made it possible to collect funds from tolls. The money for the roads now came from the users and no longer from the parishes along the roads, whose citizens had always resisted the collection of such rates. As heavy traffic increased, the road surfaces suffered greater wear, and deep ruts began to impede traffic. The designers of coaches and wagons tried to counteract this by widening the rims of their wheels, until the law had to step in to fix a maximum width of 18 inches. The iron bands on the wheels made travel especially dangerous on the poorly constructed roads. In the rainy season the latter were hardly more than quagmires, and the deep holes broke wheels and axles and overturned coaches with dismal regularity.

In France, too, road building gradually became a royal prerogative. Henry IV appointed his minister Sully as the first "Grandvoyer de France" and after that date important ministers like Mazarin, Richelieu, and Colbert improved roads and took great care to develop the state postal system. Colbert, whose policy was to try to industrialize France, took particular care to pave roads with stone cobbles or setts, still called *pavés du Roi*. When Louis XIV died he left France with the best road system of his day. New scientific methods of road construction had made this possible.

The first to study road building thoroughly was a French lawyer from Rheims named Nicolas Bergier, who, finding the remains of Roman roads on his grounds, studied them and all the literary evidence available, finally publishing his *Highways of the Roman Empire* in 1622. He dedicated this work to the French king, expressing his hopes that "this work will cause your Majesty to employ the energy and diligence of your poor (unemployed) subjects in a field that will yield great profit to the welfare of your Kingdom both in war and in peace and will be a relief to a great many poor."

Though this work attracted much attention, funds were not yet available at the time for its proper utilization. A second book of great importance was Guido Toglietta's treatise written between 1585 and 1590 in which the wheel was called the *destroyer* and the road material the *resister*. Toglietta propounded methods for the laying of paving stones and their upkeep, and proposed a road surface two inches thick consisting of a mixture of stone, lime, and sand on a foundation of gravel. Though much cheaper than the Roman type, this road surface required regular repairs.

These sound principles were frequently discussed until at the time of the second edition of Bergier's book (1728) active measures were taken. In 1716 Colbert had instituted a corps of engineers, mainly military, and in 1747 the famous École des Ponts et Chausées was opened, where mechanical and civil engineers were educated on sound principles. Jean Rodolphe Perronet, its first director, was charged with the commission "to direct and supervise surveyors and designers of maps of the roads and highways of the realm and all those appointed and nominated to such work; and to instruct the said designers in the sciences and practices needful to fulfilling with competence the different occupations relating to said bridges and highways." This engineering school had a tremendous effect on the development of civil engineering in France and abroad.

Improvement in City Services

The paving of city streets also showed a slow evolution. King Philippe Augustus (1180–1223), annoyed by the stench of the mud and dirt in the streets of Paris, ordered them paved. The condition of medieval streets can be gathered from the

Siena ordinance which forbade the throwing of refuse into the street or the emptying of vessels from windows between dusk and dawn. Most medieval streets had a central gutter closed with huge slabs. Here again, as in road building, the difficulty was to find sufficient funds. The Emperor Sigismund had ordained that the fines imposed on "felons, bawds, and whores" were to be used for this purpose, so that "what came from lewdness would go to the mud, the holes and the sewers, and bad money collected from sin would be turned to the common good." The clergy often sponsored the collection or donation of money for such funds. It was widely recognized that good government could be judged from the condition of its roads, but nothing much was actually done.

The sixteenth century saw some improvements. Louis XI of France ordered the householders of Paris to pave the streets in front of their houses (1510). This measure met with considerable opposition and even sabotage. Things grew better as a pavers' guild was organized, materials were specified, and taxes were levied to execute the paving as part of the public works. Thus the streets of the larger cities were gradually paved in France, Italy, Germany, and England. Yet English travelers of the seventeenth century marveled at the paving stones on all Dutch streets, for London at that time still had many unpaved streets and people had to go about on high wooden clogs whenever it rained. Paving blocks of uniform size had already been specified in the days of Charles VI of France (1415), but at first the paving of streets led to a rise in the cost of materials. This was a common feature in many countries and it took several centuries until good materials were easily available everywhere and streets generally were paved.

It may seem strange to find that parking was a problem in the cities of this period, but medieval towns had been built at a time when there were no coaches, so that when in the seventeenth century these vehicles began to appear in large numbers the old narrow streets and lanes were soon obstructed and congested. Paris in 1550 counted only three coaches and London saw its first coach in 1555. In the latter town their iron tires destroyed the soft pavements and Parliament forbade their use. Charles I wanted to ban them from the towns where only sedan chairs were to be allowed, but this proposal was rejected as leading to the reintroduction of slavery.

Yet by 1634 over 3,400 coaches were in use in England. They were exceedingly uncomfortable, the body of the coach being hung in the frame by leather straps or chains instead of being supported by springs. The first coaches to have little windows were designed about 1630. Not until 1670 were steel springs first applied to a coach. The C-shaped spring was a great improvement, but it was expensive as it could be manufactured only from certain types of steel that had been tempered with great skill. A few decades later the rim brake was introduced.

During the same period authorities began to give more attention to public health. Many factors contributed to this happy decision. First of all there was the new medical art of great doctors like Ambroise Paré and Thomas Sydenham, who turned from the books of Galen to the observations of patients. The scientists began to be interested in social conditions, which had hitherto been the unchallenged field of the philosopher. In the seventeenth century we even find the first social statistics or "political arithmetick" as Sir William Petty called it. Graunt in his *Observations* (1662) discussed the bills of mortality published for the London parishes since 1563. He found that "the Fumes, Steams, and Stenches of London do so medicate and impregnate the Air about it, that it becomes capable of little more." Hence greater attention was gradually given to water supply, adequate sewerage, and street cleaning.

Street cleaning proved a difficult problem. In the Middle Ages fecal matter was collected in trenches in the streets, removed at irregular intervals, and dumped outside the towns. As long as good urban water supplies were lacking, no proper solution could be attempted. In 1551 Defroissis recommended flushing the streets with water, a highly practical suggestion except that there was no water available. Surface and rain water, which did not always drain to the rivers, often remained in stagnant pools in the streets.

Nor were the streets themselves adequately lit. In Paris the ordinances of 1408 and 1413 tried to establish proper lighting but this lasted only until 1508, at which time little tallow dips were lighted at street corners for late travelers. In general, streets were completely dark at night and thieves and robbers ranged abroad unseen. If a citizen wanted to cross the street after dusk he usually went accompanied by servants carrying lanterns or torches.

As the Roman aqueducts had fallen into disuse, most towns like Paris did not have a dependable water supply. Sometimes the water from springs was led into public fountains from which everybody carried the water he needed back to his house. Sometimes an old aqueduct still served to feed these fountains. Both instances were to be found in old Paris. After the thirteenth century lead pipes were used to supply certain houses in Paris, but this service was a privilege that could be suddenly revoked when the supply of water reached a low point. Then the improved water wheels and pumps allowed Lintelaer, a Flemish engineer, to construct the first water supply in the reign of Henry IV by installing a pump that was driven by a water wheel at the Pont Neuf and feeding it into a system of lead and wooden pipes. Two aqueducts had already been constructed by 1457 to supply Paris with water. Additional pumps installed at other bridges were built after 1585 and the first big main led water from springs to the north of the town into Paris after 1606. This chaotic system of tapping water from the river and from aqueducts lasted well into the nineteenth century, and it is typical of other European water systems as well.

Sewers were built, but not systematically, and the lack of sufficient water for regular flushing became serious in the fifteenth and sixteenth centuries. In 1663 a report on Paris sewer conditions revealed a shocking state of filth, and more systematic repairs were begun. Here again the lack of regular

public funds apportioned for this specific purpose was responsible for the deplorable sanitary conditions. But as the connection between a good sewerage system and public health
was now well known, improvements were gradually achieved.
Not until the nineteenth century, however, when water was
chemically treated and no longer supplied from springs or
rivers (into which the sewage flowed), could public health
show any marked improvement.

Canals and Drainage Projects

FAR greater strides were made in other fields of civil engineering. New canal and drainage projects were now realized with
public funds. Canals had been in the plans of many great rulers.
Charlemagne had intended to connect the Main and the Danube with a canal, but this project, like many others of its
type, failed when great differences in the water level had to be
overcome. The secret of using locks was still unknown at that
date.

The origin of canal locks is still obscure. From the first descriptions and drawings dating from fifteenth-century Italy
there is some reason to look to fourteenth-century Holland.
The locks of Spaarndam (near Amsterdam) may be the oldest
in Europe. It is certain that at that time lock gates were used
in Dutch docks. On the other hand, certain authorities point
to the twelfth-century "conches," weirs or barriers, which
were used in rivers near Milan, sometimes taking the form of
single gates for a two- or three-inch head of water. The first
set was used in the Naviglio Grande canal of Milan in 1395, and
two sets were built in 1445. The use of a series of gates is proposed in a treatise written in the late fifteenth century.
Leon Battista Alberti (1404–1472), an author, poet, mathematician, and architect, was the first to suggest the use of a
double set of gates with a basin in between to overcome the
differences in water level. The brothers Domenico (1481), or
perhaps Bertole da Novate (1452), were the first to build them.
Leonardo da Vinci invented the gates in the doors for letting

water rise in the basin without difficulty. It was about fifty years later that these modern locks appeared in French canals and rivers.

Important canals were also built in Italy and France during this period. In Italy the torrential rivers running down from the slopes of the Alps and the western slopes of the Appenines had to be canalized. Florence suffered severely from flooding of the River Arno and in 1495 Leonardo da Vinci submitted plans for the control of these floods, canalizing the Arno and improving its navigability at the same time. For this purpose he had designed special excavating machines, draglines, tripod cranes for moving earth, and a system of brushwood matting to protect the banks. Financing, however, was the big problem as usual, and debate dragged on until a number of serious floods forced Viviani, another famous Italian engineer, to execute somewhat different plans in 1679.

The canals of the Milan plain were partly used for navigation, partly for irrigation, and partly for the control of floods. They formed the first European planned system of canals, a system that was started in 1160 and was then vigorously prosecuted by the Sforzas in the fifteenth century.

In France, with a total navigable stretch of 2,215 miles of rivers, the government felt the increasing need of canals connecting these rivers to form a good inland navigation system for the transport of farm products and merchandise. As in road building, they met with the serious opposition of the landlords, who, though neglecting the upkeep of the banks and quays, levied tolls on the shipping. Improvements lagged until in the fifteenth and sixteenth centuries the central government had achieved sufficient momentum to overcome these difficulties. In 1528 Francis I had the banks of the Seine cleared and a serviceable towpath constructed, while the Ourcq was made navigable by straightening the channel and installing diversion weirs but without the use of locks. The quays of Paris itself were repaired in 1530.

A very ambitious project was to connect the Atlantic and the Mediterranean by a canal running from the Garonne

River eastward. It is quite possible that this was a project of Francis I, inspired by Leonardo. In 1539 Bachelier and Casanove, "levelers," submitted a project that after many vicissitudes was started in 1603 and completed by Pierre-Paul Riquet du Bonrepos in 1681. This was the famous Canal du Midi, then the pride of France. In 1643 Doubic built a canal connecting Dixmuide and Ypres with a set of locks to compensate for a difference in water level of 20 feet. The Canal du Centre connecting the Loire and the Rhone (1765), the Canal de Bourgogne between the Rhone and the Seine (1600), and the Briare Canal from the Loire to the Seine (1639) completed a series of water connections of great importance to inland navigation and trade.

The Low Countries became increasingly important in the field of civil engineering. The Dutch engineers amassed a great deal of experience, as canal and dike building was imperative in these countries to keep the land from being flooded. Hence Dutch engineers like Sir Cornelis Vermuyden were called to England to drain the fens north of Cambridge; others, like Cornelis Meyer, went to Italy to drain the swamps of the Campania.

The origin of most instruments, machines, and methods used in civil engineering is still unknown, and this applies to the dredger as well. Dredging by hand with scoops from flatboats had been done for centuries in Holland, Italy, and France. Simon Stevin designed a large dredge net in 1589, but the modern chain or bucket dredger seems to have originated in the sixteenth century. Venturino took out a Venetian patent on it in 1561, but in the same year Pieter Breughel produced a drawing of a similar chain dredger which had been made for the Rupel-Schelde canal built by the Brussels Municipality. Other patents of a similar kind date from 1600 to 1620.

The most common dredger was the so-called Amsterdam chain dredger, which was moved by a treadmill worked by two horses, while the dredger boat itself contained a small stable for two more horses. The other types invented by the

Dutch could be run by the force of the current. Cornelis Meyer (1640–1700) was said to have invented the power dredger moved by horses about 1680 or 1685, but earlier forms of the Amsterdam dredger are known. By the time the first illustrations or descriptions of these machines appear, they are already in common use and patents of this kind are rare.

The bucket dredger was particularly suited to conditions in the Low Countries. A second and equally important type was the double-jaw dredger, which was evolved in Italy and appears fully fledged in the *Book of Fortifications* by Vuonaiuto Lorni (circa 1600). All these engines belong to a whole series of earth-moving machines mostly developed by Italian engineers of the fifteenth and sixteenth centuries. We need not wonder that many of them are illustrated in books on military art and fortifications, for the canal, drainage, and irrigation projects of those days were very often adapted to military needs.

The Ship

BEFORE we turn to technology and the chemical industry, we may pause to look at the development of shipbuilding in this period. The great discoveries of the fifteenth and sixteenth centuries opened up new continents and new trade routes. This meant not only the ever-increasing importance of ocean trade and an urge to build better and faster ships, but also the founding of distant colonies and overseas empires. These colonial possessions of European nations as well as the trade routes to them had to be watched and protected. These powerful factors led to the rapid growth of European navies. Though no really fundamental changes were introduced, a number of special types of ships were evolved to suit local demands and conditions.

To cite one instance, Pieter J. Livorn of the small town of Hoorn (Holland) invented a new type of vessel, the "fluitschip," in 1595. This was a ship with shallow draught and slender design, her length being more than four times her beam. The deck sloped toward the stern and there were three masts with sails that were easy for a small crew to handle. This new vessel had great advantage in speed and efficiency over earlier types and became a dangerous competitor. Again, in the English wars, the Dutch built standard ships at a very fast rate to replenish their neglected navy. Standardization played a great part in arsenals after those days, and the navy was one of the strongest forces in promoting the manufacture of standard parts and tools.

The introduction of artillery into the navy as early as the end of the fourteenth century was a powerful factor in the design of new ships. The fundamental tactics of the ancient navies had been ramming and boarding—that is, duplicating in so far as possible the conditions of dry-land combat. Now cannon mounted on ships required entirely new tactics. Naval battles became a matter of skilled maneuvering so as to fire broadsides at the enemy ships. The new art of tacking and maneuvering demanded ships that were easily navigable and quickly responsive to the wheel. Hence the wide range of designs in rigs and ships, ranging from the unwieldy medieval cockboat to the trim, rakish lines of the square-rigged clipper ships.

We also begin to hear of submarines. The indefatigable Leonardo designed one, but probably never experimented with it. Cornelis Drebbel, however, actually constructed a submarine in which propulsion was achieved by rowers sitting in a kind of diving bell. The description can be read in his patent of 1598, and he demonstrated it on the Thames to King James I in 1620. Papin designed another type of submarine, which foundered when he tried to demonstrate it.

The so-called "ships' camels," which were devices for lifting heavy ships over sand bars and permitting them to navigate through shallow canals, were a further boon to shipping. The earlier forms appearing in the seventeenth century consisted of wooden chests attached to the ship that were pumped dry and thus increased the ship's buoyancy. Bakker of Amsterdam in 1688 designed more efficient models that allowed certain types of repairs to be made without placing the ship in dry dock. The most efficient form (1641) consisted of two half-sections of hull that were fitted on either side of a vessel and then pumped out, thus raising the vessel partly out of the water.

Mechanics and Industry

THE printing trade was very closely linked with mechanical inventions. After the invention of printing the number of publishers grew rapidly. From a total of 382 presses established in 1480 the number grew to 1,050 by the year 1500. Who invented the first printing press has not been established with certainty, but the first illustration of a press occurs in a work of 1498 and a similar or identical press is described in a book of Jost Amman in 1568. Types were either cut or cast. A type-founding industry was flourishing in Ripoli, Florence, between 1474 and 1483, and again Amman's book describes it in detail.

From recent studies on the invention of printing it is clear that Coster of Haarlem had already printed from loose cast types and that this art was improved by Gutenberg of Mainz between 1448 and 1454. His fellow worker, Peter Schoeffer, improved on Gutenberg and enabled Fust to complete the *Psalterium* in 1457, after which date the art of printing spread rapidly. Printing was an art in which the urge for mechanization was constantly present from the very beginning.

Paper manufacture also profited from applied mechanics, a major invention of this period being the "Hollander." Producing pulp for rag paper was a tedious job, for the rags had to be pulverized by pestles or hammers, usually moved by a water wheel, to form a suspension of fibers which then served as a base material for the papermaker. A new device was accordingly invented to shorten the time for obtaining pulp. This was achieved by an oval-shaped vessel divided along its major axis by a partition which did not extend to the ends of the vessel, thus forming an O-shaped channel, open at the top. The mass of rags was forced through this channel by means of a drum fitted with knives, and extending into one of the longer sides of the channel. The knives worked in conjunction with another series of knives that were fitted on a raised part of the bottom of the vessel. The rags were thus quickly cut up into a workable pulp. The inventor of this improved process was a Dutchman who lived in the latter part of the seventeenth or early eighteenth century, which accounts for the name "Hollander" that has clung to this device ever since.

It seems that the Dutch tried to keep this new machine secret, but did not succeed, and the first Hollander was installed in Germany in 1712 and France had its first machine soon afterward.

Further great strides toward mechanization were made in the textile industry. This industry had already profited from the introduction from the colonies of new dyes that tended to displace the old local dyes. Then came Cornelis Drebbel's invention of the use of tin mordants to achieve good scarlet colors. His son-in-law, Kuffler, first put Drebbel's process into use in the dyeing works at Bow, London, in 1610. This use of mordants allowed the industry to obtain faster and brighter colors. The practice spread quickly to the continent and held its own until the twentieth century.

The last step toward mechanization was taken in spinning. The earlier spinning wheels left the twisting of the thread to the spinner and only wound up the spool. About the middle of the sixteenth century Jürgen of Brunswick attached a crank and a treadle to the bobbing wheel and thus left the operator's hands free to handle the yarn. Now a new type of spinning wheel was introduced, sketches of which are also found in Leonardo's notebooks. The spindle of this new spinning wheel consisted of a pulley and a two-pronged flyer. Between these the shaft of the spindle (a spool with a pulley of its own) was free to revolve. Both pulleys were moved by means of strings on a larger wheel which was connected to a treadle and moved by the spinner's foot. The operator supplied a thread from the sliver on his lap and passed it through a hole in the center of the flyer over a hook or "hetch" on its arm onto the spool.

As spool and flyer moved at different speeds, the thread was thus twisted automatically. Different hetches ensured even winding on the spool. Though the stretching of the thread was still done by the spinner's hands, this new spinning wheel produced a stronger yarn. The improved spinning wheel with flyer, known as the Saxony wheel, made the spinning operation continuous. In the seventeenth century a further improved form, operating two spindles and two spools, came into use.

The ancient prehistoric and Egyptian inventions applied to the loom remained practically unchanged until the early eighteenth century. But horizontal looms were used, treadles applied to the operation of the heddles, and a batten moved the weft into position. The draw loom, which was probably imported from China, allowed more intricate patterns to be manufactured. The ribbon loom, a Dutch invention attributed to Willem Dircxz van Sonnevelt of Leyden, caused a revolution in the industry. Once again we find serious opposition to it from the guilds of Leyden, for it allowed the manufacture of a great number of ribbons on one loom. The patent was granted in 1605 or 1606, but only narrow ribbons were permitted to be manufactured in this way. The States General of Holland tried to prevent the export of the loom but failed, as it spread to England, Germany, and Switzerland in the course of the century. By 1765 it had become fully mechanized.

Knitting, at first performed entirely by hand, was mechanized by the Reverend William Lee's "stocking frame" in 1589, a treadle-operated machine with a separate needle for each loop. Though not completely automatic, this machine was the prototype of subsequent knitting and lace-making machines.

Mechanization did not mean that changes were introduced into the general structure of the textile industry. It remained a typical home industry in which the stages of production from raw material to finished product were divided up among many workmen who had these simple machines in their homes and who were financed, as before, by the merchants and bankers.

Metallurgy and Chemical Technology

IN THE field of technology the greatest progress was made in mining and metallurgy. The financial powers of the sixteenth century were very deeply involved in the development of these branches of technology. The rich Fugger and Thurzo families vied with each other for the exploitation of the mines of Styria, Salzburg, Tyrol, Hungary, the Harz, Bohemia, and Silesia. Earlier attempts in these districts from the thirteenth century onward had failed because of the lack of capital and because the Black Death in the fourteenth century had decimated the population.

Now the printing presses began to pour out a series of manuals on mining, metallurgy, and assaying, called *Bergbücherlein* (mining manuals) and *Probierbücherlein* (assaying manuals). The most important of these are the German Agricola's *De Re Metallica* (magnificently translated and edited by H. C. and L. H. Hoover), the Italian Vanuccio Biringuccio's *Pyrotechnia*, and the Frenchman Bernard Palissy's *Discours*. Every aspect of these trades is dealt with in these books. Agricola (whose German name was Georg Bauer), was a doctor in the Fugger mines and wrote down what he observed there, combined with quotations from the classics. His book gives details on mining, ore dressing, the building of shafts and corridors, the location of strata, the assaying of ores, and the details on current metallurgical processes.

De Re Metallica, first published in 1556, begins with an elaborate discussion of the use of metallurgy in the service of mankind. The sections on different ores, their location, and means of surveying contain interesting descriptions of very old techniques still practiced not so long ago. The tools of the miner are described in great detail, as are the methods of assaying, which for the first time employ quantitative analyses. This meant that careful control of the efficiency of every stage in the process from ore to metal could now be established, a control that was certain to lead to definite improvements. The book also describes the first mechanical crushers used for ores—pestles, or hammers moved by water wheels, which came into use in Agricola's day.

The water wheel was very liberally applied to move bellows, crushers, hoists, and other types of machinery. In those days water power, availability of wood for making charcoal, and the relative abundance of ores determined the location of mining centers.

Anyone interested in ingenious mechanisms for the drainage and ventilation of mines (for which rotary blowers were constructed), or in the construction of shafts and hauling machinery, sluicing and panning machinery, tunneling and fire setting, or who has a love for machinery in general, should find a great deal of pleasure in examining these beautifully illustrated books.

In general, the methods of obtaining copper and iron from their ores did not undergo great changes. The blast furnaces of the early sixteenth century are generally about 30 feet high with a diameter of 24 feet. Then as now, however, more primitive forms of metallurgy survived, and were practiced alongside the more efficient and modern ones. Water power was applied to the production of air for the blast furnace and also for hammering the lumps of crude wrought iron or any object that the smith wanted to shape.

A new method was devised for obtaining the silver from crude copper. It consisted of alloying lead with crude copper and slowly heating the bars thus obtained. The lead would drip off gradually, leaving a copper (containing only traces of silver) which could then be recovered. But this so-called "saiger" process (German, perpendicular or vertical) had transferred most of the silver to the lead from which it was recovered by the processes already practiced in ancient Troy. It appears that the saiger process was invented by Venetian metallurgists in the twelfth century, but it came into common use only in the sixteenth century. The same can be said for the use of mercury in the amalgamation processes, such as the "patio" process used to extract gold and silver from ores. This, too, had been known for many centuries but became common only in this period.

A new metal, bismuth, is first described in the mining handbooks of the time, as is the metal zinc. The ancients had known and used brass but had obtained it by heating copper with charcoal and zinc ores. Now it was realized that these zinc ores contained a metal. Its extraction was still too difficult, for as it is freed from the ore by the action of charcoal it boils off, owing to its low boiling point. The zinc vapors are then readily oxidized and form the white zinc oxide deposited at the mouth of the furnace. Therefore mass production of the metal was not possible until air had been excluded from the furnaces, the latter thus becoming, in effect, giant retorts. This improvement in furnace design was realized only 250 years after Agricola's death, whose book described the metal as a freak produced in small quantities in certain cases and recognized the connection between the metal and its ore.

A metal known only indirectly was cobalt, for in Agricola's day the residue of the treatment of antimony ores was used to obtain a beautiful blue glass. Antimony, already known to the ancients, became very popular when Paracelsus and other doctors, who believed in the use of chemicals to supplement herbs as medicines, began to prescribe it for various ills. It was used in the form of pills, but the metal was also used to cast cups which, it was believed, would be beneficial for the sick to drink from.

The glass industry was well developed in this period. Along with other branches of chemical technology it was seriously hampered by the fact that the wood used for fuel was in scarce supply due to the demands of shipbuilding and metallurgy. During the Dark Ages the glassmakers of Western Europe retreated south, except for a few along the Rhine. They settled in the ninth century in l'Altare in Montserrat near Genoa. These glassmakers, like those still working at that time in Syria, Byzantium, and probably at Venice too, used the ashes of seaweeds and thus produced soda-lime-silica glass, while the Rhenish glass prepared with wood ash was of similar composition except that potassium replaced the sodium. Stimulated by the greater demand for window glass in the Middle Ages, the Altarist craftsmen swarmed out again and founded new glasshouses in Lorraine and other regions of Western Europe. When the armies of Tamerlane destroyed Damascus, the seat of Syrian glassmaking, in 1402, the exports of Syrian and Alexandrian glass to Byzantium and beyond practically stopped.

This was a great boon to the glassmakers of Venice, who had moved their glass furnaces to Murano in 1291 and had tried to guard most zealously the trade secrets they had learned through trade with Byzantium and the Syrian coast. Glass manufacture was mostly concerned with the making of art objects until new inventions were developed. Venetian glass, now well decolorized and refined, profited much from the invention of Caspar Lehmann (1600), court jeweler to the Emperor Rudolf II at Prague, who began applying the technique of jewel-cutting to glass. Lehmann, Schwanhardt, and others perfected this technique during a period when the production of Venetian glass had reached its apex both in quality and quantity. In this way Venice partly made good the loss of shipping it had sustained through the Portuguese discoveries of the sea routes to India and the East.

In England the glasshouses suffered most through lack of fuel. Though there are some indications that coal was used earlier on the continent, Thomas Percivall in his patents of 1610, 1611, and 1613 describes a successful coal furnace for the manufacture of glass. Though at first difficulties arose in the melting of the glass batch in these closed furnaces, they were overcome by the addition of lead oxide to the mixture. These coal furnaces freed the glassmakers from depending on the waning supplies of timber in the less populated rural districts. They could now concentrate in the big cities, using the supplies of Tyneside "sea coal."

The manufacture of art glass had turned the scientists and technologists to the production of new colors for glass. Thus cobalt glass became popular in Germany about 1540 and Libavius and Glauber formulated good recipes for lead glass as well as for purple glass containing coloidal gold, a type that had been known to the Assyrians. The search for differently colored and better-quality glass was greatly stimulated by the publication of Neri's L'Arte Vetraria in 1612, which was translated into English by Merrett as The Art of Glassmaking in 1662. Thus the new chalk glass of Bohemia, called "crystal glass," appeared about 1675. The English glassmakers had experimented with glass containing lead oxide, and Thomas Tilman in 1662 produced a "crystal lead" glass; however, it was George Ravenscroft who erected two glasshouses in London in 1673 and 1674, where, with the help of his assistant Bishop, he produced the first really satisfactory "new flint glass."

These improved means of producing better-quality glass had immediate success, and glass vessels slowly drove out the older pewter and wooden tableware. The period of the limited use of glass lamps, phials, and bottles, which had begun in the fourteenth century, was now at an end. New decorative processes also became possible through the use of new glass-making ingredients and coloring agents.

There was not much progress in the production of pottery. Spanish-Moorish pottery had dominated from the twelfth century, this art being first transferred to Italy, then to France. Tin glazes, later so important an element in the famous majolica plaques of Lucca della Robbia and his school, were invented about 1283. Lead and salt glazes were still frequently used, the former being applied to the

German stoves decorated with tiles that were fashionable in the fifteenth and sixteenth centuries. But these schools produced only art objects; there was no serious attempt to manufacture technical and household pottery. The first to make an effort to understand the fundamentals of pottery manufacture was Bernard Palissy (1510–1590).

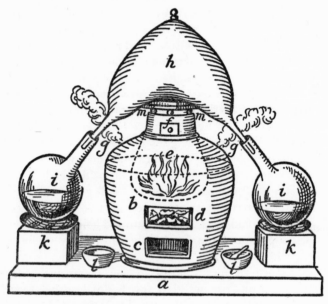

Lefebvre's bell process for the production of sulfuric acid from burning sulfur, circa 1660.

Chemical technology shows some evolution in this period. No longer were the druggists and apothecaries the sole manufacturers of chemicals. We now find substantial factories making nitre (for gunpowder), alum and vitriols (for the production of strong acids), zinc sulfate (used in tanning and dyeing), sal ammoniac, compounds of mercury (for medical use), and mineral pigments. Early chemists had learned to obtain salt from concentrated solutions by spraying them over brushwood stacks. The first factory to use this method on a large scale was built at Sulza, Germany, in 1568. Starch was also manufactured in large quantities for use in the linen and paper industries. The use of bluing for bleaching purposes seems to hail from Holland, whence it was imported into England around 1500.

The development of chemical technology, however, was held back by the paucity of chemical knowledge. Serious chemists like Boyle, Lemery, Lefebvre, and Libavius tried to penetrate the mysteries of chemical processes, but many decades of laboratory research were needed before the science could be established on a firm footing. As soon as quantitative measurements began to help lift the veil of alchemy, a sound chemical technology could flourish. This was realized only in the latter part of the eighteenth century, when the so-called Industrial Revolution ushered in a new era of chemical technology.

VIII

STEAM COMES OF AGE

(1750–1830)

THE latter half of the eighteenth century inaugurated a period which the historians of technology and culture have called the Industrial Revolution. It was characterized by the emergence of the modern world of machinery and engineering, and was accompanied by far-reaching changes and upheavals in the social, economic, and political institutions of the civilized world.

Fed by the new science of Newton and his generation and by the practical experience of engineers and technologists accumulated since the days of Agricola, two generations of brilliant technologists and inventors literally changed the face of the industrial and social world between 1750 and 1830.

The incessant religious wars and local strife during practically the whole of the sixteenth and part of the seventeenth centuries transformed Italy and Germany into backward countries, broken up into little warring states. Trade flourished in France, Holland, Scandinavia, and England. Holland had for some time held more than three quarters of international trade, but had been forced to yield first place to England, which beginning with the seventeenth century took the lead and held it for some three hundred years. The trade with the new colonies gave rise to large profits, and science, then still in the hands of those who could spend their own fortunes on research, profited in these trading countries of Western Europe.

Politically speaking, the "concert of Europe" as we know it was now consolidated. The days of the absolute monarchy were over, and through pressure from different sides the modern constitutional state began to crystallize, for it is the chief glory of the eighteenth century that it created the social sciences. Political economy and other social sciences occupied the attention of the best brains of the century.

The style of living in the eighteenth century was one of grace without the depth, fundamental honesty, and energy of the seventeenth. There was a great deal of slackness in religion, and the philosophy of the new science tended to lead mankind toward a rational belief in a mechanical world that, once having been created, had been left to its own devices without further intervention of the Creator. There was still a common belief in the general and universal tenets of Christianity, but the religion of the majority lacked genuine spirituality and fervor.

It is true that strong currents arose in protest against the rationalistic tendencies of the age. We need only mention the great philosopher and mystic, Emanuel Swedenborg, who was also an authority in the field of metallurgical and mining technique; or John Wesley and Methodists; or the many groups like the Moravian brethren, who finally sought peace and freedom in the New World. They looked to faith, not reason, as a support of religion. Still other groups used faith to justify their revolutionary tendencies. Unfortunately those who opposed the strong rationalistic current had little to say in the development of science. Their romantic protest did not begin to be heard until the nineteenth century.

Science in the Age of Reason

THE seventeenth century is often rightly called the Age of Projects. It was characterized by a great deal of ingenuity and saw the development of many contrivances that needed only time to bear fruit. This time had now come with the Age of Reason or Age of Common Sense, as the eighteenth century is variously called. For the "Newtonian world machine" and its mathematical picture of the universe appealed strongly to the eighteenth-century philosophers. It fitted in with their tendencies to create a natural religion and to find rational justification for faith and religion. They coined new terms like "progress" and "citizen of the world." The age was critical, skeptical, and worshipped common sense. It looked toward the new science to build a rational world in which every problem could be solved by the application of reason and logic.

Newton had built his philosophy of nature without "making hypotheses." These fundamental problems were for the most part ignored, for scientists now turned to the study of details and cultivated the accumulation of new facts without bothering too much about fundamentals. And so it was that they wrote lengthy books on special fields and tended to produce huge encyclopedias full of magnificent pictures and useful data on new observations. This growing mass of facts was readily absorbed by the large number of amateurs interested in science. Handbooks of technology began to appear. In France, they were written by such men as Macquer, Réaumur, Lavoisier, Baumé, Demachy, Chaptal, and Berthellot. In Germany, we find Taube, Wiegleb, Beckman, Ferber, von Poppe, Krünitz, and others, but in England, curiously enough, the first book of this type—Samuel Parkes's *Chemical Essays*—was not published until 1815.

Although by this time the Newtonian physics had penetrated the older universities, these scientific heirs of Newton turned their minds toward the abstract problems of theoretical mathematics and physics. Again they failed to establish close links with technology and engineering. This close touch with practical problems, however, was established in some of the younger universities. Accordingly Oxford and Cambridge had little to contribute to the Industrial Revolution, while Edinburgh and Glasgow played an important part in the technological development. The Scottish universities turned much of their scientific inquiry to practical applications.

The forces behind the Industrial Revolution were recruited from nonacademic quarters. When Voltaire and other philosophers translated Newton's essays from Latin into French and other languages, they unconsciously provided new food for thought for eager spirits who could not read the original. We find that after 1700 the achievements of the scientists and the different academies were absorbed by a large public of wealthy noblemen, bankers, and merchants, who discussed science freely, introduced experiments at their meetings and social gatherings, and devoted much of their money and patient labor to acquiring more than mere amateur standing in experimental and theoretical science.

The devotees in the salons and cabinets experimented and discussed practical problems. They were men engaged in trade and industry who felt that this new science could help them to perfect their products. There were also many technologists who contributed ingenious improvements. Thus in France, chemical technologists like Lefebvre, Lemery, and Glaser, most of them apothecaries by profession, were active in these fields. Germans like Becher, Blauber, and Kunckel could achieve little in their own troubled and backward country and had to emigrate to Holland and England to put forward their ideas with some practical effect.

In the earlier part of the century these men contributed largely to the rise of industry. It was not only the aristocrats, clergymen, doctors of medicine, and other intellectuals who turned from the humanities to physical science and technology as a profitable hobby; soldiers, barbers, common craftsmen, and farmers also made valuable contributions, and rose quickly in social status as a result. It is indeed very characteristic of the eighteenth century that its industrialists, contrivers, and inventors were recruited from all classes. We may even say that perhaps never before (nor since) was there such a high mobility among the different classes as there was in the Age of Reason—particularly in England.

There was a constant coming and going between laboratory and workshop. Many prominent industrialists became members of the Royal Society. Men of all classes met for discussion on scientific subjects in the Lunar Society, the Royal Society of Arts, and in other groups. New institutions, such as the Conservatoire des Arts et Metiers of Paris and the Royal Institution of Great Britain were designed to spread the new science and technology by lectures and demonstrations. In other continental countries similar societies were founded. In the United States, the Franklin Institute, founded in 1824, was the first institution in that country to be devoted to the furtherance of scientific research and the mechanical arts.

As in the early days of the Royal Society, those now keenly interested in "progress" were recruited from nonconformist groups. In England they were mostly Calvinists and Presbyterian Scots, Baptists, and Quakers. Their interest was partly due to religious opinions, but it is also true that they formed the greater part of the well-educated levels of the middle class, often possessing sufficient capital to promote new industries. The age was bustling with the idea of progress. It irritated the famous Dr. Johnson into saying: "The age is running mad after innovation. All the business of the world is to be done in a new way; men are to be hanged in a new way; Tyburn itself is not safe from the fury of innovation." Though the idea of progress spread to many, this interest would not have been sufficient in the long run to support an Industrial Revolution. What was needed were well-trained professional engineers and skilled labor.

Engineers and Skilled Labor

THE professional engineer of modern Europe is descended from the sapper and military engineer of the Renaissance

PLATE 19 Model of Smeaton's atmospheric mine pumping plant, 1772, in the Science Museum, South Kensington, London.

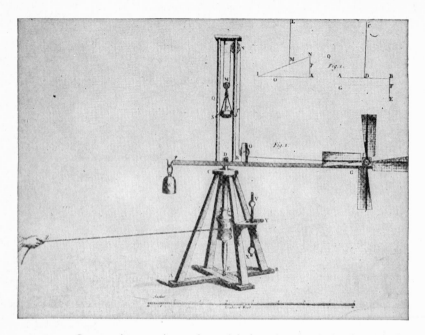

PLATE 20 Smeaton's experimental model for the determination of the power of windmills.

PLATE 21 The original McCormick reaper, 1834. (*Courtesy International Harvester Company, Chicago.*)

armies. In the eighteenth century, however, commercial and economic rather than strategic necessities determined the demands for improved roads, bridges, canals, and railroads. The methods of meeting these demands differed from country to country.

In France, the École des Ponts et Chaussées (1747) supplied the state with well-trained employees, many of whom left this service later to enter private industry. As the century progressed and mechanical engineers and chemical technologists were needed, other schools were founded—for example, the École Polytechnique and the School of Mines.

In England in accordance with the laissez-faire policy of leading economists like Adam Smith, the state did little for professional training. The English clung to practical training in famous workshops such as the Soho (Birmingham) works of Boulton and Watt. Here famous men like Joseph Bramah, Henry Maudslay, and Joseph Clement were initiated into the new arts of designing and making precise engines and machine parts. These men were not prone to write textbooks like their French colleagues; instead, they trained new generations of skilled workmen and engineers by teaching them in their shops. New machine shops like those of Dobson and Barlow, Asa Lees, and Richard Roberts formed additional centers of training.

The new machinery demanded not only ingenuity in designing, but also accurate manufacture of parts. As the guilds of craftsmen decayed rapidly into monopolistic societies of tradesmen, a trained body of workmen—"skilled labor"—arose. No institutions for educating these new craftsmen existed until well into the nineteenth century. They had to receive their training in the machine shops like the engineers. In fact, the different systems of apprenticeship proposed by eighteenth-century industrialists show how difficult it was to cope with the demands for a new type of workmen created by the new machines.

The creation of these new engineers and workmen would not, however, have yielded any appreciable results without the improved instruments used in experiments, and without a sound theoretical approach to the physical properties of materials, such as metals, wood, and stone.

The new science of the preceding era had created different types of instruments, which now became more generally available with the rise of a kind of manufacture specializing in this field. Count William IV of Hessen (1532–1592) had tried to make Cassel the center of instrument manufacture; Augsburg and Nuremberg continued to be famous for the production of certain tools, while university towns like Leyden, Paris, London, and Edinburgh could boast of skilled instrument makers. Generally speaking, scientists or amateurs of the eighteenth century no longer needed to make their own instruments or grind their own lenses as Huygens and others did before; now one could buy them ready-made from the rising class of skilled instrument makers.

One has to go back a long way to find the first approach to a clear knowledge of the properties of materials. This branch of science owed its first impetus to the efforts of Galileo and Leonardo, who tried scientifically to measure breaking strength and other properties. But their knowledge of mechanics was still insufficient and not until the days of Mariotte and Hooke (c. 1664) was science far enough advanced to attack successfully even a simple problem like the bending strength of a beam enclosed in a wall at one end. Hooke in 1670 and La Hire formulated laws for the elastic behavior of materials. The problems of the strength and shape of arches in buildings occupied such minds as those of Palladio (1550), Derand (1643), and Rondelet, who measured these values in practice. La Hire published the correct solution in 1695.

The Dutch scientist, 's Gravezande, was the first to design and demonstrate machines for measuring the tensile strength, breaking strength, and bending strength of different materials like wood, glass, and metals (1729). These instruments were greatly improved by Mariotte, Coulomb, and others. Prominent mathematicians like Euler contributed to the mathematical calculations on which these machines were based. Testing struts and beams formed the subject of a discussion between Buffon (for wood), Gauthey (for stone), and others, until Coulomb and Rondelet announced the correct solution in 1802. Réaumur was one of the first to measure the tensile strength of metals and to design an instrument for measuring their hardness. Without these theoretical discussions and laboratory experiments the machine industry of the nineteenth century would have been impossible.

The New Machine Works

THE new technology stemmed from the art of the ancient millwrights, carpenters, and instrument makers. But the skill of these ancient craftsmen had to be reshuffled and re-oriented. James Watt, himself a trained instrument maker, had to create the necessary tools and teach workmen of foundries and machine shops how to use them.

The skilled inventors coming from Boulton and Watt's workshop gave us a host of minor inventions that proved how active they were in every direction. Everything they touched apparently was transformed into a useful tool or machine.

Take the copying press, a regular feature of the old-time offices, which was invented by James Watt himself. When traveling he had no secretary and had to write and copy his letters himself. In 1799 it occurred to him that by mixing his ink with glue or sugar he could obtain writing that could easily be transferred to a moistened sheet of thin paper. He then designed a press that would ensure proper contact between the letter and the moistened paper and thus was able to make many clear copies of the original.

Among other prominent engineers and skillful inventors were Henry Maudslay and Joseph Bramah. The latter was an exceedingly fertile genius and one of the few that reaped the fruits of his inventions during his lifetime. He was the inventor of the water closet (1778, 1783) and of a patent lock

(1784) which defied everybody until Hobbs in 1851 at last succeeded in opening it with a skeleton key after 51 hours of labor.

Bramah and Maudslay cooperated for many years until Bramah refused to increase Maudslay's wages of thirty shillings a week (1797). By that time they had invented a planing machine for wood, a machine that numbered the banknotes of the Bank of England for years, and many other ingenious devices. Their main contribution, however, was the education of generations of skilled engineers and workmen, who later rose to high positions in industry.

For it cannot be stressed too often that the mainstay of the evolution of the steam engine and of the Machine Age in general lay in the precision of the machine tools themselves. The rapid development of the steam engine would not have been possible without tools and processes for accurately finishing parts that had to fit together smoothly. The practical inventors of the Industrial Revolution had an uncanny knack of inventing the proper tools that made possible the building of their engines. Henry Maudslay actually invented the screw-cutting lathe in 1797 in order to help Joseph Bramah realize his project of a hydraulic press. Tools and tolerances were the primary problems that Watt and his generation had to contend with. Out of these problems emerged a type of skilled labor that was entirely different from the old craftsmanship.

Maudslay's lathe was directly responsible for the improvement in the machining and production of tools and machine parts. The lathe originally belonged to the carpenter's shop. Even before the eighteenth century lathes had sometimes been used for turning soft metals such as tin and lead. Most primitive carpenter's lathes moved the work with the same kind of bow used for the fiddle. Then some improvement was achieved by the introduction of a treadle or handwheel to turn the work. Here again Leonardo's notebooks show plans to change the speed by using an interchangeable set of gear wheels. The Florentine genius also invented the slide rest and a better form of hand wheel. Similar ideas arose in the eighteenth century when furniture makers adopted intricate art styles that further advanced the evolution of the lathe and, incidentally, incorporated many of Leonardo's ideas.

But applying the lathe to metals meant redesigning and reinforcing its entire structure. Maudslay, Roberts, Fox, and Witworth were the pioneers of the modern lathe, which was driven by the steam engine by means of a complicated system of shafts, pulleys, and gears. New means were found to move the work in the lathe both vertically and horizontally, to adjust the depth of cut and rate of feed by screws and hand wheels, and to stop the machine automatically when the work was done. The older lathes were still moved by hand or foot, but steam eventually won out, only to be superseded in the present century by electricity.

Maudslay and Robinson had made possible the automatic manufacture of screws, and through their efforts the mass production, according to rigid specifications, of such common standard parts as screws, bolts, and nuts became a reality. The latter half of the nineteenth century saw a further evolution of the lathe. Parts such as pulleys, axles, and handles were perfected and then came the invention of the capstan or turret lathe. This was a round or six-sided block rotating about its axis and having a hole in the middle of each side to hold different tools that could be inserted at will. These could then be brought successively into contact with the work. The capstan lathe thus performed the work of six separate lathes in much shorter time. In 1855 a mechanism for automatically turning the turret was added, and in 1891 James Hartness developed the flat-turret lathe, in which the turret was replaced with a horizontal face plate that permitted greater flexibility and higher speeds. The lathes were specialized in different directions and now range from the tiny forms suitable for the watchmaker to those for boring large cannon and other huge pieces of armament or equipment. Recent progress in this field was made possible by the introduction into the machine shops of high-speed tool steel by Taylor and White. The lathe has definitely come to stay, but it will be clear from this rapid survey that it was already an essential and universal tool for the manufacture of machine parts as early as 1800.

The Industrial Revolution

IN THE foregoing pages we have cited many examples from England to illustrate the evolution of engineering in the Industrial Revolution. We must now try to explain why England became the leading country in this period.

France, though it had a strong central government—probably the strongest in Europe in those days—did not succeed in building up an industry from the decaying guilds of craftsmen. Colbert, Turgot, and other ministers interested in this problem could not get sufficient financial backing nor arouse real interest in industrial middle-class circles, where it was feared that the government was attempting to control industry. Napoleon, through Chaptal, created something of a French industry, but it went through a great crisis after his fall, for much of its prosperity had actually depended on the success of the British blockade of the continent. Holland, limited by the Act of Navigation, had too small a market of its own to support an industry, nor could industry thrive in a divided Germany. Napoleon's artificial "self-supporting French industry" failed, but free enterprise, stimulated by real support, succeeded in England and also in the United States, a country whose voice now began to be heard in the European concert.

The prominent position of England during this period is due to a fortunate combination of many factors. Through better hygiene there was a constant decrease in mortality during the century, which coincided with a high and steady fertility and an influx of labor from Ireland and Scotland. Industry, formerly concentrated mainly in the south and east of England, was still rural and migratory, but it gradually moved north toward the Midlands and beyond. The situation was eminently suited to a reshuffling of industry as demanded by the Industrial Revolution for various economic and technical reasons. Industry started to shift away from the greater towns and their stricter public control.

Through the building of a colonial empire, England had grown rich and not only had excellent sources of many basic materials for its new industry but had built up a merchant navy fully capable of handling its imports and exports. All through the century capital was freely available at a fairly constant, low rate, and land became more easily obtainable as enclosure of common pasture lands proceeded. The many poor farmers and squatters moving into the towns provided an ample supply of labor. A plentiful source of capital and an excellent banking system furnished the backing that industrialists needed.

The large class interested in science and in constant contact with it provided the initiative for the Industrial Revolution. As labor was better divided and specialized, multiple inventions prospered. The new science and the idea of progress were ingrained in a large class of individuals recruited from all social groups, and they started a series of changes that were particularly noticeable after 1760. The rich supply of technical geniuses and inventors available in England and Scotland were also an important factor in the changing industrial pattern.

The great events characterizing this period are the development of iron metallurgy, the evolution of the steam engine, the general use of coal instead of wood, the rise of industrial chemistry, and the establishment of machine industry. These events served to raise the barriers imposed by limited supplies of food, fuel, iron, yarn, and transport. They could not have occurred without the background of scientific thought provided by the scientists forming part of the generation between Francis Bacon and Isaac Newton. This background underlay all of the useful inventions of the Industrial Revolution. Since the appropriate symbol of this period is the steam engine, it will be well to review the power resources of this period. Though some writers have stressed only the seamy side of life during the era, objective research has proved that England as a whole attained a higher standard of living in the Industrial Revolution than it ever had enjoyed before.

The Beam Engines

WATER wheels and windmills still were important sources of power, but they were destined to be supplanted by the steam engine during this period. No fundamental changes took place in their design between 1750 and 1830, although it is worth mentioning that experimenting and calculation played a part in attempts to improve these earlier forms of prime movers. Smeaton was sent by the Royal Society to study windmills and hydraulic engineering works in Flanders and Holland in 1759, and proved in his report that overshot wheels were the most efficient types of water wheels.

Windmills were so important to Dutch industry that handbooks like Lindperch's *Moolenboeck* (1734) and Van Zijl's *Algemeen Groot Moolenboeck* were published to describe their construction and application to industry. Smeaton carefully studied these works and mills and experimented with scale models. He soon was able to show that the windmill could not hope to compete with the steam engine of his day, for to develop the same power as the latter the area of its sweeps would have to be increased to fantastic proportions. While the windmill was closely bound to certain climatic conditions, the steam engine, assuming there was sufficient fuel available, could be built and operated anywhere.

Stephen Hales's first application of the windmill to ventilation of dwellings was in 1752. He was led to this by the strange tax then levied in England on the total window surface of private houses, public buildings, and even prisons. It was, in effect, a tax on light and fresh air. Hales's ventilator was a boon to the inmates of prisons and hospitals, who in those days suffered from the strange disease called "hospital fever," the incidence of which was greatly reduced by increasing the amount of fresh air in the buildings.

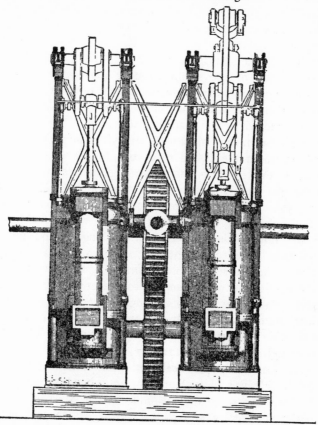

Beam engine designed in 1818 by Colonel Ogden of New Jersey for his steamboat. (Analectic Magazine, 1818.)

The steam engine came into its own in this period and has remained one of the primary sources of power ever since. Savery's engine had been of tremendous advantage to the miner, but it was definitely not a universal power engine as yet. The first practical steam engine was built by Thomas

Newcomen and John Calley (or Cawley) in 1705. This model, like most of the early types, was an atmospheric engine—that is, no superheated high-pressure steam was used, but only steam at atmospheric pressure and 100°C as evolved by boiling water. It was a typical eighteenth-century steam engine in that a beam or balance formed part of its construction. The piston of the steam cylinder moved one end of the balancing beam up and down, while the other end of the beam was connected with the pump or with the driving wheel connected with other machinery.

Newcomen and Calley used Savery's principle of condensing the steam in the cylinder for the downward stroke of the piston. But in their engine an ingenious system of valves regulated the introduction of steam into the cylinder, the injection of cold water to condense the steam, and the shutting off of the steam from the cylinder. Newcomen could not obtain a patent for his engine, and until 1716 Savery's patentees profited from Newcomen's inventions. But in that year Newcomen formed a company to promote the application of his engine to industry and soon he was successful. Many Newcomen engines were now applied to the drainage of coal mines. In due time the inventor succeeded in attracting the attention of the eminent English civil engineer, John Smeaton (1724–1792).

Smeaton was a practical man who paid great attention to details. He was pleased but not entirely satisfied with Newcomen's engine, so that he undertook a series of careful experiments with a specially designed engine that had been built for him at Austhorpe in 1769. His precise observations and mathematical analyses of its performance led to several improvements. First he attacked the problem of the boiler, furnace, and methods of firing. He redesigned the grate and increased the size of the valves and steam lines. In 1772 he reported the results of over 130 experiments, and formulated design data for engines of from one to 78 horsepower, giving recommended values for cylinder diameter, length of stroke, number of strokes per minute, size of boiler, quantity of feed water, temperature of injection water, and coal consumption. In 1774 he built a 76½-horsepower engine at Chasewater. But the days of the Newcomen engine were by then nearly over, for these pioneer atmospheric engines were rendered obsolete by Watt's improved design, and disappeared shortly after 1800.

In 1765 James Watt, a Scottish engineer (1736–1819) constructed a steam engine that used but one-third the coal of a Newcomen engine of comparable size. He achieved this result largely by applying the principles of physical science to steam production and consumption. James Watt was not only a skilled engineer; in his youth he had been trained as an instrument maker and had conversed with the great scientists of his day. He was the friend of John Robison and Joseph Black, both prominent in the universities of Scotland and both engaged in the study of the nature of heat.

This study had got well beyond the stage of theoretical discussion and was now directed toward the measurement of temperatures and of quantities of heat. Most physicists then believed that heat was a condition of matter, a form of energy caused by the motion of the particles (or molecules) of which all matter was composed. Black and a few others, however, persisted in the mistaken belief that heat was a substance that flowed from hot bodies to cold ones, a form of matter that the older chemists had called "caloric." The American physicist Benjamin Thompson (1753–1814), who accepted the title of Count Rumford from the Elector of Bavaria in 1791, was the first to refute the caloric theory. He undertook a series of experimental proofs after he had observed that a great amount of heat was evolved during the boring of a cannon at the arsenal in Munich; later he was able to boil water by the friction of a blunt tool inside a brass cylinder. Black's erroneous theory, however, did not impair the accuracy of his quantitative heat measurements, so that progress in calorimetry and thermometry continued.

By this time a number of thermometer scales had been developed. The older thermometers did not indicate anything but relative differences in temperature. Gabriel Fahrenheit, Anders Celsius, and René Antoine de Réaumur each devised a temperature scale of his own by marking his thermometer at fixed points—the melting point of ice and the boiling point of water—and dividing the scale into a fixed number of intermediate points, as Newton and others had previously suggested. At last scientists could measure the "degree of heat" by means of any one of these three standard scales.

Moreover, the *quantity* of heat could now be expressed accurately as well. Many scientists had measured the resultant temperature when hot and cold substances were mixed. Black and Wilcke independently repeated such measurements and defined certain units of heat governing these phenomena. The first of these was *specific heat*—that is, the amount of heat required to raise the temperature of a unit mass of a substance one degree. The second was *latent heat* (of fusion), which is the amount of heat required to melt a unit mass of a solid without changing its temperature. (A later concept, *latent heat of vaporization*, is similarly defined, being the amount of heat required to change one gram of a substance from a liquid to a vapor without raising its temperature.)

The phenomenon of evaporation was also better understood after Dalton had shown that every substance has a definite vapor pressure at any given temperature, the pressure increasing with the temperature until it becomes one atmosphere at the boiling point. Formulating these units meant that the changes of heat occurring in a certain system of substances could now be observed and calculated scientifically with the calorimeter, the new instrument that had been perfected by Lavoisier. It now became possible to calculate how much heat (and hence energy) was contained in steam at various temperatures and pressures.

Watt himself tells us that his discussions with Robison and Black on the nature and quantity of heat led him to the improvement of the steam engine. The most important of his improvements was the condenser, which he perfected in 1765. Watt found that the steam entering the cylinder would do more work if the cylinder were kept as hot as the entering steam. Newcomen engines consumed an enormous amount of steam when cold water was injected into the cylinder, for the walls of the cylinder were then cooled down to 20°C and had to be reheated to 100°C during the next stroke. This meant that much of the steam consumed did not perform any useful work. Watt argued correctly that the cylinder, instead of being cooled after each stroke, should be insulated and kept hot.

The upshot was that the condensing of the steam was made to take place in a *condenser*, an enclosed chamber distinct from the cylinder itself. The cylinder would then remain hot when the condenser was cooled, and the steam pressures in both would be about equal. Thus when the steam was condensed in the condenser the pressure in the cylinder was lowered at the same time, causing the piston to be sucked down but allowing the temperature of the cylinder to remain high in readiness for the next charge of steam. The new charge would drive the piston up again without any intervening loss of pressure formerly caused by the cold cylinder walls.

The Double-Acting Rotative Engine

Two years after Watt had his fruitful discussions with Black (1763), he tried to realize his ideas for the improvement of the steam engine. In this he was fortunate to meet John Roebuck, a very enterprising Scotsman and industrialist, who helped with money where Watt, who was never a good financier, would have failed. At Roebuck's Carron Ironworks Watt did not find the skilled artisans needed to make his experimental engine, so that he himself had to spend too much of his time in surveying and engineering for his employer. Therefore it was a boon to Watt that Roebuck transferred his part of the 1769 patent to Matthew Boulton.

Watt moved to Birmingham in 1774. There in Boulton's Soho Foundry he found craftsmen sufficiently skilled to make precision parts like valves and close-fitting pistons. Nearby was John Wilkison's Foundry at Bradley, which could supply cylinders accurately finished, for Wilkison had taken out a cannon-boring patent in 1774. Parliament extended Watt's 1775 patent to 1800, and at Soho Watt produced his first large-scale steam engine in 1781. It was of the single-acting type, using steam only on one side of the piston.

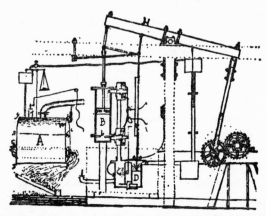

Reichenbach's sketch of a Watt engine made in 1791 at the Soho Works, illustrating the sun-and-planet gear.

Watt's first engine already showed a considerably higher efficiency than Newcomen's. Its power output per unit of steam was four times that of the latter. It was soon applied with considerable success to pump water in brine works, breweries, and distilleries. Its greater efficiency was particularly appreciated in the ironworks. Watt was lucky to have so honest and enterprising a partner as Boulton, who, with the famous William Murdoch, did much to advertise and apply Watt's steam engine. Yet Watt was not content to rest with these achievements.

For not even with his two important auxiliary patents of 1781 and 1782 would he have been able to capitalize on his inventions. Watt's first machine was still a beam engine, suitable for driving pumps but not as a universal source of power. Realizing that for the engine to be successful it must be adaptable

to all types of power requirements, Watt took out his patent
of 1781 in which he describes a means of translating the reciprocating movement of the beam arm into a rotary movement.
Since Watt could not use the crank because it had been patented by one of his competitors, he hit upon the ingenious
idea of attaching a rod with a gear wheel to the beam arm, the
gear wheel moving about a second one attached to the driving
wheel. This "sun and planet" movement converted the steam
engine into an engine with a rotating driving wheel and axle
that could be made to drive machinery by means of belts or
chains.

Watt's patent of 1782 brought two further important
improvements. His new engine became a double-acting one—
that is, steam was introduced alternately on both sides of the
piston to provide smoother operation. It was not a success immediately, for the art of accurately casting the large cylinders
needed for double-acting steam engines had not yet been mastered. Here again Boulton and Watt had a hard struggle to obtain better-fitting parts and materials of the required strength.

A serious problem arose during the construction of the
double-acting engine. The piston now had to pull and push alternately, which meant that it had to be properly connected
to the beam and be guided throughout its travel. The older
single-acting beam engine had used a flexible connection between the piston rod and the beam. Such a connection allowed
too much play when the piston was made double-acting. In
1784 Watt devised an extended three-bar motion, called the
"parallel motion," of which he was rightly very proud; he
wrote to his son that he took more pride in this invention
than in any other.

Watt also introduced his regulator in the patent of 1784.
This instrument automatically closes the supply of steam
when the piston has moved part of the stroke and thus con-
tributes materially to the efficiency of the engine. The rest of
the stroke is due to the expansion of the steam admitted, and
thus a more effective use is made of the energy contained in
the steam that is already in the cylinder. The centrifugal gov-

ernor of 1788 combined this efficient use of steam with automatic regulation of the steam supply when the load on the engine was increased or decreased. As the number of strokes per minute had to remain constant, a device had to be found that would diminish the steam supply as the load decreased. Watt took four rods connected with hinge joints to form a diamond or lozenge that was weighted with a heavy ball at each of the two outer hinges. The lower hinge was joined to a rod that moved through the upper hinge and connected with a valve that closed the steam supply. As the engine speed increased, the heavy lead balls turned faster, moving outward by centrifugal force and lowering the rod that shut off the steam.

In 1794 Watt added a new testing device, the steam gage or indicator, consisting of a small cylinder in which a piston was connected through a spring to a stylus that moved over a revolving drum. The steam from the engine cylinder acted on the indicator piston and moved the stylus, which traced a curve on graph paper wrapped around the drum. And so this "stethescope of the engineer" was able to draw a pressure-displacement curve which showed exactly how the pressure in the engine cylinder fell off as the stroke advanced, thus providing a means of controlling engine performance under varying conditions of fuel supply, temperature, and pressure.

Watt's rotative engine came at the same time as Cort's roller process for the production of wrought iron and Arkwright and Crompton's mechanization of spinning. In 1783 a Watt engine operated the first hammer for John Wilkinson. It was the start of a series of very successful practical applications of the engine, and by 1800 there were some 500 Boulton and Watt engines in operation. Together with the new mechanisms for transmitting power, the steam engine gradually displaced human labor and the water wheel in many crafts. It became the symbol of the new Machine Age of the nineteenth century.

Watt owed much of his success to William Murdoch, who besides helping with the business end of Watt's inventions also invented the sliding valves that regulated the steam supply to the cylinder and developed a mixture of iron filings and sal ammoniac to serve as a packing between the piston and cylinder. Cast-iron surfaces could not be made to fit as closely as at present, and adequate packing materials such as we have today had not yet been perfected.

Towards the Modern High-Pressure Steam Engine

WATT's genius had conceived all the fundamental parts of the modern steam engine, and the subsequent development of the engine has been in the direction of better design, more accurate machining of parts, and increased capacities and outputs. The only really serious competitors of Watt were John Hornblower and Richard Trevithick. Hornblower was the first to build a compound engine in which the steam released from the first cylinder was further expanded in a second cylinder. These compound engines, which did away with the condenser and increased the over-all efficiency, were not a serious threat to Watt's engine so long as low steam pressures had to be used. Engines could not yet be made stronger and tighter, for the materials were not available.

Trevithick (1771–1833) and Oliver Evans (1755–1819), the American inventor, were the pioneers of the high-pressure steam engine. Trevithick applied himself to the problem beginning in 1796 and finally took out a patent in 1802, which brought him into conflict with Boulton and Watt, many of whose ideas he had to take over. But the application of high-pressure steam meant more horsepower per unit of weight. When the engines became lighter there arose the possibility of using them for transportation.

Furthermore, the evolution of compound engines and auxiliary machinery could begin only when the theory of the transformation of heat into energy had been fully developed. This new theory, on which the modern science of thermodynamics is based, was the work of Sadi Carnot, Robert Mayer, James Prescott Joule, William Thomson (Lord Kelvin), and Rudolf Emanuel Clausius; it did not reach final form before

1850. We have already seen that Benjamin Thompson (Count Rumford) was also involved in the development of the new theory, having been the first to disprove the older idea of caloric, which conceived heat to be a form of matter.

During this period the rotative beam engine reigned almost supreme in England. The high-pressure steam engine could not be a success so long as the boilers could not produce high-pressure steam, for the old boilers were all vertical beehive-shaped structures not designed for high pressures or for the most efficient consumption of fuel. The first fundamental step was taken by Trevithick, who created the Cornish boiler (1812). This was essentially a cylinder heated by a furnace tube mounted inside the cylinder itself, the heat being transferred to the water from the hot flue gases inside the tube, thus contributing to increased fuel efficiency.

The old Cornish boiler met a serious competitor in the Lancashire boiler invented by William Fairbairn in 1844, which had two internal flues instead of one. The grate of this boiler was the subject of many patents, the most important of which were those for the "traveling grate stoker" granted to John Bodmer in 1834, and Juckes's chain-grate stoker, patented in 1841. The fuel economizer for heating the feed water with flue gases was introduced by Edward Green in 1845. Notwithstanding these considerable improvements, the Cornish and Lancashire boilers were still fairly inefficient.

Further improvements were made when multitubular boilers were introduced. In these the water is taken into a series of tubes built in the flue. There a better contact between the water and hot flue gases is achieved, and the water is then returned to the boiler for evaporation in the form of steam. Multitubular designs are connected with the evolution of the vertical boiler, the first practical design originating with Marc Seguin of Paris about 1829. The typical modern Babcock and Wilcox tubular boiler stems from the original horizontal water-tube boiler built by that company in 1867.

A further step away from the beam-engine type was the invention of the direct-action steam pump by Henry Worthington of New York in 1841, which was soon followed by the double-action steam pump in 1857. Toward the end of the Industrial Revolution steam had already been widely used as a prime mover in machinery in such applications as the steam hoist (1830) and James Nasmyth's steam hammer (1839).

In the meantime, the design and manufacture of machine parts had undergone a complete change. Not only could these parts be made interchangeable but their specifications now called for smaller and smaller tolerances. Cartwright's metallic packing (1797) as improved by Barton in 1816 ensured tight joints and eliminated the possibility of serious leaks.

Hence four different factors—the evolution of efficient high-pressure boilers, the rise of thermodynamics, experience with steam-driven prime movers, and the availability of close-fitting, interchangeable parts—contributed to the eventual success of the high-pressure, multicyclinder, noncondensing compound steam engine.

Arthur Woolf (1776–1837), the man who perfected the compound engine (1804, 1814), was one of Trevithick's competitors, since he too used high-pressure steam. But the steam engine still retained its beam form for quite some time, and not until about 1850 did the rotative high-pressure compound engine come into general use. Even the American Corliss engine (1849), though a decided improvement on earlier types, still employed the beam form. John McNaught in 1845 and E. A. Cowper in 1857 were the pioneers of the modern form. Three-cylinder engines were introduced by Brotherhood in 1871 and Krig in 1874, and soon became popular as prime movers of steamships, beginning about 1881.

Coal and Coke

THE Industrial Revolution, and more particularly the development of the steam engine and of metallurgy, depended on a good supply of fuel. In the old days the most important fuel for the metallurgist and technologist was charcoal. Already in the days of Queen Elizabeth a serious shortage of timber had resulted in a rise in the price of charcoal. Instead of remaining near the ore deposits, the smelting plants had to follow timber and water power into the mountain districts. This resulted in a serious disruption of production, for the various stages of producing and manufacturing metals were still handled in different plants. The moving of the smelting plants into the mountains occasioned a dire need for transport, which was as yet in a very primitive state and could not begin to meet the new demands. With the price of timber rising 80 per cent in two centuries, disaster seemed to threaten the iron and steel industry.

Coal production was still a rural craft, the miners often stopping their work at harvest time to till the soil. By the beginning of the eighteenth century open pits and outcrops no longer played a prominent part in production. Most coal mines were systems of galleries reached by shafts up to 200 feet deep. This meant that drainage and ventilation had become serious problems in coal mining.

After the thirteenth century coal had been shipped from the Northumberland and Durham collieries to London by sea. Its production rose steadily from about 50,000 tons a year in 1550 to 280,000 tons in 1680. Its use was mainly limited to domestic heating and to a few small industries. Even then production ran short and the prices of tin, alum, and soap had tripled. The metallurgist could not use this "sea coal" instead of the expensive charcoal, for the volatile constituents of coal spoiled his products.

The primitive transporting of coal in the galleries, mostly performed by women and children carrying baskets, was gradually taken over by ponies drawing sledges or wagons along wooden rails. Then from the top of the pits the coal was transported in wagons on wooden rails to the river or sea, where it was loaded into ships of 300 to 400 tons burden. The tubbing of galleries and shafts (making them watertight in water-bearing strata) was mainly achieved with wooden planks. In 1777 John Curr introduced cast-iron tubbing of the shafts.

The most important limiting factors of coal mining were

coal gas and water. Between 1550 and 1660 no less than 14 per cent of the patents granted were for devices or machines that attempted to solve the latter problem. Here the Newcomen engine, primitive as it was, became an immediate success. It was first used in the Midlands and then moved north. In 1765 one hundred Newcomen engines were in constant use in the Wear and Tyne districts.

Hand in hand with the use of the steam engine underground, though not directly connected with it, came better mine ventilation and increased protection from coal-gas explosions. Before the days of the modern high-speed centrifugal blower, ventilation in mines was obtained through convection currents set up from an underground furnace. This system was adequate for mines where noxious and inflammable gases were present only in small quantities, but there was always the danger that a large quantity of coal gas (firedamp or methane) might suddenly be released when a coal seam was opened. Many serious explosions were caused when the open flame of a miner's lamp ignited this material.

Sir Humphrey Davy (1778–1829), then a professor of chemistry at the Royal Institution of London, studied the problem and discovered that a metal gauze conducts heat away so rapidly that a flame will not pass through it. He applied this principle and invented the miner's safety lamp or Davy lamp in 1816. It consisted of a small cylindrical oil lamp surrounded by a wire gauze mounted in a cylindrical frame. The Davy lamp not only prevented accidental explosions of this nature but also warned the miner of the presence of dangerous gases by the flickering of the flame.

These and other improvements in mining technique accounted for the steady development of coal production during the eighteenth century. Production rose from two and a half million tons in 1700 to four and a half million in 1750, ten million in 1800, and sixteen million in 1829. Not only did this increase lead to further improvement of the steam engine and increased production of metals, but coal transport and export also basically affected the growth of the English merchant navy and the evolution of cheap transportation. By 1750 practically all of the present English coal fields were in operation, with continental development not far behind.

The Frenchman, Jars, traveling in England on behalf of the French government, was outspoken on the advantages of coal for industrial production. The merchant navy doubled in size during this century. Road traffic and improved roads were stimulated by the transport of coal to industrial centers, and so was canal building. Smelting plants and other industries began to return from the forests high up in the mountains to the sites of ores and coal fields.

The production of coal was necessary for domestic and industrial heating, for the production of metallurgical coke, and for the recovery of gas and other by-products important in chemical technology.

The New Iron Metallurgy

GENERATIONS of pioneers had experimented with coal as a substitute for charcoal in metallurgy. Dun Dudley in his *Metallum Martis* claims to have run a blast furnace with coal in 1621, but the evidence for it is doubtful. Coal as such continued to spoil the good iron by giving off sulfurous fumes. Though many inventors brought forward various processes for using coal in place of charcoal, the ironmasters regarded each new attempt with some degree of suspicion. Moreover, the blast in the furnaces then used was still insufficient to permit the use of coke. Some of the primitive coke produced failed because it was too soft for stacking ore in the blast furnace. This was due to the fact that indiscriminate experimenters were using all kinds of coal. The production of good hard coke was the key to the problem.

It was finally solved through the combined efforts of three generations of the Darby family. Abraham Darby senior spent his life in these experiments. He produced coke in the same kind of stacks as those used for the manufacture of charcoal. When he died in 1717, his experiments were sufficiently advanced to enable his son Abraham junior to succeed. From 1753 onward the latter could produce the right kind of coke for his blast furnace at Coalbrookdale.

In a letter to a friend dated 1775, Abraham junior's wife Abiah wrote that it had occurred to Abraham senior "that it might be practicable to smelt iron from the ore in the Blast Furnace with Pit Coal. Upon this he first try'ed with raw coal as it came out of the Mines, but it did not answer. He, not discouraged, had the Coal Coak'ed into Cynder, as is done for drying Malt, and it then succeeded to his satisfaction."

Her husband, she tells us, then spent a great deal of time in looking for further sources of this coal. He installed a "Fire Engine" for the recirculation of cooling water, for their supply of water was quite limited. He refused to take out a patent when he found that he could make "Barr Iron from Pit Coal pigs." This settled the practicability of the new process. Abiah goes on to tell us that "the Iron Trade of our own produce would have dwindled away, for wood for charcoal became very scarce, and landed gentlemen rose the prices of cord wood exceeding high. But from pit coal being introduced in its stead, the demand of wood charcoal is much lessened and in a few years I apprehend will set the use of that article aside."

Darby had a suitable high furnace and a powerful blast to go with it. The secret of successful smelting with "pit coal" was found to be the use of a hard, good-sized coke free from grit that would otherwise impede the circulation of blast air in the furnace. It was now recognized that the general type of sea coal was what we now call bituminous, and that coal from deeper strata of the anthracite type was better suited for the manufacture of metallurgical coke, as well as for domestic fuel, because it gave off little smoke. The right selection and classification of coals placed this fuel in the first rank as a source of heat and power. It now became the very lifeblood of the Industrial Revolution.

Coke production was greatly improved by the end of the eighteenth century, when beehive ovens of masonry replaced the old stacks for making coke from coal. These ovens were im-

mediately successful and led to a decided improvement in the
quality of the coke produced. Experiments with retorts gave
less promising results. The use of coke spread quickly to the
rest of Europe, so that in the Ruhr it was used from 1780 on,
and in Saarbrücken beginning about 1796. The beehive oven
was also introduced and the old-fashioned stacks were even
forbidden in 1832 because of the stench they produced.

*Sectional drawing of an early beehive coke oven. (From F. T.
Harbord,* Refractories and Furnaces, *New York, 1912, p. 126.)*

About 1840 the beehive oven became common in the United
States, where it has remained in use up to the present day,
though it has been largely replaced by the more efficient by-
product oven.

The new gas industry which started early in the nineteenth
century produced additional large quantities of coke for the
metallurgist. Although the production of gas was the main
purpose of the industry, it also succeeded in improving the
quality of the coke produced in its retorts. The old beehive
furnaces had produced from 90 to 150 pounds of coke per day,
but the new retorts and chamber ovens produced over 750
pounds, apart from the gas and other by-products.

It should be remembered, however, that the gas factory primarily produced gas and by-products, which indeed determined its economy. But its development of suitable retorts taught industry much about the proper conditions under which coke of certain specified qualities could be produced. Appolt was the first to construct a vertical chamber oven; the horizontal form that is now more common in Europe was introduced by Coppée of Belgium in 1871. Improved types in which the tar could be recovered with greater efficiency were developed by Hüssener and Carl Otto, each working independently. The fuel economy of the chamber oven was considerably improved by the introduction of preheating with spent-oven gases (Hoffman, 1883). The modern types of oven go back to the Koppers model of 1899, in which the complete recovery of all by-products was effected.

Even in its early period (1750–1850), this development of the production of coke had achieved a good fuel that could be stacked in the smelting furnaces without impeding the circulation of blast air, yet was sufficiently strong to carry the greater weight of the batch at a time when the furnaces were constantly increasing in size. The pioneers had resorted to tricks like producing coke from mixtures of coal and peat. Later manufacturers knew how to select the right type of coal for this purpose.

The earlier centuries had seen the retreat of the smelting plants into the mountains, following the ever scarcer wood. As the supply of coke grew, the plants began returning to their natural sites between coal mines and iron-ore deposits. Improved land and water traffic was stimulated as plant production rapidly increased. Metallurgy turned to coke, but at first used it only in the early stages of smelting iron ores. Charcoal was still the fuel for the refining of wrought iron, steel, or cast iron, because the earlier types of coke still contained such noxious impurities as sulfur compounds. A happy chance had led Darby to select the right kind of coal, but other early coke manufacturers had to learn by experience and patient research.

By 1800 Darby's process was widely known and the production of iron and steel increased by leaps and bounds. In 1720 it was 20,000 tons, and remained at about the same figure all during the period of pioneering with the coke process. But by 1788 production had already increased to 70,000 tons a year, and in 1806 no less than 250,000 tons were produced—quantities that may seem insignificant to us now but which were of unprecedented importance then.

The production of coke was not the only factor contributing to the swift growth of metallurgy. In 1760 Smeaton had used a water wheel to drive two pistons moving in cast-iron cylinders to provide blast air for a furnace, thus increasing the means of producing much larger volumes of air per minute. This in turn meant that the smelting furnaces could be enlarged and operated at higher temperatures. The old form of bellows disappeared quickly. When by the end of the eighteenth century steam engines began to be used to produce blast air, an added impetus was given to the production of iron and steel. The new method was first applied in the blast furnaces built by Roebuck in Scotland according to the designs made by Smeaton as early as 1760.

Lack of knowledge of what really happened in the blast furnace, how wrought iron could be transformed into steel, the composition of cast iron, and many other metallurgical problems continued, nevertheless, to impede the progress of the industry. Thus some ironmasters still believed that traces of sulfur were actually needed to transform crude iron into steel. The first man to study this seriously was Réaumur (mentioned earlier in connection with the thermometer), who in 1722 published his *Art of Converting Wrought Iron into Steel*. He was the first to distinguish the different types of iron by their structure, as observed on a freshly fractured bar. He gave a very good interpretation of the cementation process, in which the surface of wrought iron is given a steel structure by the penetration of carbon from the charcoal. He knew that differences in the quality of iron were due to differences in the carbon content, a fact that was proved many decades later by Bazin, Bergman, and Clouet. Steel was found to contain from 0.3 to 0.8 per cent of carbon; cast iron, from 1.0 to 3.5 per cent.

The chief difficulty encountered in metallurgy was not the lack of chemical knowledge, of insufficient blast air, or of properly designed furnaces, however important these factors might be; it was the need for an adequate fuel supply, for metallurgists were the largest consumers of charcoal and so depended on the landed gentry who owned most of the forest lands. There was, for example, a flourishing iron industry in The Weald (a wooded district in the south of England) during the sixteenth and seventeenth centuries, but the exhaustion of the forests caused a decline of this industry and it tended to move toward the Midlands and further north, following the forests.

Iron metallurgy at the beginning of the eighteenth century was not only fairly primitive but was broken up into a series of smaller industries. First of all there was the blast-furnace industry, producing pig iron from iron ore and charcoal. This pig iron was either delivered to small furnaces producing cast iron or castings, or bought by the forgemasters who converted it into bars of wrought iron. These wrought-iron bars were in turn handed over to slitting mills, which heated them and drew them out into rods by passing them through grooved rollers. Smelting plants, forges, and slitting mills were separate industries, often at different localities, and there was a considerable and uneconomic traffic in pig and bar iron. Cast iron was mainly used for the manufacture of pots, pans, and some types of ordnance. Wrought iron went to the manufacture of such articles as nails, picks, spades, locks, bolts, wire, and tools.

Darby's great innovation freed the furnaces and the foundries, which now tended to go back to the coal fields and ore deposits. It also caused a marked increase in the output of cast iron during the eighteenth century. Moreover, many objects formerly made of wrought iron were now manufactured of cast iron. At first the use of coke was limited to the production of pig iron and cast iron. The success of coal in this field naturally led to attempts to use it in place of charcoal when converting pig iron into wrought bar iron. Henry Cort was the first to realize this in practice and outlined his inventions in two patents covering the "puddling" and the "rolling" processes.

New types of furnaces had been developed for the refining of other metals—for example, the reverberatory furnace, in which the flue gases were led over a shallow bed of molten metal. Henry Cort and Peter Onions independently developed the idea of using this type of furnace to convert pig iron into wrought iron in 1783, using coke as the fuel. This process of puddling the pig iron consisted of agitating the mass in a reverberatory furnace with iron poles or "puddles" until it was completely transformed into a thick mass of wrought iron by the burning away of the carbon and other impurities. This wrought iron was then removed in lumps and processed by being rolled between grooved rollers, which pressed out the dross and produced a typical wrought iron with a fibrous structure that proved very resistant to corrosion.

This invention made Cort the father of the modern rolling mill, although he was not the inventor of the rolling process. We have already seen that rollers were used in shaping softer metals like lead and even precious metals. In Nuremberg in the seventeenth century, and later in Sweden, small bars and sheets of wrought iron were rolled.

The man who transformed the roller into a practical piece of machinery for metallurgical purposes was Christoph Polhem of Sweden (1661–1751), who rose from the humble status of junior clerk to the position of a titled mining engineer. By the end of his life he had succeeded in building rolling mills that could shape iron into a variety of different profiles. It was from Polhem that Cort derived the machinery that he introduced into the metallurgical practice of his day. The rolling mill reached a higher level of development in the middle of the nineteenth century, when steel rollers of sufficient size and strength could be cast and shaped, and when ample power became available to roll steel bars into rails and to shape blocks of red-hot steel or iron into bars and sheets.

Cort's new "puddling process" influenced the production of steel and indeed the whole manufacturing stage of iron metallurgy. Steel had previously been produced by heating wrought iron with charcoal in an oven for several days. It was, in fact, the cementation process of the ancient smiths, carried out on a slightly larger scale. Its results were rather uncertain and the "bilster steel" obtained was reforged into shear steel. Because the wrought iron had to be of high quality, it was usually imported from Sweden, so that the trade became localized in Newcastle because of that town's nearness to the Swedish coast.

The man who helped establish the fame of Sheffield as a steel-producing town was a watchmaker named Benjamin Huntsman (1704–1776). The steel produced in this period varied so much that he looked for some means of controlling its production. Another common process then in use for this type of steel was of Hindu origin, being a crucible process of smelting very pure iron ores with charcoal. It produced small lumps of steel of two or three pounds' weight, which were hammered into strips and bars. Huntsman conceived the idea of heating these crucibles in the hearth of a reverberatory furnace and thus obtained a fairly even and constant source of heat. Because the crucibles were closed, the noxious compounds in the flue gases did not harm the steel.

A second advantage of this process was that the steel was obtained in liquid form and could then be cast in small molds. Huntsman, however, had the greatest difficulty in obtaining the proper base materials for his crucibles and molds. The first steel he produced was so hard and brittle that he had a hard time trying to sell it. Gradually he learned to control the process and his results demonstrated to others the value of good hard steel for machine parts and instruments. This invention transferred the center of steel production and manufacture from Newcastle to Sheffield.

The industries for the manufacture of iron and steel had

tended to congregate on the coal fields just as soon as they saw that full and efficient use could be made of this new fuel. There was much localization and specialization in these industries as the century proceeded. It was much more difficult to introduce new tools and machines into this industry than, say, into the textile industry, for, as we have already pointed out, the machining and accurate finishing of metals was the very problem that impeded a speedier introduction of the steam engine. And so we find at this time that there was innovation in the types of products rather than in the processes of manufacture. After Cort's invention of the puddling process for the mass production of wrought iron, the output of manufactured steel products rose very quickly.

Through Darby's invention the foundries and furnaces were no longer tied to the forests. Cort liberated the forgemasters from the woodlands, and steel manufacture was able to move northward to the areas around Birmingham and Sheffield. Now all phases of iron metallurgy tended to be drawn to coal fields and to the ore deposits that lay close by. This grouping of all these phases led to their amalgamation in the course of the nineteenth century.

Two more events were to boost iron metallurgy. Both had definite effects only in the decade between 1830 and 1840. The first was the discovery of the "black-band ironstone" of Scotland by David Mushet. It was the first of a series of discoveries of iron ores that could be worked as profitably as the more common ores had been worked for centuries.

The second event was also British in origin. As the blast furnaces grew in size, even the new steam- or water-driven compressors could not produce sufficient blast air to develop the high temperatures needed. Neilson of Glasgow conceived the brilliant idea of preheating the blast air with the spent gases from the blast furnace in 1829. The economy of the blast furnace was such that no special preheating furnace could be used. Neilson used the inflammable blast-furnace gases to heat this preheating furnace and thus materially improved the economy of producing iron from its ores.

Neilson's invention was followed up by many minor improvements until Cowper in 1860 created the modern form of high towers of fireproof bricks. These brick towers are first heated by the burning of blast-furnace gases and are then used to preheat the blast air on its way to the furnace. They work in pairs, one being heated while the other transfers this heat to the blast air. In this way it is possible to obtain the very high temperatures of modern blast-furnace practice and to process huge quantities of ore.

The metallurgist of the Industrial Revolution also discovered and used a host of other metals that until then had been scientific curiosities or were entirely unknown. Thus the Jesuits had discovered platinum in Colombia in 1735; huge deposits were later found in the Ural Mountains about 1820. Its modern use in the laboratory was the result of many experiments by Wollaston, who in 1803 and 1804 had also discovered the related metals rhodium and palladium. In 1805 he succeeded in discovering the secret of shaping platinum into crucibles, vessels, and other forms. He kept this secret until his death in 1828, when his will allowed the Royal Society to disclose it.

Zinc had been known ever since the sixteenth century, but only as a freak; it had been described by Agricola but its possibilities were unsuspected. The proper furnaces and retorts for its mass production were not built until the eighteenth century, when such places as Goslar (in Harz, Germany) and several Belgian towns became the centers of its production. It was used for the protection of iron sheets, which were dipped into baths of molten iron. In 1805 Sylvester and Hobson discovered a method of producing this "galvanized iron" which is the common material of the roofer and tinner today.

Nickel, already isolated by Cronstedt in 1751, was first refined by Bergmann in 1775. Saxony, where it was usually alloyed with copper, became the center of nickel production. This alloy became important about the middle of the nineteenth century, when it was found to be eminently suitable for coinage. Although Faraday in 1843 discovered how to deposit a protective layer of nickel by electrolysis, the rise of the nickel industry dates from the discovery in 1876 of the rich deposits of nickel ores in New Caledonia.

The new technique of analytical chemistry, born in the latter half of the eighteenth century, soon bore fruit, and many new metals were discovered. Thus Vaquelin found chromium in Siberian minerals in 1797, Bergmann discovered manganese in 1774, Hjelm isolated molybdenum from the mineral molybdenite in 1781, Sefström discovered vanadium in 1830, and Klaproth discovered titanium in 1794. These metals remained of only academic interest until near the end of the nineteenth century, when it was discovered that steel alloyed with these singly or in certain combinations acquired very valuable properties. Nowadays they are of utmost importance in the manufacture of modern tools and machines.

The New Textile Factories

THE textile industry was an offshoot of the ancient peasant economy. Even in the eighteenth century the English farmers produced an appreciable amount of woolen cloth as part-time work. On the other hand the mechanization introduced in this industry during the preceding centuries had led to a certain concentration of specialized workers in such areas as Lancashire, Yorkshire, and East Anglia. The industry relied to a great extent on imports of raw materials, like raw silk from the Mediterranean and the Far East, flax from Ireland, and cotton from the Levant and West Indies.

The old organization of the industry had maintained itself, though there appeared some semi-independent workers. Also the clothiers and linen drapers tended to become factory managers, as the mechanization of the industry proceeded. They retained less of the characters of bankers, who themselves withdrew to remain the financial backers of the clothiers. Not only were the different industries localized—notably the silk industry in Norwich and the cotton industry in Lancashire—but the old system of splitting up the industry into

PLATE 22 Winsor demonstrating gas light at the Lyceum Theater, London, 1804. (Diorama at the Science Museum, South Kensington, London.)

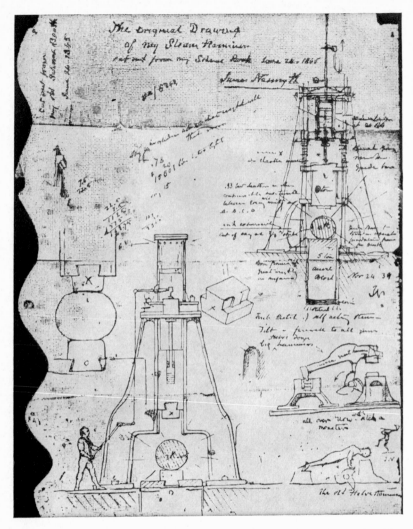

PLATE 23   John Naysmith's original drawing (November 24, 1839) of his steam hammer, cut from his sketch book in 1865. (From *The Engineer*, Vol. 69, 1890.)

Power loom weaving, from an early nineteenth-century woodcut.

substages, such as carding, fulling, spinning, weaving, bleaching, dyeing, and the like, each to be executed in separate works or homes, was still in full force. New machinery was introduced from the continent, where mechanization had proceeded somewhat more rapidly. Thus Thomas Lombe introduced silk-throwing machinery from Italy in 1717.

However, the fully mechanized textile factory driven by steam power is the creation of English inventors. The story of its creation is a curious one; it appears to have been a struggle between the inventors in the field of spinning and those in the field of weaving machinery. The first move came in the field of weaving. In 1733 John Kay, a Lancashire clockmaker, invented his "flying shuttle," a fly-shuttle that was shot through the weft by means of hammers handled by the weaver. It allowed the double width of cloth to be woven by one man. The invention was met with considerable opposition on the part of the Lancashire weavers, who destroyed several of the machines; moreover, the mechanical difficulties had been underestimated by the inventor, so that its effects did not make themselves felt before 1760.

The next improvement was in the field of spinning. Lewis Paul fully mechanized spinning in 1738 by stretching the carded wool or cotton between two sets of rollers, running at different speeds, before spinning it on the shuttle. This did away with the last phase left in the hands of the spinner after the "Saxony wheel" had been introduced. Here again mechanical trouble and unskilled workmen prevented this invention from being fully exploited before 1760. It then had an important effect, for it produced a much stronger cotton yarn. Formerly cotton yarn had been used as weft but seldom as warp, so that the industry was limited by the supply of linen yarn. Now that the warp could also be made of cotton, shortage of yarn no longer held back weaving and an industry based soley on cotton could grow up, combining spinning and weaving in one factory. The roller system proposed by Paul was later more fully realized by Arkwright.

In 1764 James Hargreaves constructed his "spinning jenny," a combination of six or seven spindles into one spinning machine to be operated by one spinner. Later the number of spindles thus operated was extended to 80. This cheap way of spinning was an immediate success and by 1788 no less than 20,000 jennies had been installed in cottages and factories. The jenny produced a rather soft yarn fit for warp threads only.

In 1768 Richard Arkwright and John Kay produced the "water frame," which used rollers like Paul's machine. This water frame gave a strong, rather coarse yarn, which was a good substitute for the expensive linen warp threads. In 1771 Arkwright set up a factory driven by water power at Cromford. Four years later he took out another important patent on carding with cylinders. This meant that carding and spinning could now be done economically in one factory. Manchester spinners got this Arkwright patent revoked after 1781 and as a consequence hundreds of factories began to use it.

In the meantime, these ideas were taken up by Samuel Crompton, who after seven years of experimenting produced his "mule" in 1774, an engine that combined the good principles embodied in both the jenny and water frame. In 1785 the steam engine was first used to drive the new spinning machines, and five years later was used to move the new mules. In general these patents on mechanization of the different stages of the textile industry led to the amalgamation of smaller industries into larger factories. The number of such factories in Manchester rose from 2 in 1782 to 52 in 1802.

Weaving did not remain far behind spinning. In 1784 Edmund Cartwright produced his first power loom. This patent was soon followed by further improvements by Radcliffe, Johnson, Horrocks, and Roberts. These power looms soon produced about ten times the amount of cloth made on a hand loom. By 1813 there were over 2,400 power looms in operation in Great Britain. Some eight years afterward the amalgamation of spinning and weaving establishments into textile factories began to take shape. Technical progress was less rapid in the woolen and worsted branches, but it came eventually in the course of the nineteenth century.

The ribbon loom was made substantially automatic by the work of Kay and Vaucanson about 1765. The old knitting machine invented by Lee in 1589 had proved its mettle, but was now improved by a series of inventions. The most important

Original model of Eli Whitney's cotton gin. (The New York Public Library.)

of these was that of Jedediah Strutt, who in 1785 introduced a second set of needles at right angles to the original set and thus produced a knitted fabric with a ribbed surface that had a far greater amount of elasticity.

These inventions were not limited to Europe, for the United States contributed materially to the progress of cotton manufacture. As early as 1790 Samuel had designed a successful power-driven cotton spinning machine. The quality of cotton and the cost of its production were radically changed by Eli Whitney's introduction of the cotton gin in 1793, in which seeds were separated from the fibers by running the cotton through a series of spikes. Whitney's device may not have been the first mechanical cotton separator ever built (though the courts upheld his patent in 1807), but it was highly successful and changed the whole economy of the South. Hogden Holmes in 1796 changed the design by introducing sawteeth to remove the seeds, but the patent granted him for this "improvement" was later annulled.

The first invention to influence textiles materially in the following period was the invention of the sewing machine in 1845 by the American, Elias Howe, who improved his invention in his patent of September 10, 1846.

The cheaper manufacture of printed calicoes and other goods began when Thomas Bell in 1783 substituted engraved metal cylinders for the copper plates or wooden cylinders formerly used in textile printing. They were further improved by Nicholson in 1790.

There was, moreover, a series of chemical inventions in the fields of bleaching and dyeing that were equally important to the textile industry. Bleaching in the Middle Ages was achieved by exposing the cloth to strong sunlight, so that medieval towns had large stretches of meadows either within or directly outside the town walls devoted to this purpose. Buttermilk and sour milk were often used to assist the natural process, for milk was not yet recognized as a valuable food. Later, when people began to realize its true worth, milk prices rose and it became imperative to look for other bleaching agents.

In 1756 Francis Hume introduced dilute sulfuric acid. This remained in use until Berthollet in 1789 found that his bleaching liquor prepared from chlorine and alkali was more efficient and less injurious to the fibers. This bleaching liquor, however, was rather expensive and Charles Tennant in 1799 succeeded in finding a cheaper substitute made from chlorine and slaked lime. His bleaching powder was also much easier and less irritating to handle. The abolishing of the bleaching fields was the direct result of the introduction of these bleaching agents, but some of the fields were kept in use, as the agents then known were too corrosive to use on silk and wool. These fabrics were usually first washed with soap and water and then bleached in the sun or by vapors of burning sulfur.

Dyeing in the early days had been a matter of trial and error. The use of a good mordant was restricted, and sometimes alum or compounds of tin were used to prepare the fibers for the application of the dye. The universities now turned to this problem, and French scientists like Macquer and Berthollet greatly improved the art of dyeing. Macquer proved that dyeing was not simply a precipitation on the fiber, and believed that the mordant and the dye formed a kind of compound. Berthollet studied this theory in 1791 and proved that light and oxygen played a part, too. Though these theories have since been proven wrong, much of the experimental work was of great practical consequence and the recipes for dyeing that were evolved did much to improve the quality of the work.

Gas and Chemicals from Coal

THE new chemical technology owed much to the evolution of the gas industry. The experiments to make good coke had shown that coal when heated gives off an inflammable gas. The first to try to use this gas was Phillipe Lebon, a teacher of mechanical engineering at the École des Ponts et Chaussées. In 1797 he began his attempts to produce illuminating gas from wood, oil, and tar. Two years later he patented his "thermolampe," a miniature gas factory for domestic lighting, consisting of a retort and a system of tubes conducting the gas to fishtail burners. But the candlepower of these thermolampes was low, and besides they had an unbearable odor.

In the meantime, Aimé Argand had perfected a circular burner for liquids and gases in which part of the air consumed by the flame was introduced through the center of the wick holder, the flame being shielded by a glass chimney. Liquid fuel was drawn up into the burner through the circular wick and gases were introduced under pressure. Argand went to England and sold a license of his patent to an agent of Boulton in 1784, but his patent was widely imitated and Argand was soon involved in lawsuits that eventually ruined him. His later efforts in the field of alchemy were unsuccessful, and he died by his own hand in 1803, broken-spirited and penniless. His burner lived on as the basic model of our modern oil lamps and gas burners.

William Murdoch, working for Boulton and Watt in Cornwall, took up the experiments of Lebon and those of the Belgian, Minckeleers, and soon established gaslighting in his own house. He discovered that a cannel coal produced an excellent gas. With a cast-iron retort and a long system of tubing connecting it to fishtail burners, he installed lights in Boulton and Watt's foundry in Soho, Birmingham, in 1798. His illumination of the factory on the occasion of the peace of Amiens drew the interest of the public toward gaslight. In 1807 a large factory in Manchester installed gaslighting, where it was proved that 900 gas burners saved over £2,350 that had been spent on candles before. Murdoch was awarded the Rumford Medal in 1808.

The German, Winzer, who between 1801 and 1810 had looked in vain for capital in his own country to develop gaslighting, came to London and after having his proposals rejected twice by Parliament succeeded in founding the Chartered Gaslight and Coke Company in 1812. The technical developments of the gas factory were largely the work of Samuel Clegg, a pupil of Watt and Murdoch. He invented the water-locked gasholder, the gas scrubber, gas valves, gas meters, and many other essential parts that are still used in gas production. The wax candles, introduced in the eleventh century, patent oil or colza oil, and other more expensive means of lighting houses and buildings soon fell into disuse. As early as 1813 Westminister Bridge had its gaslights, and in 1813 the whole of the Parish of St. Margaret's was lighted by gas.

The manufacture of gas spread quickly to the continent. Between 1811 and 1816 Lampadius carried on successful experiments in Freiberg. William and Drory built the first German gas factory in Hanover in 1825. In 1826 Unter den Linden in Berlin got its gaslight and the residents of Berlin could obtain gas until ten o'clock in the evening. Gaslighting in the United States was introduced with the experimental lighting in Peale's Museum, Philadelphia, in 1816. Soon it was adopted for street lighting in Boston (1822) and in 1823 the New York Gas-Light Company was formed.

The London gas factory had serious technical troubles to overcome but the combined ingenuity of Clegg and Accum surmounted all of them. Two important problems remained— removing the evil smell of coal gas, and finding a means of reducing high pressures in the mains, which was the cause of many explosions and much loss of gas. Gas was still considered dangerous and no gasholder of over 1,000 cubic feet capacity was allowed to be erected in Germany.

In 1847, however, Leming discovered the means of refining coal gas by passing it through iron oxide, which took away the vile-smelling sulfur compounds and which could be regenerated by simple aeration. In 1855 Beale invented the gas fan exhauster, which solved the problem of the delivery of gas through low-pressure mains. The construction of proper cast-iron gas mains required a lot of experimenting (1810–1830) until a satisfactory method of making them gastight was finally found. Improvements of the coking retorts had materially contributed to the production of a better-quality coke. The cast-iron retorts introduced by Murdoch remained in use until about 1880, when they began to be replaced by retorts lined with firebricks. The inclined gas retort was introduced at Rheims by Coze in 1888, then in 1900 the vertical retort designed by Buë came into general use, to be replaced in its turn by chamber ovens.

The efficient use of gas as an illuminant dates only from 1886, when Auer van Welsbach substituted the incandescent mantle for the fishtail burner, which dropped out of general use around 1900. The greatest improvements in the production of good coal gas were due to the work of Bunte (from

1878 to 1899) of Karlsruhe, Germany, who invented scientific methods of analysis of gaseous products and who was the first to use the calorific value as a commercial quality index. This was indeed a significant forward step, for on August 27, 1859, Colonel Edwin L. Drake had struck oil at 69 feet in Pennsylvania shale and started the prosperous oil industry. Petroleum and gas became serious competitors by 1880, and electricity soon joined the competition. Bunte's work resulted in the use of gas for cooking (1890–1905) and in the recovery of purer by-products for the chemical industry. Another aid to the gas industry was the invention of the gas engine (not to be confused with the gasoline engine) by Otto and Langen of Cologne in 1867. By 1880 there were several efficient types of gas engines available.

By-products of the gas industry became increasingly important. The old charcoal stacks had yielded tar, which was mainly used on ships, both as a paint and as a finish coat in calking decks or floors. Coal tar had been the object of much research by Alexander Cochrane, ninth Earl of Dundonald, who had done brilliant work on the use of coal as a source of chemicals. His many patents on the manufacture and application of pitch, tar, and varnish were ingenious, but he was a poor financier and the factory he erected at Culross in 1782 nearly went bankrupt. His successor, John McAdam, the inventor of macadam pavement, put these processes on a sounder financial basis.

Practical methods for refining of tar and application of its fractions had to wait for the sounder chemical theories of the early nineteenth century, which allowed a slow but steady progress in tar research. The use of tar for the manufacture of roofing felts dates from 1820. Accum in 1815 proved that the low-boiling compounds of tar, such as benzene (a quite different substance, *benzine*, comes from petroleum) were excellent paint thinners. In 1820 Reichenbach discovered paraffin wax in coal tar and wood tar. Bethel pointed out the excellent protective properties of creosote. Finally there was the first synthesis of a dye from coal tar by Perkin in 1856.

217

These new discoveries led to the evolution of modern coal-tar distillation plants, for distillation columns had already been designed and tested by French pioneers.

Distillation had been materially improved by the invention of the rectifying column by Cellier Blumenthal in 1813. Adam and Bérard had each tried to design a column for rectifying alcohol produced from wine. Blumenthal, in combining the principles used by these two inventors, had succeeded in producing a column that gave a continuous stream of rectified alcohol from a continuous feed of wine. The wine was preheated by the condensing alcohol vapors and the residue was tapped from the still intermittently. Derosne, who bought this patent, and his assistant Savalle developed the column further, and German inventors like Pistorius built models especially adapted to the thicker mashes used in their country. By 1850 very efficient distilling and rectifying columns were in use in the alcohol industry and thence passed into the coal-tar and petroleum industries.

Between 1860 and 1880 many valuable chemical products such as benzene, toluene, and xylene were discovered by distilling tar; each of these now forms the basis of a branch of the coal-tar industry. In fact, the by-products of coal tar have turned out to be far more valuable than the coal gas that was originally the sole product sought. Today there are over 3,000 compounds manufactured from coal tar on a commercial basis, among which may be listed dyes, perfumes, explosives, synthetic yarns, photographic chemicals, paints, wood preservatives, flavors, drugs, antiseptics, pain-killers (aspirin), and many varieties of plastics, including nylon.

The production of synthetic dyes started with Perkin's discovery of mauve in 1856, which he stumbled on quite by accident while trying to make quinine from impure aniline, a coal-tar product. At that time Perkin (later Sir William) was only a seventeen-year old schoolboy, whose professor, the German scientist von Hoffman, taught coal-tar chemistry at the Royal College in London. One year later mauve (or mauveine) was sold to the textile industry. Perkin followed up his discovery and in 1866 succeeded in making alizarin, another aniline dye.

An avalanche of discoveries followed on the heels of Perkin's original work. In 1859 Verguin prepared a synthetic red dye called fuchsine, and Nicholson produced the so-called Lyons blue. In 1864 aniline yellow was discovered and three years later von Hoffman produced methyl violet. Griess, working in a brewery, discovered the extremely important diazo dyes, which turned benzene and similar compounds into basic materials of prime importance. This work also contributed materially to the rise of organic chemistry.

In the meantime, Germany started producing synthetic dyes on a large scale and soon left France and England far behind. It was discovered that naphthalene and anthracene, until that time considered useless coal-tar products, were important starting points for entirely different classes of dyes. The manufacture of substitutes for natural dyes was also begun. Liebermann and Graebe synthesized alizarine red in 1868 and von Bayer succeeded in 1880 in producing synthetic indigo blue. Good fast synthetic colors such as indanthrene blue have been developed since 1902.

The Rise of a Chemical Industry

THE rapidly growing textile and other industries demanded larger supplies of chemicals. Their manufacture had mostly been in the hands of distillers, druggists, and apothecaries. They had produced on a laboratory scale, which had been quite sufficient for the limited demand. Now the growing needs called for large-scale production. Unfortunately, chemistry was still in a qualitative stage and was engaged in violent discussions on the phlogiston theory. Not until the end of the eighteenth century did chemistry, through the efforts of Lavoisier and his school, become a quantitative science to guide the chemical industry. The manufacture of chemicals was therefore dependent solely on practical experience, and the early chemical factories were typically "enlarged laboratory processes." They had to struggle through the difficult stage of adapting their "pilot" processes to large-scale production.

A striking example of this situation is afforded by the history of sulfuric acid manufacture. Until 1750 sulfuric acid was prepared mainly by distilling vitriols in earthenware retorts, a rather expensive process but one yielding a stronger acid. A weaker acid was produced by burning sulfur under a glass bell jar. The dilute sulfuric acid formed by absorbing the fumes in water could be concentrated by distilling in a glass retort.

By 1750 sulfuric acid had become increasingly important in many industries, being used for bleaching, tinning, and gilding, and for the manufacture of brass and felt. Joshua Ward, the quack doctor, was the first to burn sulfur with some nitre in big glass jars to produce sulfuric acid on a larger scale (1749). He succeeded in bringing the price per pound down to the former price per ounce. John Roebuck rightly considered these great jars (which incidentally are the forerunners of our modern carboys) too expensive and in 1746 he developed the method of letting the whole process take place in lead chambers containing a shallow layer of water that was regularly replenished. In 1749 Roebuck erected the first lead-chamber plant in Preston Pans, near Edinburgh. Preston Pans was one of the earliest all-round chemical plants, for it produced not only sulfuric acid but also soda for the soapmakers, white lead for the potters, litharge for the glassmakers, and refined potash and alum for other industries.

Roebuck's patent of 1771 was withdrawn after a year, but in the meantime the price of sulfuric acid had gone down to sixpence a pound. In 1772 the first acid factory was built in Battersea, London, and 1776 saw the first continental factory at Rouen, France. The old "vitriol-distilling plants" soon disappeared.

Then de la Follie in 1774 improved on these methods by burning the sulfur in a separate chamber and leading the vapors into lead chambers in which nitric acid was injected. He also discovered that the injection of steam increased the yield of acid. Gay-Lussac was the founder of the modern sulfuric acid plant. He introduced a scrubbing tower between the lead chambers and the air to remove the nitrous vapors with acid and to readmit them to the process. This is now done by introducing the acid from the Gay-Lussac tower into the Glover scrubber (1859) that is built between the sulfur burners and the chamber. In 1818 Thomas Hills succeeded in using the sulfurous fumes produced by roasting or oxidizing iron and other pyrites (ores containing sulfur) to make sulfur by the lead-chamber process, thus combining the production of copper or iron with that of sulfuric acid.

The size of the lead chambers—and therefore the efficiency of the process—was seriously limited by lead-soldering techniques. Soldering hard lead with a hydrogen flame was discovered only in 1838 by Desbassayns de Richemond. After 1850 this discovery allowed the building of even larger lead chambers and the production of greater quantities of sulfuric acid.

But in 1831 P. Philipps had acquired a patent for the so-called "contact process" in which the sulfur dioxide resulting from burning sulfur was converted with oxygen and water into sulfuric acid by means of a catalyst (a chemical that stimulates a process without taking part in the reaction). This basic patent had to rest until 1900, when Winkler and Knietsch clarified the problems of catalyst poisoning, the optimum temperature for the process, and related factors. Then it became a formidable competitor of the older lead-chamber process, which it has now practically displaced.

A new way of producing soda or sodium carbonate was also discovered during this period. Soda had previously been imported in a crude natural form from Egypt, or it had been extracted from the ashes of kelp, varec, and seaweed in Marseilles, Brittany, and Ireland. The production of glass, soap, and textiles was bound up with the production of soda. As the demand rose, the French Academy offered the large sum of 100,000 francs for a process of manufacturing soda from common sea salt. As Duhamel had pointed out the chemical relation between salt and soda, and Margraff had proven the difference between sodium carbonate (soda) and potassium carbonate (potash), the road seemed clear and several solutions were proposed.

A correct and efficient one was finally found in 1789 by Nicolas Leblanc, who invented the process which bears his name. First he made sodium sulfate by mixing sulfuric acid and sodium chloride in a furnace. Next the sulfate was heated with coke and limestone (calcium carbonate) in a rotary furnace to form "black ash," a mixture of sodium carbonate, calcium sulfide, excess lime, and carbon. The sodium carbonate was then extracted by mixing it with water, the resulting pure soda being obtained in the form of large crystals. The sodium sulfate was cheaply obtained as a by-product of the manufacture of hydrochloric acid. Thus the manufacture of soda, hydrochloric acid, and sulfuric acid became an integrated operation of industrial chemistry.

In 1789 Leblanc obtained money from the Duke of Orleans, who had the process investigated by Professor Darcet and his assistant, Dizé. The latter entered into partnership with Leblanc in 1790 and they started work at St. Denis, where the first factory was built. It was entirely successful, though Dizé and Leblanc soon quarreled. However, during the French Revolution Leblanc was deprived of his patent because the process was essential to the State, and new factories sprang up everywhere in France. The price fell from about 90 francs per hundred pounds to ten francs. Leblanc was ruined, and after trying to get damages for his factory and to collect the prize money from the Academy (which, sad to relate, was never paid), he committed suicide in 1806. Not until 1855 did his family get damages after the fraudulent claims of Dizé had been dismissed. The process was introduced into England and Scotland (St. Rollox) by Tennant, and it flourished after the damaging salt tax had been abolished in 1823. Muspratt proved that the new pure soda was superior to the old in the manufacture of glass.

The new soda soon displaced the older potash from the market but was itself in danger of being superseded when Ernest

Solvay (1838–1922) discovered in 1860 a method of converting ammonia, carbon dioxide, and salt into soda. Indeed, the Solvay process has now made the Leblanc process practically obsolete today.

We should also cite an example in which the lack of chemical knowledge held back an industrial process. Many scientists had tried to find a good method of manufacturing nitre. This valuable product, used for gunpowder and after 1830 also as a fertilizer, was formerly manufactured by extracting mixtures of dung and lime, which had been aerated. Also "flowers of nitre" were collected from clay walls, and often formed part of taxes in kind that were levied in the East. Not until the natural deposits in Chili were discovered did Europe have access to larger quantities of nitrates, and not until very recent times was science able to convert the nitrogen of the air into useful nitrates.

Many other new chemical industries, such as those concerned with the manufacture of starch, glue, mordants, etc., grew up during this period, but we must restrict ourselves to just one more typical industry, that of beet-sugar production. Until this period sugar was always prepared from sugar cane grown in colonial possessions, although refining was often done in the home country. In 1747 Margraff presented an important paper to the Berlin Academy pointing out the natural sugar content of many plants, such as beets. Sugar could be extracted from these plants and the process could be controlled scientifically. Achard, Margraff's pupil, started growing beets in Silesia, building a factory at Kunern. In 1786 he had his first harvest of beets and his experiments were concluded in 1798. In the meantime, another factory had been built in Bohemia in 1795. The Cunern factory worked commercially from about 1802 on, pressing the beets which were cut up into slices in large screw presses. The extracted liquor was then boiled, treated with lime, and inspissated. Only three per cent of sugar was extracted from the beets, which through careful selection and modern extraction methods now yield up to 16 per cent of sugar.

When the Continental Blockade cut off Europe from supplies of colonial cane sugar during the Napoleonic wars, beet-sugar manufacture boomed and Chaptal started building new factories in France, the first of which was erected at Passy in 1808. The refining of sugar was a national problem, but Delesert developed the modern refining process of beet-sugar in 1812 and was personally decorated by Napoleon in the Passy factory. A sharp decline followed after the fall of Napoleon. But the exertions of clever mechanical engineers and technologists like Derosne, Savalle, and others resulted in better machinery and more efficient processes. After 1840 it was clear that beet sugar had come to stay.

Some Technical Innovations

THE development of pottery in the Industrial Revolution was determined by a rapidly growing demand for household ware. This was partly due to the increasing shortage of lead and tin and their rising prices. Also, the mounting demand for tea and coffee in Europe and America led to the manufacture of a greater variety of household pottery. This work was still concentrated in a host of smaller shops, especially in England, whence itinerant "cratemen" distributed these wares throughout the country in paniers or baskets on the backs of donkeys.

There was little scientific research into the properties and manufacture or porcelain and pottery. The interest in Japanese and Chinese porcelain that had arisen during the eighteenth century was one of the chief stimulants to a practical search by trial and error for better clays, better glazes, and more suitable and economic means of decoration. About 1750 the "pyrometric bead," a little clay cone, came into use for the control of the temperatures of pottery ovens. It contributed toward more uniform standards and methods in pottery manufacture. About the same time copper plates came into use for impressing designs on ware.

Astbury, by admixing bits of fireproof bricks to clay, obtained a very hard type of pottery which nearly equalled porcelain. It was first produced by Josiah Wedgewood in his factory at Burslem, Staffordshire, in 1759. Wedgewood contributed much to the improvement of British pottery. He combined an artistic sense with a proper feeling for research on materials. He was the first to employ a steam engine to move his lathes, and ran his factory efficiently, instituting a well-planned division of labor. He is also rightly famous for having shown a really modern and exceptional regard for the welfare of his workmen.

Von Tschirnhaus was the real discoverer of porcelain, which he made in small batches from pure kaolin in 1687, as he stated in a letter to Leibnitz in 1694. In 1701 this porcelain created a great sensation in Paris. Tschirnhaus submitted plans to the King of Prussia, who had a factory built in Berlin, and installed Tschirnhaus as its director. Böttger, his successor, usually mentioned as the inventor of porcelain, did not start working on this problem before 1705; he, too, finally decided to use kaolin as a base material. The famous Meissner porcelain was first sold at the Leipzig fair of 1710, and shortly afterward the recipe was smuggled abroad and a new factory was built at Vienna in 1717, to be followed shortly by many others as porcelain became the rage among the rich.

The centers of the glass industry were now Thuringia, Silesia, Bohemia, France, and England. A major invention helped to stimulate its development, for in 1665 Nehon had discovered a method of casting glass, which was improved by Louis Lucas in 1688. This new method enabled the French glassmakers to cast glass panes by pouring molten glass onto large tables. Thus they learned to manufacture much larger windowpanes and mirrors than had been hitherto possible, and the French for some time held a monopoly in this field.

In the eighteenth century a real glass industry established itself in America. Unfortunately it did not gain great importance until the turn of the century, when Americans invented the automatic processes of glass blowing and pressing that led directly to the mass production of common tableware. As early as 1739 Caspar Wistar and his son Richard operated a successful glasshouse in New Jersey, and in 1765 Henry William Stiegel began producing a very decorative type of blown flint glass in Pennsylvania. The renowned Boston and Sandwich Glass Company was founded in 1825 and continued for some sixty years to produce the excellent "Sandwich" glass that is still highly valued today. E. D. Libbey and M. J. Owens developed the first automatic bottle-making machine between 1899 and 1904, a vacuum-operated molding mechanism that reached its full development about 1920. This machine made possible the automatic production of bottles and jars of all types. Irving Colburn, another American, invented the process, named after him, of making flat glass by a continuous drawing and rolling process, and installed the first machinery for this process in Charleston, W. Va., in 1917. Other machinery was developed to produce electric-light bulbs, tubing, and rods of glass by automatic methods.

Returning to the invention of cast glass, we should point out that this invention was an important step in the evolution of scientific instruments, as it was coupled with the discovery of various compositions of glass, such as flint glass and optical glass. The basis of the modern techniques of producing optical glass was laid by Pierre-Louis Guinand of Switzerland in the years 1774–1805. From France this technique was brought to England, where Faraday spent some years (1824–1830) of research on the subject.

Optical glass, which had not existed before 1790, has to be chemically homogeneous and substantially free from physical impurities. This was now possible with the new casting methods and the use of purer ingredients and improved methods of refining. The purer soda manufactured by the Leblanc process previously described was introduced with great success in glass manufacture by Deslandes in 1770. Optical glass also needs a wide range of refractive indices, and this requirement was fulfilled by the many new qualities of glass now perfected.

Great scientists like Isaac Newton and Christian Huygens had been obliged to grind their own lenses and were often hampered by the impurities present in the glass. Now good instrument makers were available in Holland, England, and France who could produce lenses of fine quality and workmanship, and had perfected methods of cementing together glass of different optical qualities to form lenses that were substantially free from chromatic aberration. Ordinary lenses produce fringes of color around the image due to the different angles of refraction of the various wavelengths of the spectrum; each of the colors that make up white light is focused at a different point. Gregory, Newton's disciple, had suggested the combination of different media in 1695 to overcome this deficiency, but the first achromatic lens was perfected by Chester Hall in 1733, who combined a flint-glass lens and a crown-glass lens in such a way that the aberration of one lens cancelled that of the other. John Dollond, the instrument maker, first realized the commercial production of such an achromatic lens in 1758.

The technique of fashioning laboratory glass instruments was studied and described by Johann Kunckel, who virtually originated modern glass-blowing methods in the laboratory. The production of optical glass gradually became more and more important. After Faraday and other English scientists, modern scientific research into the properties and composition of optical glass begins with the work of Carl Zeiss and his friend Abbe, who about 1870 laid the foundation of the famous optical glassworks of Jena, Germany. This plant made Thuringia the world's center of optical glass manufacture and instruments, a role that is now being gradually taken over by the United States in such cities as Corning, N.Y., and Pittsburgh, Pa.

Optical glass not only helped improve existing scientific apparatus, but also stimulated the evolution of important new inventions such as the camera, which proved to be a valuable tool for science and industry as well as an adjunct to the historian and the artist. The ancestor of the modern camera is the "camera obscura" (dark room) or pinhole camera, mentioned as early as the year 1100 by the Arab

Alhacen. Renaissance scientists like Leonardo da Vinci and Geronimo Cardano investigated its possibilities, and artists used it to draw pictures from nature. D. Barbaro and G. Porta substituted a convex lens for the pinhold and thus obtained sharper images. The astronomer Kepler suggested a combination of a convex and concave lens in order to increase the magnification of the image.

Two different lines of evolution are then seen to emerge. On the one hand, Athanasius Kirchner used lenses for a primitive projector, which Christian Huygens completed, using it to cast pictures from a painted glass plate onto a screen in 1659. A second possibility was the recording of the image formed inside the camera by the lens. This could be done only if the image could be focused on a sensitized plate or paper within the camera. The idea originated with the invention of lithography by Anton Senefelder in 1796, an art that some twenty years later became a craze in Paris. One of those interested was Jean Nicephore Niepce, who tried to fix the image upon a lithographic stone, as he himself could not draw. Together with his brother Claude he succeeded in producing a photographic image on a paper coated with silver chloride. Real success was achieved only when Niepce joined forces with the artist Louis Jacques Daguerre in 1829. Ten years of experiment finally resulted in the well-known "daguerreotype" (1839). A silvered copper plate was exposed to iodine vapor and placed at the focus of a camera obscura, the image obtained being then developed and fixed by chemicals. This daguerreotype process did not, however, allow for the direct reproduction of the original picture.

A further development became possible through the invention of nitrocellulose by Christian Schönbein, the Swiss chemist, in 1846. An English architect, Scott Archer, perfected the wet collodion process in 1851, in which a glass plate covered with a sensitized solution of nitrocellulose was prepared immediately before the exposure was to be made. The limitations of this process, which required the outdoor photographer to carry a portable darkroom about with him, as Matthew Brady did during the Civil War, were overcome when B. J. Sayce and W. B. Bolton succeeded in 1864 in preparing an emulsion of silver bromide in collodion, which was then applied to a glass plate and allowed to dry. Upon exposure the plate was developed and fixed as before, but with this "dry-plate" method the portable darkroom was no longer necessary and photography became a less cumbersome process.

A marked improvement in sensitivity and sharpness of image was obtained in 1871 when R. L. Maddox made emulsions of silver bromide in gelatine, and greater flexibility and simplification of camera design came in 1884 with the invention of roll-film photography by W. H. Walker, in which the emulsion was carried on waxed paper (later cellulose acetate). In the following year George Eastman patented a machine for the production of continuous photographic film. Subsequent advances have been in the field of color photography, high-speed photography, stroboscopic cinematography, and other specialized applications.

The period 1750–1830 is also remarkable for the first steps in mechanized farming. The first farming machines, such as sowing machines and cutters, were introduced in 1799. As early as 1636 Sir John van Berg had invented a threshing machine, but only the improvements of Andrew Meikle in 1788 turned it into an efficient piece of machinery. It not only threshed the corn, but also blew away the chaff and separated the grain from the weeds by sieving. In 1794 James Cooke invented a chaff-cutting machine which prepared the cattle fodder. However, the days of mechanized farming were still far off, and these new machines had no great influence on farming during that period.

The progress of agriculture lay rather in the adoption of new methods which spread very slowly across England, starting in the south and east. The influence of the Continent on this progress is evident, particularly that of Holland.

After the thirteenth century more and more fields were enclosed. This concentrated ownership of land in fewer hands, though many yeomen became large leasehold farmers. Many of the small cottagers and squatters left the land and turned to the new industries, which thus found a sufficient supply of labor for their rapidly increasing needs. On the other hand, enclosure resulted in better productivity and increased yields.

This improved agriculture was not wholly due to the efforts of Jethro Tull, whose fame is probably overrated because of the number of his experiments and proposals. The improvements also came through the increased sowing of turnips, clover, and new grasses. Norfolk led in the introduction of a rotation of crops on sandy soils composed of marl and clay. Formerly, enclosure had often led to a greater development of pasture lands and the raising of sheep. Now the farmers turned instead to a combination of grain and cattle. Lord Coke and Viscount Townshend were foremost in the promulgation of better methods of farming and animal husbandry. The system of four-crop rotation (turnips-barley-clover-wheat) spread to the Midlands and further north. Through this system the cattle were maintained better during winter and produced more natural fertilizer for cereals and root crops. In the old days the cattle were usually brought south for fattening, but this was now unnecessary.

After 1760 enclosure proceeded at a much more rapid rate. Joseph Elkington propagated better methods of drainage of farmland, while Robert Bakewell, by methods of inbreeding, appreciably raised the yield of beef. Nor was the landed gentry alone in arousing interest and helping to spread these methods. Sir John Sinclair in 1793 set up the Board of Agriculture, which reported regularly on progress and new methods. The farms no longer used the markets to dump their surplus but actually began to produce primarily for the market. As a result, potatoes came into general use and meat was no longer considered a luxury. As a whole these new agricultural methods gave England a better and more varied diet. English farms at the end of the century produced 50 per cent more per acre than French farms.

A second round of mechanization set in when the American

pioneers in their drive to the West settled in what is now the Middle West and began to cultivate the rolling plains. Mechanization began with the use of reapers. Smith had patented a reaper in 1811, but McCormick's reaper of 1834 was a vast improvement over this primitive tool. Marsh used the conveyor system, then being introduced in industry, in his machine of 1858, in which the cut grain was carried on a continuous belt to a binding platform, thus combining raking and reaping in one operation. These early machines had not yet succeeded in binding the straw, a feature that was eventually mechanized in Appelby's machine of 1880.

All these early harvesters and their progeny were still horse-drawn. Full mechanization became possible only after the evolution of the tractor (1915) and particularly after the introduction of the balloon tire (1932) to facilitate movements in muddy and clayey soil. The first "baby" combine that not only reaped and threshed the wheat but also bound the straw and packed the grain in sacks was introduced in 1936. It meant that full mechanization of agriculture had been attained, and it transformed the homestead into a factory-farm engaged in the "manufacture" of wheat.

IX

The Conquest of Distance

(1750–1930)

T HE beginning of large-scale production, which we call the Industrial Revolution, would hardly have been possible without the support of organized commerce, credit, and a developing system of transport. The quick and efficient movement of base materials and the distribution of finished products were the key elements in the structure of the new industry.

Better transportation in England itself meant new roads, bridges, and canals; communication with the colonies and with European nations meant better shipping. The professional engineer created by the French schools and the English practical experience of the eighteenth century together proved equal to the task of constructing roads, bridges, and canals. As mechanical skill developed, new professional classes arose that undertook to apply steam power to land and sea traffic and who dared to attempt the conquest of the air.

The New Science of Road Building

THE English Turnpike Act of 1662 and similar laws on the continent made it possible for companies with sufficient capital to improve the highways and to reap the harvest of their labor by the imposition of tolls on the traveler. Early in the eighteenth century this system worked steadily but slowly. It was not much before 1750 that a fairly satisfactory road system was established connecting London with the new industrial districts in the Midlands and the north. An adequate beginning could be made only by establishing more scientific methods of road building.

This phase began in France after the establishment of the École des Ponts et Chaussées in 1747 and its reorganization in 1760 by Trudaine and Perronet. The Corps of Royal Engineers was completely reorganized in 1750–1754 and now embraced all state officials that had anything to do with road building and civil engineering. It was high time that something was done, for there were hardly any skilled workmen or specialists in this field. Though the corvée or tax in the form of labor for public works was established in 1730 for the country people, it was hardly a success; the minister Turgot eventually had to discontinue this practice.

The results of the work of the new professional engineers, so important for the government, soon made themselves felt. Gautier had invented by 1720 a system of making roads by building two low walls of masonry or stone blocks between which the road surface, consisting of clay and gravel or crushed stone, was rammed. A much better construction was introduced by Tresaguet in 1775. By 1788 France had over 12,000 miles of well-paved roads, much more than any other European country could boast of, and at least as many miles were under construction at that date. Le Large had even invented a paving machine in 1717, which, however, was little used. But the road roller, an invention of Cessart (1787), usually made of cast iron and moved by men or horses, was far more important, as it largely displaced the old road rammers.

England, relying on practical experience rather than on state education, followed suit comparatively late. Between 1760 and 1774 Parliament passed more than 452 acts establishing turnpike trusts, to whom the task of improving and building new roads was largely entrusted. General George Wade had proved the strategic importance of good roads when quelling an uprising in Scotland about 1740. The first

English road engineers received their practical training in working for the turnpike trusts.

The new roads were very badly needed, for it was common for a load of timber to take one year to reach the coast from inland. A contemporary print shows a sailor with a wooden leg declining a ride on a mail coach because he was in a hurry. Road building could hardly meet the demands of the growing trade and industry, and on some roads the speed of the mail coaches was not more than five miles an hour by the end of the century. Road building was also important for the postal service, which in 1784 started to use mail coaches.

The first experiments to speed up traffic were directed toward a better construction of vehicles so that we find a stream of pamphlets and books on this subject issued between 1760 and 1820. But as the turnpike trusts grew richer they gave larger contracts and the road engineers thus had a chance to show their ability.

One of the pioneers was John Metcalf, who, like Appius Claudius, had lost his sight and accordingly became known as Blind Jack of Knaresborough. With his contemporary, Thomas Telford, he understood that the proper basis for good roads was the establishment of well-drained foundations. Water and ice were the chief enemies of roads. The English engineers proved that the French foundation of heavy stone paving blocks was not always necessary and that gravel, loam, and stone chips were good materials for road carpets, if this foundation was properly built and drained. These new roads were generally 20 to 25 feet wide, their slope being about five per cent.

Parnell, Edgeworth, Walker, and McAdam continued the excellent tradition of the English road builders. John L. McAdam became famous for his wearing surface (still known as macadam), constructed from light stone chips, which he built after many experiments that were often paid for out of his own pocket. His central idea was that as traffic crushed some of the stone chips, the resulting grit would form the cementing and binding element for lower layers of chips, which had already been bound with sand or loam during their construction. Thus traffic would cement its own roads.

This system was a great success as long as traffic consisted mainly of horses and wheeled vehicles with iron tires. In 1815 it was recognized as the standard system of road building in England. The water-bound macadam road remained superior until the advent of the automobile, whose rubber tires sucked the crushed grit from between the chips, thus destroying the road surface.

The coming of the railroad stopped road construction in England for a time. When Parliament awarded McAdam a large sum of money for all the personal financial sacrifices he had made, he was told that the days of road building were at an end, now that railroads seemed to be getting ready to take over all kinds of traffic!

On the continent, road building made slow progress (even though engineers like Lüders produced excellent handbooks), because there was little or no financial backing from the governments. Yet construction was sometimes speeded up for very curious reasons. The Empress Maria Theresa of Austria, for example, had a good road built from Krakow to Bohemia so that cattle would not have to be transported through enemy territory in Silesia. In such countries as Spain, no attention whatever was paid to roads; the mail coach from Madrid to Toledo in 1830 still followed an old track that was entirely unpaved. Traveling in stagecoaches was decidedly uncomfortable.

In France, road building declined during the Revolution, but boomed again under Napoleon, who recognized the strategic value of good roads in time of war. Between 1804 and 1814 he built many hundreds of *routes nationales* throughout Europe, using the experience of the English engineers. This system, often following the old Roman highways, is still the backbone of the European road network. The roads built over the Alps were especially famous. For the first time since Roman days these routes became fairly safe all the year round. These roads served as excellent propaganda for road building and definitely conquered the old reactionary resistance of innkeepers, landlords, and the landed gentry. It should be mentioned here that turnpikes were also established in America with great success, the first national road, the Cumberland Route, being constructed in 1818.

The macadam road reigned supreme in the nineteenth century, as it was eminently suited to the type of horse-drawn vehicles then in common use. A second phase in the evolution of road construction began with the rapid growth of city traffic. The old pavements in city streets—so far as they existed at all—were very unsatisfactory. The rising clatter of vehicles on cobblestone streets eventually led townspeople and municipal authorities to press for noise-abatement measures. The earliest attempts in this direction were based on the use of creosoted wooden blocks. This idea, imported from Russia, was quite a success in London and Paris in the early nineteenth century.

Other systems employed natural asphalt, which had been newly discovered by French technologists in the course of the eighteenth century. The bituminous limestone of Neufchatel, Val de Travers, and Seyssel, and later that of the Trinidad asphalt lake, supplied the "rock asphalt" that was used abundantly in the early nineteenth century.

Asphalt and Concrete Roads

DE SASSENAY in 1820 and Malo in 1850 had shown that an excellent road surface could be made from this natural asphalt when mixed with hot tar oil and then spread and troweled. The first experiments on the bridges and sidewalks of Paris were a complete success (1810–1820). In 1835 the Place de la Concorde in Paris was paved in this way, and other streets in Paris and London followed. In 1837 de Coulaine discovered that natural asphalt could be powdered when hot, and that this powder, after spreading, could be compressed with a steam roller into a watertight pavement. This type of surface proved highly satisfactory in Paris after 1851, when Polonceau had completed his heavy roller of 1838, which could give much better compression than the old light Cessart rollers moved by hand or drawn by horses.

For several decades it seemed that science had now invented the ideal wearing surface both for country and city. All this changed at the beginning of the present century when automobiles began swarming over the roads in increasing numbers. The development of the automobile therefore ushered in the third and modern phase of road building.

The older horse-and-carriage traffic had merely hammered down the wearing surface, so that repairs were usually limited to the filling in of ruts and depressions. The automobile, however, with its rubber tires and greater speed, sucked at the road surface and hence scattered the grit and other binding material holding the larger stones in place. In the early 1900's the whirlwinds of dust and grit that resulted became a serious hazard as well as a source of discomfort to travelers.

Here again France found the solution. In southern France experiments were begun to brush the damaged macadam surface and to pour on a thin layer of tar, which was then covered over with gravel or chips. Then, after 1910, asphalt from crude oil was also used for these surface coatings which prolonged the life of the old macadam road.

But the increasing quantity and weight of motor traffic demanded more lasting and stronger roads, which would react as one mass of stones (i.e., concrete roads), or as a tar- and asphalt-bound mass, impassive to the suction of tires. This first required better rollers, for the road roller as conceived by Polonceau was not heavy enough to roll thicker road surfaces into a solid mass.

Even hollow rollers filled with water or with sand and stones, both tried in 1853, proved no solution, as they were too heavy to be handled. The correct answer was found in Lemoine's steam roller of 1861, which was improved the following year by Ballaison, who introduced two rollers of equal size. England preferred for a long time the three-wheeled roller designed by Clark and Batler in 1863. That country also produced the first motor-driven roller in 1902. These heavier rollers were easily handled and proved to be the proper solution for the construction of well-compacted foundations and pavement courses.

In England as early as 1838 rolled courses of chips had been grouted with tar. This tar-macadam came into common use about 1895, and ten years later it had also spread to the continent. Tar surface dressings were introduced by Guglielminetti at Monte Carlo in 1901 to combat the dust of macadam roads.

Natural-asphalt surfacing was further improved. De Smedt in 1870 and Clifford Richardson in 1894 had introduced well designed mixes of stones, sand, and fillers in which the minimum amount of voids was achieved, the voids being filled by adding the requisite amount of tar or asphalt to the hot mix in the mixers. When these mixes were spread on the road and properly compacted, watertight constructions such as asphaltic concrete were obtained. They were first tried out and perfected in the United States before being built in Europe about 1910. Asphalt-macadam followed tar-macadam in 1910, and other forms of bitumen, such as emulsions and cutbacks, allowed for the construction of asphalt roads without the necessity of heating the mixes.

Another type of road material, which became a serious competitor of asphalt, was concrete. In 1827 Hobson had taken out a patent for grouting macadam roads with cement mortar. Joseph Aspdin in 1824 had succeeded in burning a mix of slaked lime and clay to produce what he called "Portland cement," but the real inventor of Portland cement was I. C. Johnson, who in 1844 combined the practical information obtained by Aspdin with the scientific researches of Smeaton, Vicat, Frost, Parker, and others, and heated the mix to vitrifying temperatures, thereby obtaining a good artificial hydraulic cement for the first time.

In the United States, David Saylor began in 1870 to manufacture cement at Coplay, Pa. Soon this excellent building material was tried on the roads. Concrete roads were made in Scotland from mixes of stones and cement beginning in 1865, after some earlier experiments in Austria had been successful. Early New York experiments date from 1869. Germany followed, first in Breslau in 1888 and then in Vienna in 1898. The first concrete road in France came in 1892. Good spreaders and mixers were built after 1897, but did not become popular until the 1920's. Now they are, of course, a symbol of concrete road construction.

Road building in the eighteenth century was left to private enterprise. During the nineteenth century, governments awakened to the importance of their road systems for trade and industry. Gradually they drew the control into their own hands. Nationalization of roads became more urgent as the coming of the automobile withdrew a great deal of traffic from the railroads, giving it back to the roads. In Great Britain, the control now rests largely upon the country councils. By an act of 1909, a Road Board was established, which is now merged into the Ministry of Transport. It makes grants from the government Road Fund towards the expenses incurred by road authorities and so coordinates activities.

In the United States, New Jersey inaugurated in 1891 the policy of state cooperation in road building. Other states followed. These State Highway departments were coordinated by the Federal Aid Act of 1916, later amended as the Federal Highway Act of 1921. The Bureau of Public Roads now coordinates planning, improvement, and research in road building.

Modern nations had to cope with the same difficulties as the older empires in obtaining sufficient funds for road construction. Tolls now have generally been abolished except on certain state highways in the United States and on some European roads; the necessary funds are obtained mainly by taxing automobiles and gasoline.

239

Bridges and Canals

As ROAD systems were established, and more particularly when the railroad came to stay, a great era of bridge building began. For railroads required bridges where the highway could avoid them (and often did) on account of the cost. Moreover, in the older traffic system, seagoing vessels usually sailed up the rivers and waterways as far inland as possible. As industrialization proceeded, a canal system was established and ports moved to the mouths of the rivers. Bridges could now be built further downstream, where former generations had had to avoid building them so as not to impede water traffic.

Up until the Industrial Revolution most bridges had been of wooden or stone-arch construction, built according to rules accumulated in practice. Thus, for instance, there was a rule that the thickness of the piers of stone arches should be one fifth of the span of the arch. The foundation of the École des Ponts et Chaussées and its first director Perronet (himself a builder of fine bridges like the Pont de Neuilly) changed the situation materially.

Bridge building now gradually became a science, with the help of the growing knowledge of the strength of materials and of applied mechanics. The École des Ponts et Chaussées had a lasting influence on the science of bridge building in England and in other countries. Technical means were developing, too. Thus the invention of good caissons in 1790 enabled builders to construct solid foundations for piers even in the middle of a river, a difficulty that neither Roman nor later engineers had been able to overcome properly.

New designs sprang up all over Europe. Telford's beautiful bridge over the Severn, with its three elliptical arches, is only one example. In the art of bridge building the English engineers often distrusted the elegant calculations of the French school and sometimes even boasted that they did not use them at all. English engineers like Edwards were often endowed with

PLATE 24 The first cast-iron bridge in the world, crossing the Severn at Coalbrookdale, erected in 1779. (After an engraving in Gloag and Bridgewater's *History of Cast Iron*, Allen and Unwin, London.)

PLATE 25 Saylor's first Portland cement mills at Coplay, Pa., 1870. (*Courtesy Portland Cement Association, Chicago.*)

PLATE 26 Gail Borden's vacuum condensing pan of 1853 used in his condensed milk experiments. (*Courtesy The Borden Company, New York.*)
PLATE 27 Replica of the first (1879) incandescent lamp, made by Edison himself on October 19, 1929, at Dearborn, Mich. (*Thomas Alva Edison Foundation, Inc.*)

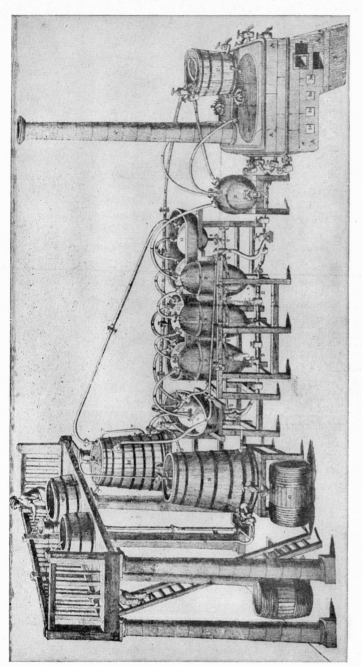

PLATE 28   Adam's apparatus for the distillation of alcohol from wine, 1801.

PLATE 29 The steamship *Curaçao*, which crossed the Atlantic from Holland to Surinam by steam in 1816.

PLATE 30 Duryea's "horseless buggy" of 1892. (*Photograph from the Smithsonian Institution.*)

a marvelous feeling for the correct and mechanically efficient proportions without having recourse to the theory of stresses.

At the same time, timber spans were being constructed with great skill. In the eighteenth century the Swiss brothers Grubenmann built their large timber spans over the Rhine near Schaffenhausen in 1755, and these were followed by a similar wooden bridge over the Limmat near Zurich in 1758. In these bridges the modern idea of struts radiating from the abutments and connected with vertical and horizontal members can be found. Yet these designs are now regarded as primitive, because proper calculations would have allowed lighter and more efficient construction. But the Swiss engineers did not have the benefit of the science of applied mechanics in those days.

Like the Swiss engineers, the early American settlers built many timber bridges, for this material was still abundantly available. Early American builders like Palmer, Wernwag, and Burr built combinations of span and truss bridges, relying more on their practical feeling than on mathematical concepts underlying the construction of bridges.

The early span bridges had one grave defect. They depended to a great extent upon arch action for strength, and the extended horizontal thrusts tended to overturn the piers. American engineers set out to avoid these difficulties, and in 1820 Ithiel Town patented a type of truss bridge entirely free from this defect. These "lattice trusses" were soon improved by new patents taken out by other inventors and served as the foundation of modern designs of iron truss bridges. In 1840 William Howe devised a patent truss that used verticals of wrought iron (later steel) and thus forms the link between the older timber and the modern steel bridge. Howe's truss bridges were used in American railroads for many decades.

The older materials—timber, brick, and natural stone—were partly displaced in the nineteenth century by new materials like cast iron, wrought iron, steel, and reinforced concrete. Accordingly it became possible to build longer bridges. Thus while the limit of a masonry arch is widely recognized to be 400 feet, the steel-arch bridge in Sidney, Australia has a span of 1,650 feet and the Bayonne Bridge in New York tops this by just two feet, one inch. Along with the new materials came new types of construction, based on sound scientific principles and tested engineering practices.

It was natural that the greater production of cast iron and wrought iron during the Industrial Revolution would lead to experiments in the use of these materials for bridge building. The first experiments with cast iron in Lyons failed in 1755. Abraham Darby III and John Wilkinson, the famous foundry owner, succeeded in building the first cast-iron bridge over the Severn, near Coalbrookdale, for the transport of products from their works. This bridge is still in working order. Darby received the gold medal of the Society of Arts for this feat in 1787. Other countries followed England's lead and for a time cast-iron was very popular for bridge building. In France, the Pont du Louvre, built in Paris in 1803, was one of the earliest examples of this type. The first American cast-iron bridge was built at Brownsville, Pa., in 1836.

George Stephenson of railway fame built the first cast-iron railway bridge to carry the Stockton and Darlington Railway south of Durham in 1824. By that time engineers had already come to distrust cast iron as a building material. Failures and partial failures of cast-iron bridges made them aware of the fact that this material, while strong in many respects, is weak in tension. Hence after 1840 cast iron was not used widely as before. Attention was now drawn to wrought iron and steel.

Robert Stephenson (George's son), when designing the Britannia Bridge over the Menai Straits (Wales) on the railroad from Chester to Holyhead, adopted a system combining a new material, wrought iron, with a new design. His bridge was really an immense tubular beam instead of the suspension bridge originally planned. It was completed in 1850 and contained two spans each 460 feet long. Many more tubular railway bridges followed.

William Fairbairn, a shipbuilder, who had cooperated in designing the Menai bridge, was the first to make wrought-iron beams by riveting. This combined the economical form of the cast-iron girder with the toughness and ductility of wrought iron. He used it in a bridge over the Leeds and Liverpool Canal in 1846. An American engineer, James Millholland, used the same construction in a railway bridge near the Bolton Depot on the Boston and Susquehanna Railroad in the same year.

Soon afterward, with steel becoming more readily available, the development of modern steel bridges started, the first patents being those granted to Thomas and Caleb Pratt of Boston in 1844. In general, American engineers have contributed greatly to the development of the modern steel-truss bridge. Men like Squire Whipple and Herman Haupt wrote the first books on the theory of trusses, and English and German engineers continued their excellent work.

Steel proved to be the ideal material for bridges. In the early days mild steel was generally used, but at the present time high-tension steel is produced for this purpose.

The early nineteenth century is, however, even more famous for the introduction of two new types of bridges— the suspension bridge and the cantilever bridge. Primitive suspension bridges, made from ropes suspended across a ravine, firmly anchored at each end and hung over fixed supports, are, of course, much older. The strength of suspension bridges lies in their rope-like construction, which gives flexibility without breaking, if properly designed. They allow much larger spans to be bridged. Whereas the span of a truss bridge is now limited to about 800 feet, that of a suspension bridge may be as much as 7,000 feet. The longest suspension bridge in the world at the present writing is the Golden Gate Bridge in San Francisco, with a main span of 4,200 feet. In 1949 the nine largest suspension bridges in the world were the Golden Gate, the George Washington, the Transbay, the Bronx-Whitestone, the Ambassador, the Delaware River, the Bear Mountain, the Williamsburg, and the Brooklyn, all in the

243

United States, while the tenth largest was the Lions Gate Bridge at Vancouver, British Columbia. On November 7, 1940 the Tacoma Narrows suspension bridge at Puget Sound, Washington, then the third largest suspension bridge in the world, with a span of 2,800 feet, collapsed and fell in a 42-mile gale because of faulty design, although this type of aerodynamic failure had been clearly understood as early as 1867 by John Roebling, who took the utmost precautions against it in building the Brooklyn Bridge over the East River in New York (completed in 1883).

Primitive suspension bridges have a bending and swinging floor attached to the ropes. An American, James Finley, conceived the brilliant idea of constructing a suspension bridge with a stiff and level floor and thus became the inventor of the modern suspension bridge in 1801. In 1810 he designed a bridge over the Merrimac River above Newburyport, Mass., which still stands. His patent of 1808 soon became known over the whole world and it forms the basis of later improvements and patents. Renowned English bridge builders like Rennie and Telford used this system with much success. Telford built his great suspension bridge over the Menai Straits in 1826, connecting Wales and the Island of Angelsey, and thus considerably shortened road traffic from London to Dublin.

The system was tried out for railway bridges, with John Roebling building an 821-foot suspension bridge over the Nigara River in 1851–1855. It was finally replaced in 1897 by an arch bridge, for by that time it had been found that suspension bridges were less suitable for railway loads than for highway traffic. Roebling died in 1869 without seeing the completion of the Brooklyn Bridge, but his son, Washington Roebling, carried the work through despite the fact that he had become paralyzed from the "bends" contracted during the sinking of the pneumatic caissons for the piers. The Brooklyn Bridge, first in the world to use steel wire for the suspension cables, is still one of the most imposing monuments of nineteenth-century bridge building. After having served continuously for 67 years, the bridge was closed to traffic in 1950 to permit strengthening and widening of its roadway.

The modern cantilever bridge came in the last three decades of the nineteenth century. Primitive forms have been built of timbers projecting from massive abutments. The word cantilever means a projecting beam or span supported only at one end. The modern form of cantilever bridge consists of two such projecting spans anchored on massive piers and joined together by a shorter suspended span. Each of the spans is made up of a steel truss which is a modification of the older iron trusses of the Whipple, Parker, and Warren types. The first modern cantilever bridge was built in 1867 across the Main River in Germany; it was designed by Heinrich Gerber and had a span of 425 feet. Perhaps the most famous cantilever bridge in the world is the renowned Firth of Forth Bridge, erected in 1882–1890 with two main spans of 1,700 feet each. Its builders, Sir John Fowler and Sir Benjamin Baker, used tubular chord members to form the trusses, which are spread out at the base and rest on massive concrete piers. Its construction became possible "'soon after the invention of Bessemer made steel cheap," according to Fowler and Baker.

The Firth of Forth Bridge held the world's record for length of span until 1917, when the Quebec Bridge over the St. Lawrence River was completed with a span length of 1,800 feet, still the longest cantilever bridge in the world at the present writing. The construction of the bridge was marked by two disasters. The first structure collapsed during erection in 1907 with the loss of 82 lives; twelve more lives were lost in 1916 when the suspended or connecting span fell into the river while being lifted into place.

The third largest cantilever bridge in the world is the Howrah Bridge across the Hooghly River at Calcutta, India, completed in 1943 with a span of 1,500 feet.

A few words should also be devoted to the subject of canals. During the Industrial Revolution it was quite well understood that bulky goods could be transported more cheaply and safely by water—that is, by river or sea. The towns at the mouth of navigable rivers now became more important than those further inland, which until now had been at "the head of the river." The new seaports like Liverpool helped to develop interregional trade and localization of industry. During the eighteenth century many landowners and industrialists formed companies to improve waterways, and especially the smaller rivers that were navigable only for very shallow barges. These canal plans met with much opposition, largely because tolls had to be levied for the use of the canals to pay the costs of construction and operation.

Robert Southey, the early-nineteenth-century English poet, tells us that "the present Duke of Bridgewater, whose fortune has been amply increased by the success of his experiments, first tried to build new canals in the industrial districts. His engineer Brindley was a singular character, a man of real genius for this particular employment, who thought of nothing but locks and levels, perforating hills, and floating barges upon aqueduct bridges over unmanageable streams. When he had a plan to form he usually went to bed, and lay there working it out in his head till the design was completed. Being asked before the Houses of Parliament for what he supposed rivers were created, he answered after a pause—to feed navigable canals."

And indeed, after Bridgewater had constructed the canal connecting his collieries at Worsley and Manchester, a period of development ensued wherein the rivers became feeders of a more efficient system of canals by the end of the eighteenth century. The Midlands were connectd in 1768 with great harbors like Liverpool, Bristol, and Hull through such canals as the Grand Trunk, the Wolverhampton, and others. Coventry and Oxford obtained canals leading to the Thames. Indeed, in the period of 1790–1794 canal planning reached such a height that we can almost speak of a canal mania. This period of canal building came to an end with the coming of the railroad.

In the United States the first canal was built in 1792–1796 at South Hadley, Mass. Many more famous canals followed the building of roads in this period. De Witt Clinton started

"Clinton's Ditch," now the Erie Canal, on July 4, 1817, in an attempt to connect Lake Erie and the Atlantic Ocean. Other American canals of this period contain long tunnels such as the 400-foot Schuylkill Tunnel and the 728-foot Union Canal Tunnel. Canal building was continued with great activity in the earlier part of the nineteenth century until about 1837, when the growth of the railroads checked their development. However, some 4,500 miles of canals had been built, about half of which have been modernized and are still in use today. European countries were also active in canal building. In Sweden the famous Trolhättan Canal, connecting Göteborg and Stockholm was completed in 1800. In Russia a canal connecting St. Petersburg and the Volga had been built by Dutch engineers summoned to Russia by Peter the Great. Another big canal connected the Don and the Volga

This canal-building activity had a definite effect on industrialization. It materially lowered the cost of transporting coal and other goods. Thus, for instance, the cost of shipping goods from Liverpool to The Potteries at Staffordshire inland had been about £2 10s. 0d. a ton, which the canals reduced to 13s. 4d. a ton. Formerly a horse had carried only one sack of wheat; now one horse, pulling along the canal bank, could draw a barge loaded with forty tons of wheat. The trains of packhorses disappeared from the roads.

It should be remembered, however, that these early canals were boat or barge canals—that is, they had a limited depth and breadth and were navigable only to small vessels like barges. The depth was between three and six feet, the width some 30 to 40 feet at the water level. The modern ship canals were a creation of the last three decades of the nineteenth century and the early decades of the twentieth. They serve an entirely different purpose. They either shorten the voyage between two seas by cutting through an intervening isthmus (Panama Canal, Suez Canal), or they convert important inland towns into seaports (i.e., the canal connecting Amsterdam with Ijmuiden on the North Sea). From an engineering point of view these modern canals differ from the old barge canals only in the magnitude of the works involved. They do not, however, belong to the history of the Industrial Revolution but to that of the modern Age of Steel.

Steam Power and Land Traffic

EARLY in the history of the steam engine there was already no doubt in the minds of inventors that steam would one day move the carriages that were then drawn by horses or mules. A Frenchman, Cugnot, had constructed a steam-propelled vehicle, but it crashed at the first trial in 1769. William Murdoch was more successful with his experiments at Cornwall in 1785. A far better carriage, driven by high-pressure steam, was demonstrated by Trevithick in 1801. It attained a speed of from eight to nine miles an hour on the road. After more experimental models demonstrated by Evans in 1804 and others, Gurney and Hancock were able to open steam-coach service by 1831 with their "Automaton," which was the cheapest form of transport at that time, with the exception of the new railroads. The latter, however, ran only on a limited scale and in a limited area and did not serve city traffic.

At first the steam coaches were strongly opposed by many people who believed that they would cause unemployment; the turnpikes exacted heavy tolls in order to offset the damage done to the road surface by these ponderous vehicles. They were also slow in starting, consumed much fuel, and left a trail of smoke and cinders in their wake. Finally there was the famous Red Flag Act, which ruled that self-propelled vehicles must be preceded by a footman carrying a red flag or lantern to warn pedestrians of their approach. Curiously enough, this act was not taken off the law books until 1896.

The steam-propelled vehicle was not destined to rule the highway. It was to succeed on a road of its own, on rails made especially for it. Its great future lay in the direction of mass transportation of goods. As early as the year 1530 Haselberg's *Ursprung des gemeynen Berckrechts* shows ores transported in wagons running on wooden rails. Such primitive railways moved by manpower or horsepower continued in use near mines and quarries using wooden longitudinals, which in 1767 were replaced with cast-iron rails devised by Richard Reynolds of Coalbrookdale. These early rails had an L-shaped cross section until Smeaton advised Reynolds in 1789 to take the flange from the rail and make it part of the wheel. At about the same time the cast-iron rail was displaced by the rolled wrought-iron rail, which remained in use until steel rails appeared in 1860 following the invention of the Bessemer process. In 1784 William Symington and William Murdoch designed the first locomotives. A railroad on which a steam engine was used only for the transport of goods was opened between Wandsworth and Croydon in 1801.

Trevithick also designed a high-pressure "tram engine" which made a successful trial run on February 21, 1804 from Merthyr to Abercynon, Wales. The earliest models of "locomotives" were not economical. Those of Blenkinsop in 1811 and Hedley in 1813 were better, but not perfect, though the latter made an engine that was used for the carrying of coal for many years. George Stephenson was the designer of the first universal engine used for passenger service and freight. The years between 1813 and 1829 are filled with a host of locomotive designs and experiments. Protests against the railroads took strange forms. A committee of the Royal Society concluded that speeds of over 30 miles an hour would cut off the air from the compartments and thus asphyxiate the passengers. Others proclaimed that cows along the railway line would give less milk when frightened by the roaring monster.

The first public railroads were opened in the north of England (the Stockton to Darlington Railroad of 1825), a region that was without canals. Stephenson's *Rocket* won a clearcut victory in the 1829 race at Rainhill, Liverpool, attaining a speed of over 15 miles an hour. Nevertheless when building the railroad between Manchester and Liverpool the engineers hesitated for four years over whether to depend on the new engines to haul freight trains up slopes or to build windlasses to do the job. Stephenson's success lay in the fact that he connected the piston of his steam cylinder directly to the wheels of the locomotive, thus getting the maximum amount of power from the fuel. He also used a tubular boiler and created a forced draft by the injection of steam. His association with one of his competitors, Rennie, led to the foundation of the first locomotive plant in 1830.

Stephenson was most optimistic about the future of the railroad. He said: "Railways will come to supersede all other methods of conveyance in this country—mail coaches will go by railway and railroads will become the great highway for the King and all his subjects. The time is coming when it will be cheaper for a working man to travel on a railway than to walk on foot." This prophecy came only partly true, for railroads reigned supreme only until the coming of the automobile and airplane. The cause of the railroad's success was the inability of the canal system to keep abreast of growing production, a failure that was partly due to the rivalries of the canal companies and the steepness of their tolls, and partly to the different dimensions of locks, which made free passage from one canal system to another fairly difficult. The rapid growth of industrial cities and of coal transportation provided the growing railroads with abundant passengers and freight.

The dire prophecies of the farmers and others did not materialize. The success of the railroad was complete and spread from England to the continent. Baader had patented a railway track for horse-drawn vehicles in 1815, and in 1835 the first German line from Nuremberg to Fürth was opened. France started with the line from Saint-Étienne to Lyon in 1830, and Holland with the line between Amsterdam and Haarlem in 1837.

In the United States, railroad building began even earlier, for the construction of two pioneer lines of the Baltimore and Ohio and Charleston and Hamburg railroads was undertaken as early as 1828. These early American lines even experimented with auxiliary sails for their wood-burning locomotives. The first English locomotive, the *Stourbridge Lion*, completed a successful trial run in 1829. The first American-built

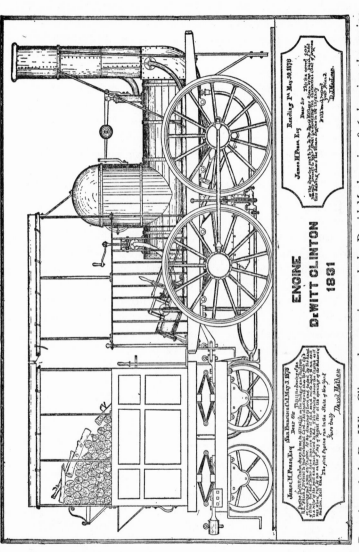

Drawing of the De Witt Clinton locomotive made by David Mathew in 1876 showing the engine as it appeared when run by Mathew on August 9, 1831, at the opening of the Mohawk and Hudson Rail Road. (Courtesy University of Michigan, Ann Arbor.)

locomotive, the *Tom Thumb*, is said to have transported 40 passengers at a speed of ten miles an hour, but better engines were made after Phineas Davis designed his *York* in 1831.

The earlier English railway cars were faithful copies of the stagecoach. Then by 1840 coaches with more logical and functional shapes were built, and these gradually took the form we know today. In the matter of comfort to the traveler the American railroads were more advanced than others. As early as 1836 sleeping cars were used in Pennsylvania, although they were rather uncomfortable until George M. Pullman remodeled them in 1858 and the first Pullman car ran the following year. Pullman cars were taken over by England and other European countries. In England the first sleeping car appeared in 1873, the first dining car in 1879, and the first corridor trains in 1890.

The main improvements in locomotives were not concerned with the fundamental design as laid down by Stephenson and his generation. They consisted of four other points which were the fruit of experience. The first was the use of swivel bogies in 1874, these being four- or six-wheeled trucks pivoted beneath the chassis of the engine that enabled the engineers to build longer and more powerful locomotives. Then the driving wheels were coupled to give the necessary frictional grip in starting heavy trains. The third was providing the engine with safer and more powerful brakes. Here the outstanding invention was George Westinghouse's straight air brake of 1869. The fourth improvement was streamlining the engine and coaches to lessen wind resistance at high speeds. Reversing machinery for locomotives was introduced in 1833.

Traces of their more primitive origin still clung to the railroads. Strangely enough, the standard-gage railway track, derived by the early locomotive builders from the width of the axle of road vehicles of their day, remained at 4 feet 8 inches—the same gage as that of the prehistoric wagon tracks of Malta and the tracks for the temple wagons in ancient Assyria!

On the other hand, the railroads were quick to adopt up-to-date techniques for the improvement of their signaling systems. The crossbar and lamp signals had been in use since 1834; in 1841 the semaphore arm was adopted, deriving from the "optical telegraph" devised by the Frenchman Chappé in 1793. Light signals of different forms appeared soon afterward. A good signaling system was possible only after the invention of the electric telegraph. The first telegraph line (from Paddington to West Drayton, extended in 1842 to Slough) was not opened until 1839, whereupon it was immediately used to assist railroad signaling.

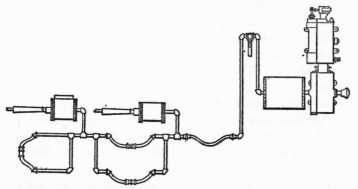

The Westinghouse "straight air brake" of 1869. (Courtesy Westinghouse Air Brake Company.)

After 1854 block-signaling systems were added. There was, of course, a vigorous effort on the part of railroad and government officials to make these systems as foolproof as possible so as to reduce accidents and safeguard passengers' lives. Gradually central watch towers were built to control the operation of points and signals, which were still largely manual. Then in 1875 W. Sykes invented his "lock and block" system, in which each passing train "freed" the points and signals for the train behind. Sykes introduced the operation of signals by compressed air instead of by hand and soon compressed air and electricity were used jointly. Then automatic signaling was introduced at Liverpool in 1893. This system proved highly effective and spread rapidly in the first decade of the twentieth century.

Electricity was not used only for signal operation on these early railroads. As early as 1838 a locomotive was run on electric batteries, but its performance was hardly economical. The electrification of trains had to await the invention and development of the electric motor. Siemens designed the first practical electric locomotive in 1879, and a year later Thomas A. Edison demonstrated his "electric car."

Though electric trains are clean, do not pollute the air, and can be quickly accelerated, the capital investment for electrification of railroads is very heavy and its economy is closely bound up with cheap electricity. Hence some countries started to build electric railroads or electrify existing lines only when they had sufficient water power to produce electricity cheaply. The first all-electric track was opened at Portrush, Ireland, in 1883. The first electric locomotive in the United Stated hauled freight train at Baltimore in 1895. After 1900 the electrification of railways made steady progress, especially for passenger traffic in densely populated areas, as on suburban lines with frequent stops. Other countries like Switzerland, blessed by nature with natural resources of hydroelectric power, were quick to carry electrification to its limits.

The rapid development of railroads in heavily populated areas like Western Europe was a logical outcome of the traffic situation in which road and canal traffic could not adequately serve the growing needs of passenger and freight transportation. In North America the situation was different. When the eastern part of the United States and Canada had become crisscrossed with railroads, the westward march of settlers began, prompted by entirely different factors, mainly political. In 1854 the Chicago and Rock Island Railroad was extended to the Mississippi west of Chicago, and the line between Cincinnati and East St. Louis was joined—only a year after the completion of the great bridge across the Mississippi between Rock Island and Davenport. From this period until about 1890 the railroads, supported as they were by the land grant policy of the United States, quickly conquered the vast plains and mountains west of the Mississippi. The slowing down after

1890 coincided with the saturation of the West and a policy of Federal regulation. A new era of improvement of track and rolling stock followed on the rapid extension of the railroads to the Pacific Coast. In Canada, a similar development started after the Railway Act of 1851, which was brought to a close with the completion of the railway line stretching from Montreal to Vancouver.

Bus, Streetcar, and Bicycle

THE coming of the railroad solved the problem of swift communication between towns and countries, but the problem of local traffic remained to be settled. While earlier experiments with steam cars had been a failure, the manufacturers of wheeled vehicles profited from the experiments and designs made in the latter part of the eighteenth century. The improved quality and greater supply of steel made possible the introduction of an important invention, the elliptical spring, early in the nineteenth century—a device that increased both the speed and safety of coaches. Combined with superior roads, coach travel now began to surpass ancient Roman travel in speed and comfort. It was, however, limited to passengers and mail, the trains taking the bulk of the freight, supplemented by the canal boat.

New types of carriages like the cabs of 1820 and hansom of 1834 made their appearance, but had little success outside England. Primitive bus services had been in operation in Paris and other large cities since 1650. In 1829 George Shillibeer introduced his horse-drawn omnibuses from France, but heavy taxes soon nearly wiped out this new London enterprise. Subsequent models were the "knifeboard" omnibus, which had a long seat on the roof, and the "garden seat" omnibus, which supplanted the former in 1890. Then the internal-combustion engine brought mechanical travel back to the road in the beginning of the present century. Though motor buses appeared as early as 1880, the chassis was subject to constant change. The standard London motor bus dates from 1923. It proved an excellent means of connecting the suburbs with the city and with railway stations.

On the other hand, transport developed quickly in the cities. The use of rails to guide vehicles is, of course, even older than the railroad itself, for it dates back to the old railed trucks used in the transportation of coal and stone centuries ago. It was quicker to develop in countries like America, where the first streetcar connected lower Manhattan with Harlem in 1832, and France, where the first streetcar was put in operation at Paris in 1855, because there was no entrenched bus system to prevent its introduction. The main difficulty, however, was the fact that the high rails impeded road traffic until the engineers solved this in 1870 by sinking the rails into the road surface. Horsedrawn trams appeared in the Midlands of England about 1860 and proved faster and more economical than horse-drawn buses. Their electrification dates from 1890. The disadvantage of the fixed track was partially solved by the introduction of the "trackless trolley" or trolley-bus, but generally speaking the motor bus had its way and supplanted even electric streetcars in many towns.

During the nineteenth century another strange and "individual" vehicle appeared in the streets—the bicycle. As with other vehicles, we find a long ancestry behind the modern bicycle. A kind of "scooter" moving on two wheels is depicted on Greek tombstones. Mechanically propelled vehicles, looking somewhat like our modern wheel chairs, were devised by Hautsch in 1640 and Farfler in 1655. Sivrac put on paper some very good ideas on the construction of bicycles, though he was never to realize them. Again, a kind of four-wheeled bicycle, propelled by a valet by means of two pedals, was in use in France between 1770 and 1790.

The first real velocipedes, on which the rider sat between a front and rear wheel and propelled the vehicle by pushing the ground with his feet, were made by Blanchard and Magurier in 1780. More practical machines came when Karl Drais von Sauerbronn constructed the modern handle bar and perfected a light, sturdy frame in 1818, which resulted in the "draisine" or

"dandy horse." The latter was a whim of fashion and contributed little to the solution of the traffic problem.

Still, these earlier models were an inspiration to a Scotsman
named Kirkpatrick Macmillan, who constructed a machine in
1840 that was propelled by two pedals connected with cranks
to the back wheel and had a handle bar and a fairly comfortable
seat like that of the modern bicycle.

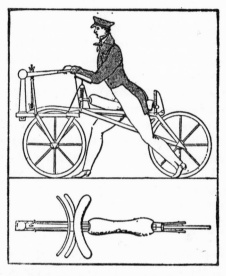

*Drawing of the "Draisine" in the original patent application of
January 5, 1817.*

A Frenchman, Lallemant, in 1865 used modern forms of
pedals to move the front wheel, thus adding something to the
power of the rider, though hardly to his comfort. These
"boneshakers" were soon followed by the "penny farthings," in
which high gearing was introduced to gain speed, though to
the detriment of the rider's safety.

With the coming of good mass-produced steel, strong,
cheap parts could be constructed. Madison introduced the
idea of frames of hollow steel tubing and wheels with steel
spokes in 1867. This was turned to account in the safety bicy-

cle of Lawson, introduced in 1876, which was propelled by a chain drive on the back wheel. This model soon swept the older types off the road. Starley began their mass production in the Rover factory in 1885.

Two further inventions made bicycle riding safer and easier. One was tangential spoking, which made the wheel lighter, safer, and stronger. The second was the pneumatic tire, which came after Goodyear had made his epoch-making discovery of the vulcanization of rubber in 1839. Thomson in 1845 proposed to use a hollow rubber tube filled with air, but his ideas could not be realized at the time. It was Dunlop who succeeded in 1889 in introducing the present combination of an inner tube and an outer casing on which a tread was molded. The introduction of ball bearings in bicycles in 1877 finally completed the evolution of an easily operated, self-propelled road vehicle. Yet a further change came with the invention of the internal-combustion engine, for in 1884 Daimler produced the first gasoline-driven motorcycle, two years before he made his first automobile. The Daimler motorcycle is the ancestor of all modern types.

The Development of the Automobile

WE HAVE noticed the profound effect that the internal-combustion engine had on the evolution of mechanically propelled road vehicles. The steam engine was too bulky to be used as a source of power for such vehicles; what was needed was an engine that would combine the fire box, boiler, and cylinder of a steam plant in a small lightweight unit. The internal-combustion engine, in which injected fuel mixed with air is exploded to drive the piston in a cylinder, proved to be the answer. It could supply more power per weight than a steam engine, and its moderate fuel consumption made long-distance travel not only possible but economical.

The evolution of the internal-combustion engine was conditioned by the increasing supply of cheap fuel and cheap steel. The supplies of gas or alcohol were too limited for a rapid development of the use of automobiles. It was then that petroleum entered the picture.

Colonel Drake had shown, beginning in 1859, how to produce crude oil in ever-increasing quantities from the deeper strata of the earth. The automobile was a boon to the oil refiners, for in the earlier days they had been forced to burn or throw away all light fractions that could not be used in lamp oil. But after 1900 gasoline production and hence the automobile too could develop freely.

Equally important for this development was the growing abundance of good, cheap steel in the latter half of the nineteenth century and the studies on the nature and combustion of gases, begun in the eighteenth and continued into the nineteenth century.

The earliest patent for a gas engine (as distinguished from a gasoline engine) was taken by Lebon in 1784, following his experiments in the production of gas. While Rivaz's gas engine of 1807 was a decided improvement, it was not until 1863 that the first practical gas engine with preignition was designed by Lenoir. As early as 1838 Barnelt had constructed an engine using compression. Lenoir adopted this principle in a double-acting engine which he built into a vehicle that completed a successful trip of ten miles from Paris to Joinville-le-Pont.

The next important step was made by Marcus of Vienna in 1875, who constructed a slow four-stroke engine having magnetic ignition. Unfortunately, however, his engine was so noisy in operation that he was forbidden to make further experiments. When, therefore, in 1880 and 1881 several electric automobiles driven by Faure's accumulators made their appearance on Paris streets, it seemed for a time that the development of the engine would take a different turn.

Then in 1882 Daimler and Maybach started building the first practical gasoline engines. These were so compactly built that they were suitable for light vehicles, and attained speeds of up to 900 revolutions per minute. In 1885 one of these engines was mounted on a kind of wooden bicycle; then, the following year, on a four-wheeled carriage. The latter was the first automobile to complete successful trips through Cannstatt. At the same time Benz of Mannheim patented an automobile with a four-stroke engine and a body constructed of hollow tubing, giving a more suitable over-all weight in relation to the capacity of the engine. In America Charles E. Duryea demonstrated the first horseless carriages between 1891 and 1893.

These experiments drew great attention in France, where an automobile industry began to develop, using the patents of Benz and Daimler. In 1894 the first automobile races were held there. The winner achieved the incredible speed of fifteen miles per hour. The experimenting phase was over; the automobile was no longer a plaything or a freak. To use a well-worn phrase, it had come to stay.

Two important developments now took place, the first of which was the redesigning of the body and parts of the automobile. The older types had been true "horseless carriages," for they had been built along the lines of the earlier horse-drawn vehicles and still retained all their characteristics—for example, the higher back wheels, splashboard in front, open top and sides, and bench-type seat, under which the engine was placed. In 1901 Daimler produced the first car with a low body and forward engine, a vehicle really designed as a functional automobile. This was the Mercedes, and its design was soon followed by the Rolls-Royce in 1904. A windshield and a folding top were added to protect passengers from wind and rain. This materially added to the weight and wind resistance of the automobile, and spurred research into lighter, stronger bodies, which would overcome friction and wind resistance at higher speeds. The modern automobile tire, fashioned after the earlier Dunlop bicycle tire, was introduced in 1896 and greatly added to the absorption of shock and vibration while allowing lighter construction and greater speed, combined with better traction. The construction of the modern tire is due to Welch.

In 1896 Bosch built his low-voltage magneto, which was

immediately applied to automobile ignition, together with his spark plug. The Daimler "honeycomb" radiator appeared about the same time and lent itself perfectly to later attempts at automobile streamlining. The earlier type of wheel was derived from the horse-driven carriage, but as a heavy type was needed, the gun-carriage wheel, invented in 1887, was usually adopted; although tangentially spoked wheels of the type used on bicycles were also employed for a short time. Then, in 1910, Rudge Witworth introduced his wire wheel with the hub so constructed that the wheel could be detached easily from the axle. During the period 1910–1935 the steel-spoke artillery type wheel was popular, until modern methods of pressing steel led to the introduction of the pressed-steel wheel that is in almost universal use on today's automobiles.

These improvements made possible large-scale introduction of the automobile. Early attempts at mass production date from 1899 to 1901, when the manufacture of the Opel, Horch, Adler, and Protos cars was started. By 1893 Henry Ford had constructed his first automobile, but it was not until 1903 that the first Ford car was introduced to a mass market with the founding of the Ford Motor Company at Dearborn, Michigan. This heralded the era of supremacy of American automotive production. At the same time a serious competitor of the gasoline engine appeared in the form of Rudolf Diesel's heavy-oil engine (1908–1909), which not only captured a large segment of bus transportation but was also used with great efficiency in locomotives and on ships.

The greatly increased use of the automobile during the First World War, which brought the tank in 1916, and other motor-driven engines of war, stimulated the use of trucks and automobiles in general. Not only did this extended use influence the design of modern roads, making them better able to handle the increasing number and heavier weight of motor vehicles, but it also built up a strong demand for cheaper and simpler cars having higher speeds. The First World War had shown the great importance of the introduction of standardized motor parts. Both standard parts and better organization of assembly formed the foundation of real mass production.

The earlier cars, as we have seen, had retained much of the design of the horse-driven carriage, but this now disappeared, and the so-called "touring car" with open sides and collapsible top gave place to the fully enclosed sedan or coupe. The enclosed car allowed for greater comfort as well as for adequate streamlining, which gave a more pleasing appearance whether or not it had much effect aerodynamically at ordinary legal speeds. At extremely high speeds the streamlining of the automobile does reduce fuel consumption, but under average conditions the greatest resistance is not from the air but from contact of the wheels with the ground. At any rate, streamlining and the manufacture of cheap standard parts were greatly assisted by the introduction of pressed steel, special steel alloys, and the use of aluminum alloys and molded plywood for the car body.

This second phase of mass production differed greatly from the first phase. Formerly the body and frame of the automobile was handmade, and the individual assembly of cars was the normal procedure. Now the conveyor system was applied to production, resulting in the familiar assembly line that has made possible the manufacture of more than four and a half million automobiles in a single year (1929), bringing a cheap form of transportation to millions of people and reshaping road traffic and road construction along entirely different lines. Ford, Morris, and Austin were among those who adopted these modern assembly methods in the early 1920's.

The New Engines Come to the Ship

THE Act of Navigation, the creation of the colonial empire, and the Industrial Revolution had given England predominance on the seas of the world, a position she was to retain until the 1930's. The quick growth of ocean shipping helped develop better instruments of navigation; the invention of the sextant in 1731 and of the chronometer in 1735 made shipping more reliable and safe. The eighteenth century also was an age of great activity in cartography, and the seas of the world were practically all mapped in that period.

The English merchant navy doubled in size not only during the eighteenth century, but again between 1790 and 1820, and this rise continued for a considerable period. Formerly the larger merchant ships had been owned by combined of merchants; now there were many privately owned sailing vessels averaging 250 to 400 tons' burden, the larger ships rarely exceeding 1,000 tons. A certain state control over shipping was inaugurated by the compulsory registration of shipping that was instituted in 1786. Other laws regulated insurance and passenger traffic. The Navigation Acts, no longer a protection to British shipping, were gradually dropped by the time the steam engine had been tested as a prime mover for ships.

Earlier attempts at marine propulsion by steam, such as those of Papin, had failed. Then in 1786 John Fitch designed a ship in which steam moved a set of oars, and in 1807 Robert Fulton's *Clermont*, a paddle-wheel steamer, made a journey of 150 miles up the Hudson River in 32 hours. In the meantime, the steamship had come to be used as a tugboat and as a freighter in the north of England. Henry Bell's passenger steamer, the *Comet*, began making regular runs on the Clyde in 1812. On May 22, 1819, the *Savannah*, a sailing vessel equipped with auxiliary steam power, left Savannah, Ga., for Liverpool, England, and arrived there in 27 days, having used her steam engine for a total of 80 hours. The first successful Calais packet in 1821 was the signal for the institution of many inland and coastal services both in Europe and in the United States. Finally, in 1830 Bell built the first ship designed only for passengers, and progress in steamship construction began to move quickly.

Though the possibility of steam-driven, ocean-going ships was by now demonstrated and coastal services had become well established, the steamship was still too costly a means of transportation to serve anything else than passenger transport. Only when high fares were exacted could the fuel-consuming paddle-wheel ships, driven by beam engines or similar efficient models, pay their way. The streamlined body copied from the graceful clipper ships of former days and, above all, the introduction of the screw propeller, together with new high-pressure steam engines of better design—all of these improvements were adapted to the steamship in 1858. The sailing ship, however, remained superior as a cargo vessel for a long time to come.

The introduction of the screw-propelled ships dates from the experimental trips of the *Archimedes* in 1839, a ship of 240 tons. The *Great Britain*, laid in 1839 and floated in 1844, was the first large steamship (over 3,000 tons) to be fitted with screw machinery, and was also the first British ship to be constructed of iron. The screw began to displace the paddle wheel and after 1850 the latter had become a rarity on ocean-going steamships, although the Cunard Line used the paddle on their mail ships until the early 1860's.

The earliest steamships had been really sailing vessels with auxiliary steam power. Developments led to the gradual abandonment of sails on the steamer, which was soon to be moved by steam alone. As early as 1816 a Dutch steamer in the command of an English captain had steamed from Brielle, Holland, to Curaçao in the West Indies without the use of sails. The *Sirius* and the *Great Western*, both English ships, made the trip from Liverpool to New York in a fortnight—half the usual sailing time—on steam alone. This sealed the fate of the sailing ship, which was always dependent on favorable winds. In 1835 the British Navy had over 1,300 steam vessels. Much of the credit for the success of transatlantic steamships was due to the English engineer, I. K. Brunel, who designed the *Great Britain* and the *Great Western*, as well as the *Great Eastern*, which laid the first successful transatlantic cable in 1866.

The sailing ship made a last bid for mastery of the sea. The beautifully rigged, streamlined California and China Clippers and their famous "tea" and "wool" races represented a lost cause, however. The opening of the Suez Canal and the establishment of bunker stations along the most important shipping lanes allowed the steamship to compete with the Clipper ships in speed, safety, and comfort. Gradually and mercilessly the Clipper ship was displaced. In 1870 only 16 per cent of the world tonnage afloat consisted of steamships, but this figure rose in 1900 to 60 per cent.

Lloyd's Register, established in 1834, classing the ships in groups each with its own insurance premium, was a great stimulant to the building of safer ships, for Lloyd's was very scrupulous as to safety measures. It certainly speeded the introduction and adoption of iron and steel ships. The development of the Bessemer process in 1856 and the Siemens-Martin process in 1866 made cheap steel available for shipbuilding. As early as 1855 Lloyd's classification of steel ships was given, after the firm had registered the first iron-frame ship in 1837. In 1870 over five sixths of the tonnage under construction in Great Britain consisted of iron ships, three quarters of which were steamships. The first twin-screw steamer sailed the ocean in 1863.

Brunel's *Great Eastern*, mentioned above, was the largest ship of her day in 1854, having a gross tonnage of 18,914 tons. The size of ships was then generally limited by that of the ports and quays, which were now gradually improved and enlarged. The size of the ocean-going ships kept increasing. The great *Mauretania* (30,696 tons) of 1907 was not surpassed by the British until 1936, when the *Queen Mary* (80,773 tons) was launched, followed in 1939 by the *Queen Elizabeth* (83,673 tons), at the present time the largest passenger liner afloat. Other countries had, however, built liners that exceeded the *Mauretania* in tonnage, notably Italy with the *Conte di Savoia* (48,502), France with the *Ile de France* (43,450) and the ill-fated *Normandie* (83,423), Germany with the *Bremen* (51,731) and the old *Vaterland*, renamed *Leviathan* (54,000). The largest passenger built by the United States is the *America* (35,000 tons). Both the extent of shipping and economical reasons set a limit to the size of steamships.

The increase in tonnage, the certainty of arrival of cargoes at fixed dates, the huge stream of immigrants to new countries, and the fast-growing export business of European countries contributed to the rise of the steamship. Better design of hull and engine followed this rise. In 1894 Parsons experimented successfully with his *Turbinia*, and in 1905 a new era in shipping was opened when the first two turbine-driven liners were launched. Oil as a fuel for ships, used for the first time by the British Navy, soon began to displace coal, because of its cleanliness, efficiency, and ease of handling. The Diesel engine proved a valuable acquisition for shipping. The first Diesel-electric ship, the *Wupperthal*, launched in 1936, may hold much promise for the future.

Masts and funnels, rudiments of the old types of ships, remain part of the ship's design, though their function has changed radically. They now serve as radio antennas and ventilators respectively; sometimes a dummy stack is added merely to create a pleasing symmetry or streamlined effect. Moreover, specialization in various types of ships has proceeded far beyond what was formerly attempted. Tankers, tugs, speedboats, steam barges, warships, and other forms differ widely in design, each type being built to serve a highly specialized function.

The Conquest of the Air

AT THE turn of the present century, man began to realize his long-cherished dream of flying. This dream, as old as mankind, played a part in many legends and myths, such as that of Icarus, whose artificial wings allowed him to escape from prison in Crete only to drop into the Agean Sea when he flew too close to the sun. Leonardo da Vinci studied the flight of birds in great detail and conceived many forms of artificial wings, both rigid and movable, but his experiments did not bear fruit.

After the invention of the air pump, the idea of using an evacuated balloon to carry people through the air was suggested by many scientists. The Jesuit de Lana in 1760 imagined a ship carried by metal balloons from which the air had been exhausted. Unfortunately the metal globes would have been too thin to withstand the internal pressure caused by the expansion of the remaining air at high altitudes. Joseph Gallien in his book published in 1755 suggested that the balloon be filled with the "light air of the upper strata of the atmosphere." Only when the science of gases was properly studied could correct solutions be advanced. Thus Black proposed the use of hydrogen, the lightest element, for filling balloons.

The first practical balloon was the product of two French papermakers, Joseph and Étienne Montgolfier, who made use of the fact that hot air is lighter than cold air. Their first experiments were made in 1783. In the same year the physicist Charles showed all Paris a balloon filled with hydrogen and made airtight by means of a rubber solution. The first man to ascend in a balloon, Pilatre de Rozier, used a "Montgolfière" and rose to a height of 80 feet in October, 1783, though his was a "captive" balloon, that is, fastened to earth by a cable. His second flight in a free balloon was a complete success. Unfortunately the fire used in these hot-air balloons caused many accidents. Nevertheless experiments were continued in many countries and Jefferies and Blanchard succeeded in crossing the English Channel in a free balloon in 1785.

Scientists like Cavendish soon used the balloon for the exploration of the atmosphere. It was also used for reconnoitering, as in the Battle of Fleurus. An old invention of Leonardo's became a reality when in 1797 Garnerin jumped with a parachute from a balloon at a great height. The hydrogen gas used for inflating the balloons was still very expensive, so that coal gas was used as a substitute after Green in 1821 had shown its usefulness—though coal gas, too, was highly inflammable.

In the meantime, Guyot had tried to solve the leakage problem by proposing an egg-shaped balloon in 1784, and Meusnier had solved it by using a series of small balloons enclosed in an outer envelope.

Though the airship was still at the mercy of the winds, the

elongated shapes used by Guyot and Meusnier formed a good basis for the development of the dirigible. In 1850 motor propulsion was tried. First came Giffard in 1851, who used a five-horsepower steam engine. In 1878 Professor C. E. Ritchell flew over Hartford, Conn., in a dirigible powered by a steam-driven screw propeller. Renard and Kreb tried an electric motor driving a propeller in 1885, but not until 1898 did balloons become fairly independent of winds and air currents with the development of the gasoline-powered aircraft by two inventors working independently—the Brazilian Santos Dumont, working in Paris, and Count Zeppelin of Germany. The latter was responsible for many improvements of the dirigible, but this type of aircraft was not, however, destined to shape the course of future development in aviation.

Heavier-than-air aircraft had been among the dreams of generations of inventors. As early as 1617, Fleyder seems to have lectured on flying at the University of Tübingen. Aircraft with steam-engine propulsion had but academic value, though a model by Samuel Langley in 1896 flew half a mile, and Sir Hiram Maxim built some ingenious models also.

The airplane was successful only after Lilienthal's experiments with gliders in 1895, which showed the value of studying aerodynamics, including air currents and airfoils, or cross-sectional shape of the wings. Four forces were shown to determine the movement of the airplane. The *lift* was the upward thrust on the lower surface of the wing caused by the pressure of the moving stream of air. The *drag* was a backward pull caused by air resistance of the airplane body. The *weight* of the plane pulled it down vertically due to gravity. The *thrust* was supplied by the propeller (later by the jet) and pulled the airplane forward through the air stream. In a properly designed plane, the thrust overcomes the drag and creates lift by moving the wing against the air, thus overcoming the weight or gravity at the same time. The plane then flies, subject to the movement of the controls.

Streamlining the airplane was the work of later generations. They gave it specialized forms for different purposes. They improved the design of the propeller and even created the autogiro and the helicopter.

In 1900 the Wright brothers, Orville and Wilbur, began their experiments with gliders. They introduced the vertical rudder and the movable wing sections or ailerons to change the angle of attack and thus regulate lift. In 1903 they built their first airplane, powered by a four-cylinder, 12-horsepower gasoline engine. In 1905 they were able to fly for a half hour at a time, covering about 25 miles. Farman, Santos Dumont, and others improved the plane considerably. On July 25, 1909, Blériot flew across the English Channel, and Latham flew nearly twice as far. In 1909 and 1910 Paulhan flew a biplane successfully, reaching a record height of 1,200 feet. He also covered the distance from London to Manchester in 24 hours, making only one landing (April 27–28, 1910).

The planes of this period all had four-stroke engines, which gradually acquired a typical shape of their own. The search was on for lighter materials for these water- or air-cooled engines. The evolution of new alloys of magnesium and aluminum and of special aviation gasolines that allowed for higher compression ratios has given a great impetus in the direction of more efficient aircraft engines. Experiments with Diesel engines for planes date from the 1920's, and at the present time jet-propulsion engines are widely used for military aircraft and to an increasing extent for commercial transport planes.

The turning point in the history of the airplane was certainly the year 1908. Practical experiments had already shown the possibilities, but now mathematical calculations based on physical laws, were formulated with scientific accuracy. Langley (1891) and Zahm (1902–1903) had started the new science of aerodynamics and had studied the behavior of air currents flowing over different types of airfoils. The investigations of Lord Raleigh, especially those recounted in his *Manchester Memoir* of 1899, are rightly famous. In Germany an inquiry into the possibilities of aircraft had been undertaken, and the final report of 1907 stressed the importance of making actual tests on airplane models in wind tunnels. These conclusions, for the greater part the work of Prandtl of Vienna started aircraft research on a real scientific basis. In England the National Physical Laboratory soon undertook similar investigations and other countries contributed additional research.

The Second World War had a tremendous effect on the further development of the airplane. Broadly speaking, the commercial airliner is still in an early stage of evolution. It has, however, clearly demonstrated its value in the swift, world-wide transportation of mail and passengers. Its possibilities for the large-scale handling of goods have only been recently explored. The experience of the Berlin airlift in 1948–1949 has shown that a well-organized air transport is quite capable of handling large quantities of all types of goods, including heavy machinery.

Two new types of aircraft power plant have come to compete with the internal-combustion engine, namely jet propulsion and rocket power. In neither case are we out of the research stage as yet, but both types of power are due to create demands for new types of fuels and new construction materials able to withstand the higher temperatures and the greater strains encountered. This becomes particularly important in supersonic flight—flight at speeds above that of sound. It is even probable that these new forms of propulsion will create entirely different types of design, such as we have already observed in the "flying wing" and sweepback wing.

Private flying in light planes has grown in importance since about 1929, having been greatly stimulated in the years immediately preceding the Second World War, but while the light plane finds many applications in business and industry, it is a long way from being a competitor of the automobile, there being only about 120,000 private planes registered in 1949 as against some 50 million automobiles. The helicopter, once thought to be the coming "flivver" of the skies, is still far too expensive and too complicated a machine for the average homeowner to think about. While it possesses distinct advantages in maneuverability over the conventional plane, its relatively slow speed and present difficulty of handling has restricted it to special applications such as patrol and rescue work.

The present state of aircraft development bears a striking resemblance to that of the steamship a hundred years ago. It would be difficult to predict the designs and types of planes that will be used even ten years hence, nor the part they will play in transportation and communication between the peoples of the world. Neither can we judge the place that aircraft will have in the society of the future, although there is little doubt that they will continue to break down the barriers of time and distance.

X

STEEL AND ELECTRICITY

(1830–1930)

THE Industrial Revolution gave birth to a completely new set of social problems. As the old-fashioned artisan disappeared, the skilled workman took his place. Technical schools had to be founded to train skilled workmen and engineers, who were to be the leaders of the new industries. Gradually the stream of farmers moving to the towns increased, for there was always the strong attraction of higher wages in industry to draw them. The governments, still unable to cope with the new social order, soon saw themselves confronted with labor troubles, the exploitation of women and children in factories and mines, and the evolution of an industrial proletariat cut loose from its origins in the country districts. This led to a series of conflicts, culminating in the Revolution of 1848 in Paris, following which society gradually learned to adapt itself more or less to the new conditions.

The great material successes of the Industrial Revolution made the scientist of the nineteenth century cocksure. His successes in investigating and conquering nature led him more and more toward materialism. The essential philosophical background that had been supreme in the seventeenth century became increasingly vague. Natural philosophy became natural science, but the philosophers like Hegel and his school were so preoccupied with theories of the social order

PLATE 31 Steel converter installed at the Cambria Iron Works by William Kelly in 1861-1862. (*Courtesy Bethlehem Steel Company*, Bethlehem, Pa.)

PLATE 32 The first experimental Burton cracking unit, developed and operated at the Standard Oil of Indiana Whiting refinery. (*Standard Oil Company of Indiana.*)

PLATE 33 The first ascent of a "Montgolfière" with a human passenger, October, 1783.

PLATE 34 Proposed statue to MacAdam, "from the oculists and eyeglass manufacturers," sketched by a contemporary French cartoonist.

PLATE 35 Otto Lilienthal in one of his experimental glider flights.

HARPER'S WEEKLY
A JOURNAL OF CIVILIZATION

Vol. XXII.—No. 1124.]   NEW YORK, SATURDAY, JULY 13, 1878.   [WITH A SUPPLEMENT PRICE TEN CENTS

Entered according to Act of Congress, in the Year 1878, by Harper & Brothers, in the Office of the Librarian of Congress, at Washington.

PLATE 36 Wood engraving from a photograph of Prof. C. E. Ritchell flying over Hartford, Conn., in 1878, using a primitive form of dirigible. (*Harper's Weekly*, July 13, 1878.)

PLATE 37 Morse's sending and receiving telegraph instruments of 1837. (*Photograph from the Smithsonian Institution.*)

PLATE 38 Model of Alexander Graham Bell's first telephone instrument through which speech was first transmitted electrically in 1875. (*Photograph from the Smithsonian Institution.*)

that they not only overlooked natural science but even rejected the scientific method.

This gap between philosophy and natural science and the ever-deepening cleft between religion and science characterize the nineteenth century. By the end of this period the scientist, emboldened by his successes, believed that everything in nature, including the evolution of man and his works, could be explained in terms of matter. There might be a few more details to be solved, but the picture seemed perfectly clear. Evolution and the struggle for existence seemed to determine human actions.

One of the outcomes of this scientific philosophy was an even closer bond between natural science and technology. And as cooperation brought great success, these branches of knowledge became more and more intertwined. Research, both pure and applied, came to stay. Turning to technology and engineering, we find that the nineteenth century brought great changes in both fields.

The supremacy of England as an industrial country was slowly but relentlessly broken. By 1850 England had already begun to relinquish her leadership in different fields to Germany. The latter country, though politically broken up into small units, had tenaciously built up a good scientific training for its scientists, engineers, and skilled labor and began to apply it quite fruitfully. France, hopelessly crippled by her lack of metallurgical coke, was reduced to the status of a second-class industrial nation, notwithstanding the considerable number of French scientists and inventors.

Some quarter of a century later the United States became a serious competitor of England and Germany. Driven by youthful enthusiasm and enterprise, it not only gained new industrial strength with each passing decade, but by the beginning of the twentieth century it was the undoubted leader in mass production. One of the most important reasons for American success was the unusually close cooperation between science and technology in that country, which found its expression in many research foundations established through the foresight and magnanimity of American industrial leaders.

The nineteenth century shows the typical impact of industrialism upon an older and more stable organization of society and industry. We still live in a society that is adjusting itself to this impact. This adjustment was evident generally throughout the nineteenth century, but manifested itself particularly in three important phenomena at the turn of the century.

The first of these was the growing concentration of the population in towns and cities. The total population of Europe increased almost threefold, but in 1900, 75 per cent of the population of England and 65 per cent of the population in Germany lived in towns and big cities.

The second factor was the rapid growth of the industrial regions, where industry, now freed by the machines from the lingering traces of the medieval craft system that had restricted its expansion, could reap the advantages of centralization and cheap raw materials. Coal and iron ores acted as magnets in this centralization process.

Third, there was the expansion of world trade, which, like the other two phenomena mentioned, was both a cause and an effect of the industrialization of Europe and America. A large percentage of Britain's exports was made up of coal that was exchanged overseas for raw materials. Over 70 per cent of the exports of Britain and Germany at the turn of the century consisted of manufactured goods.

Rise of the Steel Industry

THE expansion of iron and steel metallurgy was the dominant feature of nineteenth-century industry. The Industrial Revolution had introduced crucible steel, coke-burning blast furnaces, and the preheating of blast air. The harnessing of the steam engine to the blowers and the introduction of Neilson's "stoves" greatly increased the size and output of the blast furnace, but they had little effect on its fundamental processes. No further improvement was added to the blast-furnace process, which seemed nearly perfect, until in very recent years it was found to yield more and cheaper pig iron of a better quality when worked under pressure (Avery, 1938).

The combination of blast furnace and puddling process produced nearly 75 per cent of Britain's iron in the form of wrought iron in 1830, 20 per cent of which was exported. The rest was mainly cast iron. Steel remained a special product produced in small lots, its price being about five times that of wrought iron. In 1850 England produced three million tons of pig iron and only 40,000 tons of steel. Unfortunately, both wrought iron and cast iron had serious disadvantages as construction materials. The problem of producing steel on a larger scale became acute around 1850.

We owe the process for the mass production of steel from crude pig iron to two inventors working independently. In 1862 William Kelly installed his "steel converter" at the Cambria Iron Works in Pennsylvania, but he had been anticipated by Sir Henry Bessemer in 1856. The latter, a professional inventor during the Crimean War, had directed his attention to the making of guns, having been attracted by a prize of money offered by Napoleon III. Realizing that he needed more and better steel than could be produced locally, he made numerous experiments and discovered that a blast of air introduced in a vessel containing molten crude iron will first oxidize the impurities present, and that this rapid oxidation will heat the mass still further. Thus a molten wrought iron or steel remains in the vessel, which is called a converter. By adding the proper minerals, the oxidized impurities were slagged and the molten wrought iron or steel produced could be cast. These converters, of course, had to be properly protected by a refractory lining, which in the early converters consisted of siliceous materials.

The first converters were used in France in 1858, and the process was taken up very quickly. Within a few years the converters were able to produce 20 tons of steel in 25 minutes from one loading of pig iron, and this increased output made larger and stronger castings available.

Bessemer and Kelly came to an understanding about their patents, but it took many more years of experimenting to perfect the method. The American, Holley, finally made the process continuous by using two converters alternately. Since about 1910, however, the Bessemer process has largely yielded to the Siemens-Martin open-hearth process (described below), which was invented about 1860 by William Siemens and first used commercially by Martin in England. Through the Bessemer process and its later competitor, the amount of wrought iron produced declined both in England and in America, and with it the use of the puddling process. At the present time, the output of Bessemer steel in the United States is less than 7 per cent of that produced in the open-hearth furnace. This is mainly due to the fact that better steel can be made by the latter process from low-grade ores.

The Bessemer process is known as the "acid process" because of the acidic nature of the lining of the converter. This limits the use of the process to the conversion of iron ores and pig iron of low phosphorus and sulfur content. The difficulty was that such ores are relatively rare and the larger part of the iron ores available in northwestern Europe have a high phosphorus content, at least above one tenth of one per cent.

Producing from ores containing phosphorus did not prove to be an insoluble problem. Thomas, a clerk, and Gilchrist, a chemist, in 1877 hit on the happy idea of lining the converter with basic materials, such as dolomite. These achieved what the siliceous bricks could not—they absorbed the phosphates formed by the blast air in the converter and bound the sulfurous compounds to slag. This "basic Bessemer process" was a boon to the French and Germans working the phosphoric iron ores of Lorraine (a bone of contention in every war between these countries) and to Belgium and Luxemburg, where they are outcrops and strata of the same nature. The process materially contributed to the rise of German steel production.

As the Bessemer plants went into production, they marketed a "mild steel," the properties of which lay between those of wrought iron and the "hard" blister steel produced in crucibles by the older processes. This mild steel proved an ideal material for rails, boiler plate, bars, structural steel for ships, houses, and reinforced concrete structures, and for sheet metal, such as that gradually demanded by the rising canning industry.

Much research was therefore devoted to some modification of the puddling process that would convert pig iron into mild steel and keep it liquid until ready for casting. A second problem that soon grew important was the use of scrap iron as a base material. It seemed impossible to melt scrap iron in a reverberatory furnace. William Siemens and his brother Ernest von Siemens had pointed out that it might be possible to heat such furnaces to the correct temperature with gas and air preheated in turn by the flue gases escaping from the furnace. Le Chatelier tried this method successfully on steel, and together with the Siemens brothers took out patents in 1856 and 1863.

The correct lining to be applied to these open-hearth furnaces at first still presented some difficulties. Martin and Le Chatelier solved them by producing high-class siliceous bricks which made the Siemens-Martin process completely successful. The first open-hearth furnace was built in the United States in 1873. Today the "basic" modification of the process accounts for nearly 91 per cent of all the steel produced. Five per cent of the total production is converter steel, and four per cent is electric-oven steel. In 1879 the open-hearth process was adapted to the conversion of scrap iron containing phosphorus and sulfur, when Pourcel and Valrand used such basic materials as dolomite and magnesite for the lining of the hearth.

These different processes for the mass production of steel solved many industrial problems. Between 1856 and 1870 the price of steel dropped 50 per cent and its production increased sixfold. Already by 1860 steel plates were in general use for boilers, allowing far higher steam pressures to be used. A steel rail outlasted twenty iron rails. In 1863 the first steel ship and the first steel locomotive were produced. As steel became established as the most commonly used form of iron, different compositional types were recognized.

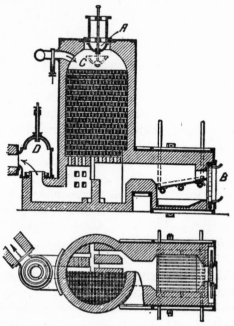

Cowper's preheating brick towers, 1857. (Dingler's Polytechnical Journal, *Vol. 158, 1860.*)

This progress in metallurgy, as we have pointed out, became possible only through the close contact between science and metallurgy. Sorby, experimenting along the lines laid down by Réaumur and Bréant, founded the science of metallography, which studies the crystalline structure of metals and alloys to determine their properties. His researches of 1857 were perfected when the microscope was introduced into metallography in 1864. Austen, Osmond, and Le Chatelier were among those who perfected research in this field in order to guide and improve metallurgical operations. It materially assisted the study of the thermal properties of metals, in which Tschernoff, Heyn, Baur, and the other scientists mentioned above cooperated.

Toward the end of the nineteenth century this led to important advances, such as the development of alloy steels for specialized applications—tungsten steel (Mushet, 1845), chromium steel (Brustlein, 1878), nickel steel (Marbeau, 1883), manganese steel (Hadfield, 1882), and vanadium steel (about 1914). Many of these metals were soon being produced in appreciable quantities and no longer were the laboratory freaks they had been for nearly a century.

Temperature control of these processes became all-important. First, this control was achieved by means of the little siliceous cones of different melting temperatures that had been developed by Wedgewood for pottery manufacture about 1750. When Le Chatelier introduced the thermoelectric pyrometer in 1891, temperature control became far more scientific. The prophecies contained in Faraday's articles in the *Philosophical Transactions* of 1822 were now fulfilled. Alloys became even more important than the original metals themselves.

A successful competitor of the old crucible-steel process was born when electricity became available in large quantities. This phase began when Clerc in 1879 constructed the first successful electric furnace, using the heat of the electric arc to melt steel and scrap. Many inventors (Héroult and Cowles among others) improved this electric furnace between 1887 and 1890. The experiments of Henri Moissan after 1892 have contributed to the efficiency of this furnace.

A new and intriguing type of electric furnace, the induction furnace, became possible through the work of Northrup in 1916 and Ribaut in 1920. In this furnace the iron or steel is heated by the eddy currents set up within the metal itself as a result of the rapidly changing magnetic fields produced by the flow of alternating current in the external electrical coils. The metal then acts as the core of a transformer, the electric coils surrounding the metal acting as the secondary. This means of heating the metal internally without having it come in contact with the current itself, or with gases or flames, is very important for melting precious metals and various alloy steels.

Electric furnaces proved of great value when temperatures up to 3,000°C had to be reached or when metals had to be melted in the presence of certain gases. They are even more

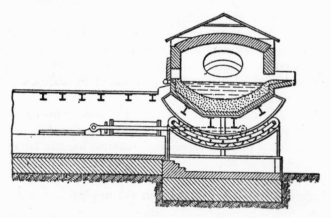

Campbell's design of a tilting Siemens-Martin furnace. (From F. H. Harbord, The Metallurgy of Steel, *1904, p. 144.)*

important for controlling processes more accurately at high temperatures and for producing deoxidized and desulfurized steels, the properties of which have been materially improved by the removal of the last traces of oxygen and sulfur.

In America and Italy, where cheap electricity is readily available, electric steel has virtually displaced crucible steel, but in other countries the greater part of the high-carbon hard steels are still made by the crucible process.

Some of the latest processes in metallurgy, such as that of Ugine-Perrin, filter the molten metal through a bed of slags and chemicals to purify it. Thus deoxidizing and dephosphorizing proceed much more quickly, and it is possible that these processes mean an entirely new departure in metallurgy.

A freak metal that came into its own is aluminum. Little disks of aluminum had been produced by Wöhler in 1827 when he was repeating Oersted's experiments of 1825. In France, the production of aluminum had been attempted by Sainte-Claire Deville, but chemical processes proved too expensive. Electricity had to come to the rescue.

Electrolytic production from molten alumina (the oxide of aluminum) proved possible if this mineral was dissolved in another mineral, cryolite, which melted much more easily.

The electrolytic cells that first produced aluminum at Pittsburgh.

This process, developed by Charles Martin Hall in 1886 and duplicated independently by Paul Héroult of France, was the beginning of the era of light metals and their alloys. Mass production of aluminum is closely linked up with cheap electricity. Aluminum and magnesium alloys, together with other light metals, now dominate such fields as air transportation, electric power transmission, cooking utensils, and building construction. They have succeeded in ousting steel and copper from many fields which these older metals had held for centuries. Since the Second World War aluminum and its alloys can be cast, forged, extruded, rolled, spun, beaten, and sprayed to suit the requirements of their numerous applications.

The demand for iron, steel, aluminum, and the new alloys and metals became so great that much care was given to the collection and refining of scrap metal. The problem of corrosion was also studied more closely. Though it is well known that aluminum and certain other metals and special alloys are fairly resistant to corrosion (more particularly, to atmospheric corrosion), this is hardly the case with many ordinary types of steel and iron. This corrosion became more serious as wrought iron was generally supplanted by mild steel.

The process of galvanizing iron by dipping it into molten zinc, as invented by Hobson in 1805, had originally been applied to thin sheets of wrought iron. As soon as the rolling mills were sufficiently improved to turn out equally thin sheets of mild steel, these were used instead, as they were much cheaper. However, the galvanized steel sheets had only about 25 per cent of the life of galvanized wrought-iron sheets. Evidently the production of these sheets (which were consumed in great quantities outside Europe and America) constantly wavered between cost of production and real protection against corrosion.

A better combination to combat corrosion was that of tinning mild steel by dipping sheets into molten tin after appropriate pickling with chemicals. As tin is fairly resistant to corrosion by the acids in food and by the atmosphere, this combination was ideal for the preservation of food in the canning industry, which still is one of the main consumers of tin. Tin cans are also used as containers in the petroleum and fatty-oils industries on a very large scale.

Metallurgical science, in combating corrosion, also introduced chemical treatments of metals after the fashion of the old cementation process of the ancient smiths. Charpy in 1913 treated iron with aluminum and zinc powder in furnaces and achieved protective coatings. Fry in 1921 in his nitriding process treated steel with ammonia in airtight containers, thus obtaining the same effect as the early smiths, who carburized their wrought iron.

Generating and Transmitting Electricity

THOUGH in the nineteenth century the old sources of power continued in use, their relative importance changed greatly. The windmill remained in use for drainage purposes. Because of their limited power, windmills were soon displaced in industry by steam engines, which came to the fore very rapidly, but were not unchallenged. The eighteenth-century experiments with electricity in laboratories and salons had soon led to research into the possibilities of storing electricity. The famous Leyden jar, invented simultaneously in 1745 by a German Lutheran pastor and a Dutch scientist, van Musschenbroek, gave little more than a flash of "static" electricity when discharged.

A regular supply of electricity was obtained by Volta, when he designed a plate form of substitute for the Leyden jar in 1775. This was gradually improved until it became a true "voltaic pile" or battery. As early as 1800 Nicholson and Carlisle used it to accomplish the first decomposition of water by electrolysis, making electricity do work for the first time. These piles or batteries consisted of two different metals or surfaces in a solution of a chemical. They transformed chemical energy into electrical energy. The old voltaic pile with its copper and zinc plates was not improved until Daniell produced his battery in 1836. Grove followed with a new type in 1839 and in 1842 Bunsen invented his carbon-zinc cell. However, the electromotive force of these cells was rather small, and large batteries had to be used to produce electric phenomena. Thus Davy used 2,000 cells to produce an electric arc in 1808. In 1850 Robert Hunt calculated that electrical power was still 25 times as expensive as steam power.

Unfortunately, when producing electrical energy these batteries were gradually destroyed because the zinc plate was eaten away in the chemical process. In the meantime, another form of transforming energy into electricity had been discovered—the dynamo. It was, however, still important to have some way of storing electrical energy. For this purpose the storage battery, using lead plates immersed in dilute sulfuric acid (designed by Gaston Planté in 1859) was a decided improvement. Clark in perfecting his standard zinc-mercury cell in 1873 contributed much to the proper understanding of batteries. This knowledge enabled Faure in 1880 to develop his openwork grid for battery plates, which reduced the weight of the storage battery considerably. Correns then designed the present form of battery grids in 1888.

By this time the battery had become sufficiently light and economical to be used by William Morrison of Des Moines to operate an electric automobile in 1891. It had also become adaptable enough to be installed in a hydroelectric plant to meet peak-load requirements (Hartford, Conn. 1896). But the sulfuric acid in the batteries still remained a serious drawback, preventing, for example, its use in submarines. Hence Edison turned his fertile brain to the subject and in 1908 he began marketing his "nickel-alkaline" storage battery, which though much lighter, stronger, and more durable, had a lower voltage than the Planté battery.

The answer to the problem of converting mechanical energy into electricity (the generator) and of converting electricity back into mechanical energy (the motor) was derived from a single experiment that is known to every schoolboy. In 1820 the Danish professor Hand Oersted discovered by accident that a current flowing in a wire caused a nearby compass needle to swing at right angles to the wire. It meant that there was some relation between magnetism and electricity. Oersted rightly supposed that both a magnet and an electric current build up a "field of force" and that the two can act upon one another. Until then, every scientist had believed that all physical phenomena could be described in terms of gravitational attraction, but now apparently a new physical force had been discovered.

This discovery created a great sensation in academic circles, and only a few months later the French physicist Arago was able to prove that a needle in a coil through which an electric current was flowing became magnetized. This "induced magnetism" was permanent in steel, but wrought iron cores lost their magnetism rapidly. The "electric solenoid" was thus a new means of making a magnet. Ampère was another French physicist who was highly interested in Oersted's experiments, which he repeated, showing that two parallel wires carrying current in the same direction attract each other, but that if the currents flow in opposite directions the wires repel each other. The *ampere,* unit of current strength, was named in his honor.

Unfortunately Ampère's essays were far in advance of his contemporaries and were so highly mathematical in nature as to be largely unintelligible to many of them. This, combined with the chaotic state of terms referring to electrical phenomena, caused academic interest to subside for a time. The popular demonstrations of William Sturgeon, who constructed the first electromagnet in 1825, also aroused much attention in general circles, but little progress could be expected from that quarter.

It took several years for these new phenomena to bear fruit. The American, Joseph Henry, revealed in 1831 a series of remarkable facts. He discovered the phenomenon of electrical induction and applied it to transform magnetism into electricity. He had constructed the first electric motor in 1829, discovered the principle of the "step-down" and "step-up" transformer, and demonstrated a telegraphic instrument using a one-mile length of wire. Unfortunately his discoveries, though published in *Silliman's Journal* and known to most scientists of the day, did not have the effect they deserved.

Faraday was luckier in ths respect. He, too, had pondered and experimented for several years on these phenomena, and in the same year as Henry he discovered the means of transforming magnetism into electricity. A coil connected with a galvanometer and a coil connected with a battery wound on the same cylinder of wood formed the first instrument he used. When he closed or opened the circuit of the second coil, a current was induced in the first coil, as indicated by a reading of the galvanometer. The same phenomena was observed when the wooden cylinder was replaced by an iron ring. Faraday discovered that moving a magnet in and out of a coil also induced a current in the coil. He went on to construct a 12-inch copper disk which rotated between the poles of a horseshoe magnet. A wire taken from the shaft and one taken from a brush rubbing the edge of the disk were made to form a circuit in which an induced current could be detected.

These demonstrations before the Royal Institution in April, 1832, created quite a sensation. When one of the visitors asked Faraday what use this new toy had, he is said to have replied, "What is the use of a newborn child?" It was soon proved that the newborn child was a lusty infant. The coil and magnet contained the principle of the generator, wherein mechanical energy is transformed into electric current, as well as the principle of the motor, which transforms electrical energy into mechanical energy.

The generator or dynamo was therefore understood in principle at least by 1832, but many obstacles stood in the way of constructing a practical working model that could serve as a source of power. One of these was the lack of properly insulated electric wire. When Morse was perfecting his first telegraph in 1837, the only insulated wire available on the market was that used by milliners for the skeleton of the "skyscraper" bonnets then worn by fashionable ladies in New York. Other inventors had to go through the tedious process of winding silk thread around copper wires by hand.

Nor were the primitive demonstration generators of Faraday and his contemporaries of any practical use. Clarke in 1835, Weber and many others improved them on several points. First of all, the field was no longer set up by permanent magnets, but by electromagnets energized from a battery; secondly, the single loop of wire moving through the magnetic field in the original model was developed into a series of loops to form a coil or coils known as the armature.

The early models of generators built by Pixii in 1831 and Saxton in 1832 were considered as useless substitutes for the batteries of the period, for these generators produced alternating current—that is, current whose polarity or charge alternated from positive to negative a definite number of times each second, whereas battery current was direct current, its polarity remaining constant. This difficulty was overcome by William Sturgeon's invention of the "unio-directed charger" or commutator in 1834, which periodically reversed the direction of the alternating current by means of a rotating contactor, thereby producing a mechanically rectified direct current, the same type as that produced by the batteries.

This important improvement had by 1845 definitely established the superiority of electromagnets over permanent magnets for use in the generator. Nollet, using a model designed by Woolrish in 1842, built a few generators that were used by the Compagnie Alliance of Paris in this decade. A better "self-excited electromagnetic machine" was designed by Hjorth in 1855, using both permanent magnets and electromagnets, for by 1851 it had been realized that the magnets could be energized by using part of the current generated by the machine itself. However, the generator was far from being a practical source of power as yet.

One of the most difficult problems encountered was the design of the armature. In 1856 Siemens developed the shuttle-wound armature for generating an alternating current. This double-T form of armature was soon improved in 1860 by Pacinotti, who used an iron wing with slots to receive the armature conductors for the magnetic circuit of the armature, and who made several additional improvements. In 1863 he designed a model that could be operated either as a generator or as a motor. A few years later Henry Wilde, Cromwell Varley and Samuel Varley, Siemens, and Wheatstone simultaneously developed working models of the self-exciting generator, the first satisfactory generator for practical use. Siemens, Hjorth, and others demonstrated their models at the great Paris Exhibition of 1867. It was Siemens who introduced the word "dynamo" in an address to the Berlin Academy.

By 1870, therefore, practical types of generators producing either direct or alternating current were available. Industrial applications of the generator now began to be found in rapid succession. Weston used it for electroplating in 1872, and in 1875 for an electric furnace. Arc lamps began to be used for street lighting, thus providing a fairly constant consumption of electricity for the new electric generating companies that were being formed in a few large cities. By the application of so-called "compound-wound field magnets"—that is, by combining shunt and series windings on the field coils—a substantially constant voltage could be maintained over the full range of load connected to the generator.

A new source of trouble was the question of alternating current versus direct current. The older generators of the alternating-current type were of as little use as a single-cylinder engine for an automobile. As advances were made in generator design, however, the polyphase alternator was perfected, whereby two or three separate currents, or "phases," mutually out of step by a certain constant time interval, could be generated simultaneously to provide more flexible power supplies and a more balanced distribution system. Furthermore, it simplified the problem of long-distance transmission of electrical energy, as we shall see below. But as long as electricity was used in small areas only—for instance, in stores and office buildings generating their own power, or on shipboard—direct current seemed preferable, particularly for electric motors, which were far more versatile than the existing a-c types.

The choice between d-c and a-c current soon took on a different aspect when it became related to the problem of long-distance transmission of electricity. As the demands for electricity rose in proportion to its increasing possibilities and growing number of actual applications, large central power stations were planned. It was clear that the cheapest source of raw energy was to be found in the water power available at waterfalls or rapids or created by impounding water at dams. But such sources are generally far from the industrial centers where the current is needed, making long-distance transmission necessary.

Such transmission is economical only at high voltages and correspondingly low currents, because only then can the cross-sectional area of the copper conductors, and hence the cost of installation, be kept reasonably low. The voltage-current relationship of direct current cannot be altered without introducing appreciable power losses; the d-c voltage generated in the central station must be the same as that delivered to the customer. (D-c voltage transformation can, of course, be accomplished by having the received current drive another generator, but large-scale use of such motor-generator sets is impractical for ordinary service, for it means added power consumption.) The first central stations, which began operating in a few big cities about 1880, generated direct current only, because all lamps and motors were then direct-current devices. With the invention, about 1887, of the a-c motor, alternating current began to be used more widely, although at first only for generation and primary distribution, being converted at substations to direct current for for secondary distribution to the customer's premises. As central-station systems increased in size, however, it became advisable to use alternating current throughout the entire system because of the increased efficiency of transmission and distribution which the device known as the transformer made possible.

The transformer operates on the principle of induction, and changes the voltage (or current) of an electrical circuit to a higher or lower value, depending on the arrangement of its windings and the number of turns of wire used. (It cannot work on continuous direct current, but only on an intermittent or alternating current.) The principle of the transformer had been known to Henry, Faraday, and others, but its application had to wait until the development of central-station power. Moreover, the use of high-voltage generators and other equipment had to await the development of better insulation materials and safety devices. Today practically all electric light and power service, except for specialized applications, is a.c., for the remarkably high efficiency of the transformer (98 per cent) has made this by far the more economical type of current. In a typical a-c system, a number of alternators generate power at 13,200 volts; this is transformed to 132,000 volts by suitable transformers and carried to the long-distance overhead transmission lines to substations, where it is "stepped down" to 13,200 volts for underground transmission in urban areas; thence to another substation, where the voltage is again stepped down to 2,300 volts, and finally to manhole or pole transformers, which further step it down to the 208-volt, three-phase network, from which 120-volt lighting service is taken from each phase or 208-volt power service across phases. Transmission-line voltages of as high as 200,000 volts have been used in commercial operation.

The discussion of the relative merits of direct- and alternating-current transmission was started by a public lecture delivered by Charles W. Siemens in London in 1877. Research on the construction of commercial transformers had been carried on for a number of years, but now it was intensified. The first official demonstration of a transformer, designed by Marcel Deprez and Jules Carpentier in 1881, was unsatisfactory. Better results were obtained by L. Gaulard and J. D. Gibbs of Paris, who filed the first of their patents in the same year. Their transformer was successful in trials in northern Italy and Great Britain. A few years later came the German patent of Déri, Blathy, and Zipernowski (1885) and this transformer was successfully installed near Rome.

In the meantime George Westinghouse had been impressed by the results of the Gaulard and Gibbs transformer, and with the help of Reginald Belfield, their representative in the United States, his engineering staff looked into the problem. Headed by William Stanley they developed the first truly commercial transformer in 1886, which was installed in the new Buffalo plant. A year later Westinghouse patented the air-cooled and oil-cooled transformer, the prototypes of the modern forms.

At that time scientific circles were not yet convinced of the superiority of long-distance a-c transmission. When, for instance, the waters of the Niagara River were harnessed it was finally decided to produce a.c. instead of d.c., in accordance with the advice of Lord Kelvin, the famous British physicist. The decision eventually proved to be right.

There remained a strong opposition to long-distance transmission at high voltages on the assumption that it was very dangerous. The battle raged until 1890, when it finally died down. The introduction of a.c. meant a great impetus to American industry and to that of other countries having sufficient water power at their disposal.

The generator was first used commercially for the electric arc lights in city streets. This application was mainly due to Brush, who in 1876 designed a practical "arc-light machine." Many inventors, including Brush, Jablochkoff in 1876, and Weston in 1877, improved the "electric candles," the origin of which goes back to the days when Davy demonstrated his voltaic piles. The generator was constantly improved, particularly by Thomas Edison, whose machines were reported to have an efficiency of 90 per cent—considerably more than that of competing machines.

In 1879 the California Electric Light Company, the first company in the United States to sell electric current, installed Brush generators for arc-lighting service, exactly one year after the installation of 16 Jablochkoff "candles" near the Paris Opera. In 1880 New York followed, and as the incandescent lamp, invented by Edison in 1878, was developed in the course of this decade the number of generating stations grew. In 1882 Edison opened the first electric-lighting plant at the

Pearl Street Station of the Edison Electric Illuminating Company in New York, which provided 800 lamps with electric current. Within 14 months the number of lamps rose to 12,732, and Edison invented a meter to measure the current used by the customer. In 1882 the first hydroelectric plant was opened in Appleton, Wis. Alternating current was introduced by the Westinghouse Electric and Manufacturing Company in 1886.

In the same year Buffalo became the first city in the United States to receive alternating current and electric light and power on a large scale. At the Vienna Exhibition of 1883, practically all the electric appliances of modern life, such as electrical hot plates, pans, cushions, and sheets, were shown, but the great consumption of electricity was due to the evolution of the incandescent lamp. It stimulated the growth of network distribution and the production of huge quantities of electricity in power plants, lowering the cost per kilowatt hour until other electrical appliances became economical to use. In 1890 the first power station in England (at Deptford) was opened and the first subway of "underground" made its appearance in London. Brown's oil circuit breaker increased the safety and flexibility of electric power systems.

The period 1880–1910 was, therefore, characterized by experimenting and the search for new applications of electricity. In the course of this period, smaller power stations were now gradually consolidated under one management, and after 1890, as hydroelectric plants were developed, there was a growing tendency to build large power plants supplying cities and countries with electric current. The Columbian Exposition of 1893 at Chicago had much to do with this development. The power plant built at Niagara Falls transmitted its first current to Buffalo in November, 1896. The evolution of large power grids in different countries can be considered as beginning about 1913.

After 1910, electric traction, not electric lighting, was the main consumer of electricity. This meant more economic use of the installed capacity of electric generating stations, for the lighting load was applied, naturally, only during the hours of darkness. The average load of the older plants was only 10 per cent of their peak load. With the growing number of electric streetcars, subways, and motors, this load was evened out over the entire day, and production became more normal and economical. During the period 1910–1920 electricity became technically and commercially accepted as an important power source, and since 1920 has increased enormously in terms of total output. This is also due to the development of hydroelectric power stations, and the use of electricity in producing aluminum, carbide, and other chemicals.

The present development of electrification is largely concerned with the decreasing cost of electrical energy and its production on an increasingly larger scale. England, for example, consumed about a million kilowatts in 1906, but some thirty years later the total consumption was about four million kilowatts and the price per kilowatt-hour had been reduced to one tenth of the 1906 price.

At the Vienna and Chicago exhibitions earlier there was already a variety of possible applications of electricity to be seen. Many of the present household appliances have a much longer history than is generally believed. The earliest vacuum cleaner dates back to 1858, dishwashers using the centrifuging principle first appeared in 1865, and the first washing machines were sold in 1869. The possibility of similar household machinery driven by electricity depended on the cheap supply of "electric juice" to every home. In a fairly young country like the United States, which was in the midst of a large expansion during the nineteenth century, electrification came much more naturally than in many European countries deriving their heat and power from coal, coal gas, and petroleum, the supply of which was already well organized when electricity began to be widely used. Except in Scandinavia, Italy, and in parts of Switzerland, France, and Great Britain, electricity met with much competition from other power sources.

Thus the mechanization of the household through electricity prompted by social and economic causes, which in the

United States became quite pronounced around 1935, has not yet penetrated to many parts of Europe, though the same social forces are active there. In the United States only three or four per cent of the power supplies in 1900 was from electric generators, whereas this figure had risen to 70 per cent just before the Second World War. Europe began to apply the electric motor more generally only about 1920.

The Applications of Electricity

THE development of batteries and generators created, as we have seen, the possibility of supplying electricity on a large scale. The first important application was the transformation of electricity into mechanical energy by means of the electric motor.

It is strange, indeed, to find that, though generator and electric motor clearly work on the same principle, their development for a long time followed different lines. The earlier models by Faraday and Barlow, demonstrating the principle of the electric motor, were mere toys. Thomas Davenport, buying one of Henry's electromagnets, succeeded in developing a practical electric motor in 1835. Improving his first patent application of 1836, he later built a motor that drove a printing press in New York in the year 1839. At the same time, von Jacobi, inspired by Faraday, reported his experiments to the French Academy and drove a small boat along the River Neva in St. Petersburg by means of an electric motor in 1838. However, the spread of the motor had to wait for a source of cheap current, for batteries were too expensive for this purpose.

The success of these two inventors was due to several improvements. First of all, they had substituted rotary motion for the oscillatory movement adopted in the earlier demonstration models of Faraday. Secondly, they applied the use of electromagnets, which were much stronger than permanent magnets. They also introduced Sturgeon's commutator, which as we have pointed out converted or rectified the original alternating current of a generator into direct current. In applying the commutator to the d-c motor, they made the current reverse in each conductor so that it always carried current in the same direction as it moved around the magnetic field, thus making possible the continuous rotation of the motor in one direction.

These early electric motors were clearly designed to be used with batteries, thus "consuming" zinc as the competing steam engines consumed coal. This proved uneconomical, and the application of the electric motor had to wait until the first practical dynamo appeared on the market and made electric current sufficiently cheap to compete with steam.

The combination of generators, circuits, and motors proved a very versatile way of distributing and utilizing energy when compared with the less flexible steam-driven machinery. It stimulated tremendously the application of machinery in general. Though scientists like Herschel, Babbage, Lenz, and others had repeatedly asserted that the generator and motor were based on the same principle, this was not clearly demonstrated until the 1880's.

Pacinotti in developing his generator in 1863 showed that it could also be run as an electric motor, and Weston did likewise in 1878. Another typical experience was that of Gramme, who had mounted two of his generators side by side on the grounds of the Vienna Exhibition of 1873. One generator was installed and running when a careless workman connected the wires of the stationary machine to it and thus converted the second generator into a motor by sending a current through its windings.

A better study of the windings of the electric motor lead to the development of three types of alternating-current motor—synchronous, induction, and universal—along with the older type of direct-current motor. Only in recent years has the alternating-current motor come to be comparable in ease of control, efficiency, and general versatility with the direct-current motor. This development took place through the gradual application of the electric motor to various uses in industry.

A number of generators and motors of different types were shown at the Vienna Exhibition of 1883; a year earlier, in 1882. Frank Sprague had exhibited his first direct-current motor for electric traction. Philip Diehl produced a variable-speed direct-current motor in 1884 for dental machines and sewing machines. In 1887, however, Tesla, Bradley, and Hasel-wander each patented an alternating-current induction motor and thus laid the foundations for general use of the electric motor. They gradually proved their worth, especially when in 1900 the Manhattan Elevated Railway was electrified. Commercial manufacture on a large scale started about 1908.

The most important application of electricity in the earlier period was for lighting, as it constituted the greater part of the consumption of electricity before the electric motor came into its own. Unfortunately the electric arc, widely used for street lighting between 1870 and 1900, was a heavy consumer of electricity, and municipalities abandoned it in favor of the incandescent lamp as soon as the latter had been sufficiently developed.

The story of the incandescent lamp is another instance of a series of inventors' struggles to realize a simple idea. De la Rue is said to have made the first lamp with a coil of platinum wire in 1820, but the record is not clear. Farmer was fairly successful in constructing similar lamps in 1859, and Swan, a year later, started experiments using strips of U-shaped carbonized paper as filaments for a vacuum lamp. The Russian, Lodyguine, in 1872 used a carbon rod.

In 1878 the Edison Electric Light Company was organized to finance Edison's experiments in the development of a commercially successful incandescent lamp. In 1879 Edison, independently of Swan, produced a lamp with a platinum-wire spiral in a vacuum chamber, and also developed another lamp containing a carbonized filament, first made of cotton and then of bristol board. The first electric-light installation on board the S.S. *Columbia* was very favorably received, and Edison started manufacturing his lamps in 1880, using filaments made from bamboo. These early lamps were quite low in candlepower and were fragile and short-lived besides, so that at first the competition from the arc light was very strong.

The further development of the electric light began with the competitive feats of Edison in the United States and Swan in England. Edison's first plant on Pearl Street in New York (1882) proved the merit of the filament lamp versus the arc light. Though the use of arc lights still continued to spread for a while, theirs was a lost cause. In 1885 Weston developed the first lamp with a homogeneous carbon filament produced from pure fiberless cellulose. In 1891 Phillips began the mass manufacture of incandescent lamps in Holland, developing after 1920 the gas-discharge lamp, the sodium-vapor lamp, the ultrahigh-pressure mercury-vapor lamp, and wire-filled photoflash bulbs.

Unfortunately the carbon-filament lamp was consuming more than three times as much current as a metal-filament lamp. It was therefore a great step toward the modern electric lamp when von Bolton and von Welssbach succeeded in rendering tantalum so pliable that it could be drawn to filament wire (1897–1906). The metal-filament lamp now began rapidly to replace the arc light, especially when Just and Hanamann developed in 1903 a method of making the much cheaper tungsten wire for filaments.

Electricity also proved an efficient source of power for long-distance communication by wireless or radio. The essentials of this application are: generation of high-frequency oscillations in an antenna, the modulation or molding of these high-frequency currents to carry the intended signals, the broadcasting of this modulated "wave," the detection of the signals at the point of reception, the amplification of these signals, and the selection of the desired signal from a number of signals received simultaneously.

Early attempts at wired telegraphy not only encountered difficulties in the procuring of proper apparatus and materials, but also ran into spirited opposition from some segments of the population. In southern Kentucky, for example, a telegraph line was destroyed in 1849 "because it robbed the air of its electricity, the rains are hendered, and there ain't been a good crop since the wire was put up!"

Though Grout took out a telegraph patent as early as 1800, nothing came of it, but Sommering used the current from voltaic piles for the transmission of signals in 1811. The current was led through a salt solution at the receiving station and the electrolytic action was used as a signal, for an electrolytic cell had to be used for each letter. Ampère devised a system using tiny magnets in 1820, and Dyar even established a commercial telegraph system to send results from from a racecourse on Long Island. But none of these systems covered any appreciable distance, at least not sufficient to make the telegraph popular. A long series of inventors tried their luck at devising telegraph systems (Schilling in 1832, Weber and Gauss in 1836, and Cooke in 1836), but these systems never carried more than a few miles.

Henry had realized the first four essential points in his telegraph. His switch was evolved into the telegraph key by Morse and Wheatstone. In 1836 Morse made his first telegraph instrument from an old picture frame, and took out a patent for "telegraph signs" in 1840. After seven years of solid experimenting, he persuaded Congress to construct a telegraph line between Washington and Baltimore at a cost of $30,000. On May 24, 1844, he transmitted his famous message, "What hath God wrought!" (Num. xxiii:23).

Morse's experiments definitely established the telegraph as a medium of long-distance communication. In 1845 the first public telegraph between London and Gosport, England, was opened to the public. The Magnetic Telegraph Company was incorporated in 1846, its offices being established in New York, Philadelphia, Baltimore, and Washington. The Morse telegraph had been used by the railroads since 1851, where it proved to be of great service in dispatching and controlling the movement of trains.

Transmission over very long distances became possible as soon as gutta-percha was available for the insulation of cables in 1847. The construction of these cables also led to the development of very sensitive galvanometers and other electrical instruments. Cyrus W. Field organized the New York, Newfoundland, and London Telegraph Company with the assistance of Peter Cooper, Moses Taylor, and Marshall Roberts in 1854, and two years later founded the Atlantic Telegraph Company in London, along with John Brett and Sir Charles Bright. Both Great Britain and the United States then subsidized their efforts to lay a telegraph cable across the Atlantic from Valentia, Ireland, to Trinity Bay, Newfoundland, which was completed and put in operation in 1858, after many hardships including the loss of hundreds of miles of cable during the first two unsuccessful attempts to lay it. The work was done by the English ship *Agamemnon* and the American *Niagara*, sailing vessels with auxiliary steam power, both of which were nearly lost during the severe Atlantic storms that raged throughout most of the operations.

The new cable had been in operation only about a month when it failed on September 1, 1858, and the disappointment was so intense that no further efforts were made to lay a new cable until 1865, when new insulation materials and better engineering techniques were available. This time the 18,914-ton steamship *Great Eastern* (mentioned in an earlier section) was made available to Field and a new cable was laid—only to be lost a scant 600 miles from its destination on shore. Though it had sunk in about two miles of water, it was successfully grappled for and raised to the surface in 1866, by which time a second cable had been laid from shore to shore, making possible the operation of two Atlantic cables instead of one. This was the beginning of a series of transcontinental and international cables connecting the civilized countries of the world.

Transmission over these long cables was at first difficult because of the apparent sluggishness with which the signals were transmitted. This defect was finally overcome when

Buckley introduced a layer of tape made of permalloy into the sheathing of long-distance cables in 1924.

The evolution of the telephone was much more complex. Though Wheatstone in 1860 had used the word "telephone" for a nonelectrical transmitter of sounds and human speech, it took many years before the transmission of the human voice over a wire became a reality. Boursel in 1854 predicted that sound would soon be transmitted by electricity; in 1861 Philip Reis of Germany transmitted the sound of a tuning fork by electrical means and improved his device in 1863. In 1876 Berliner of Washington invented a loose-contact telephone transmitter, known as the Berliner microphone. The microphone used by Reis and also by Bell in his earlier experiments was based on the varying contact between a metal diaphragm and plate when vibrating under the impact of sound waves set up by the human voice.

Also in 1876 Alexander Graham Bell, after having experimented for five years, transmitted the first complete sentence over the telephone, using a chemical form of transmitter. His simple message was directed to his assistant: "Mr. Watson, come here; I want you." A few hours after Bell had filed his patent application, Elisha Gray of Ohio filed a caveat covering virtually the same idea, and using a carbon-granule microphone, which Bell had patented in February, 1876, but did not use for the transmission of his historic summons to Mr. Watson. Bell's claim to the invention of the telephone was subsequently upheld by the courts. Later the Bell Telephone Company and the Western Union Telegraph Company quarreled over certain technical details, and the latter company thereupon instructed Edison to improve the telephone but later withdrew from the field in 1879. In 1877 the first news dispatch by telephone was sent to the Boston *Globe*, and this feat inaugurated the public use of the telephone. Research now concentrated on improving the microphone or transmitter.

The modern telephone transmitter was evolved through the efforts of Hunnings, Edison, and White. No further improvements in modulation or reception of telephone signals came for some 50 years after 1890, because most efforts were centered on providing better telephone service to a rapidly increasing number of subscribers in towns and cities all over the country. The telephone became a more useful and efficient instrument with the development of automatic switchboard machinery and improvements in telephone exchanges, cable, relay equipment, and long-distance service.

The first telephone exchange in the world was opened at Hartford, Conn., on January 28, 1878. The first telephone exchange in London was put in operation in 1879. The first experimental telephone line between two cities was placed in service between Boston and New York in 1884, and this was followed in 1886 by the line between New York and Philadelphia. In 1892 the New York-Chicago circuit was completed and put in operation. By 1880, approximately 50,000 Americans had installed a telephone in their homes or offices, yet while this may have seemed a huge volume of subscribers at the time, it was a small number indeed when compared with the 34,866,758 phones in the United States in 1948.

Two inventions contributed materially to the improvement of long-distance telephony. One of these was the "loading spool" or loading coil, devised by Pupin to increase the over-all inductance of telephone lines and thereby decrease voice distortion and attenuation. The coils are inserted in the line at intervals ranging from a fraction of a mile to a little over a mile in length. The second was the vacuum-tube amplifier, invented by Fleming and perfected by De Forest and others, a device that has had its greatest application in radio and electronics.

In 1892 the first automatic telephone switchboard was installed at La Porte, Indiana. In 1906 the art of making and laying telephone cables had improved so much that the first underground cables for telephone service were installed between New York and Philadelphia, although it was not until 1914 that underground lines were installed between New York and Washington. A great improvement was the system of carrier telephony intoduced by the Bell Laboratories in 1918, whereby a number of messages could be carried simultaneously over the same pair of wires by superimposing high-frequency currents on the ordinary line frequency. By 1931 transoceanic services were extended to Java, Sumatra, Bermuda, Hawaii, and the Canary Islands.

Radio and Television

ALTHOUGH the beginnings of radio may be traced back to Morse's telegraph of 1844, the art of communicating by means of electromagnetic waves was developed largely in the first quarter of the present century and seems to have reached its peak at the present time. The line of development runs from Faraday's discoveries in electromagnetism between 1841 and 1856 through Maxwell's formulation of the underlying physical theory in 1873, Helmholtz's studies of electric oscillations in 1870–1875, and his pupil Hertz's discovery of the so-called Hertzian waves in 1887; thence to Marconi's brilliant adaptation of Hertzian waves to telegraphy in 1895 and his subsequent successes in transmitting dot-dash signals over long distances, culminating in 1901 in his spanning of the Atlantic by wireless.

Yet this was not radio as we know it today, for Marconi's spark oscillator could not produce the continuous waves needed for the transmission of speech and music. Poulsen in 1902 used an array of high-frequency a-c generators to produce continuous waves, which he succeeded in modulating with a voice microphone, but his system was too cumbersome to be practical. Professor J. A. Fleming of England, following up the so-called "Edison effect" in 1904, discovered that the filament of an incandescent lamp in which a metal plate had been installed gave off a stream of electrons that flowed toward the plate, allowing only direct current to pass. This "Fleming valve" was actually the world's first radio tube, for it could be used to rectify high-frequency a-c wireless oscillations into low-frequency d-c currents that "detected" the signals by operating a telephone receiver. However, while entirely correct as to principle, the Fleming valve was not practical because of its low amplifying factor and poor sensitivity. It remained for Lee De Forest, an American inventor, to add a third element to Fleming's valve and thereby revolutionize all existing wireless circuits and bring about the actual birth of radio. He placed this element, known as the grid, between filament and plate and connected it to the antenna. By varying the amount of current or voltage on the filament and plate it was then possible to amplify the incoming signals enormously. De Forest's triode (or "audion," as it was named by Babcock) was the first and perhaps most important step on the long road toward practical radio broadcasting and reception, radiotelephony (of which Fessenden had dreamed in 1907), and television. About 1913, four physicians and engineers—Armstrong, Meissner, Franklin, and Langmuir—discovered simultaneously that it could also be used to generate high-frequency, continuous-wave oscillations, thus replacing Poulson's cumbersome alternators and making possible Fessenden's "heterodyne" or beat system of reception.

Further developments in radio came at a rapid pace. In 1915 a 500-tube transmitter at Arlington, Va., transmitted speech to Paris, France; in 1919 radio was used for the first time in aviation on the Alcock-Brown flight in the famed NC4; in 1920 radio station KDKA in Pittsburgh began the first regular broadcasting service in the world by reporting the returns of the Harding-Cox election on November 2; Dame Nellie Melba sang over the radio at Chelmsford, England in the same year and was heard as far away as Persia. By 1922 there were 60,000 receiving sets and 400 broadcasting stations in the United States alone. In 1925 Chelmsford relayed the first radio program to the United States via short wave, which was then rebroadcast to American listeners by the Radio Corporation of America, which had been organized as early as 1919. Toward the end of 1926 David Sarnoff and others organized the National Broadcasting Company, and a year later the Columbia Broadcasting System was formed. Short-wave broadcasting to distant parts of the world received added impetus when Queen Wilhelmina of the Netherlands addressed the East and West Indies from Holland over station PC-J in 1927. In that year there were more than 700 transmitters on the air and more than 6,500,000 receivers.

In 1927 President Herbert Hoover set up the Federal Radio Commission to regulate commercial and amateur broadcasting in the United States, which has since become the Federal Communications Commission. In the same year Major Edwin Armstrong invented the superregenerative receiver, to be followed shortly by his invention of the superheterodyne receiver, and, still later, by his revolutionary principle of frequency modulation (1936).

In the meantime, progress was being made in the development of television. Over 100 years ago Alexander Bain proposed a transmitter and receiver for sending and receiving pictures (1842), which may be considered a forerunner of modern facsimile and television systems. In 1875 G. R. Carey devised a rudimentary selenium cell for converting light into electricity, and in 1887 Hertz experimented with photoelectric effects. In 1884, Paul Nipkow invented a flat circular disk with a spiral of holes for breaking up an image into pulses of light, which could then be converted into pulses of electricity by means of a photoelectric cell. This, with slight modification, was the familiar scanning disk of the late 1920's. By 1925 John Logie Baird in England and C. F. Jenkins in America were able to demonstrate wireless television with these disks, but produced only shadows of objects, not real images. The following year Baird succeeded in transmitting the first image of a living human face; two years later he was successful in transmitting images across the Atlantic.

However, these first television images were of uniformly poor definition and illumination. It was not until the invention of the first cathode-ray tube that all-electronic television, and with it a high degree of definition and brilliance,

PLATE 39 Model of Joseph Saxton's magneto. (*Courtesy of the Franklin Institute, Philadelphia.*)

PLATE 40 Replica of von Jacobi's motor of 1838. (*Museum of Science and Industry, Chicago.*)

PLATE 41   The Brush Central Station, interior view, Philadelphia, Pa., in 1883. (*General Electric Company.*)

became possible. The Russian scientist Boris Rosing is credited with making a cathode-ray tube as early as 1906, but nothing came of it because technical development had hardly begun at that time. In 1923 another Russian living in America, Vladimir Zworykin, invented the iconoscope, an electron tube used as the camera tube in modern television (to be distinguished from the kinescope, which is the cathode-ray tube used for receiving the image). This was followed in 1928 by Philo T. Farnsworth's invention of the image dissector (a somewhat different type of camera tube) and the invention of the image orthicon, a camera tube requiring a minimum of light, by Rose and Iam in 1939. Meanwhile, coaxial cable for transmitting television images over a network had been developed, together with ultrahigh-frequency radio links, in order to overcome the limitation imposed on television reception by the curvature of the earth. By 1941 the RCA Laboratories had perfected high-definition theatre television, color television had been successfully demonstrated, and three television stations had begun regularly scheduled telecasts. By 1949 television in the United States had become a serious threat to broadcast radio, with close to 200 TV stations in operation or with FCC applications pending. The number of television receivers in use at that time was estimated at nearly 2,600,000. However, this was still a small number compared with the estimated 75,000,000 radio sets in use in the United States alone and the world total of 146,000,000.

In 1924 Zworykin had laid the foundations for a remarkable extension of the conventional or optical microscope, using the new knowledge of the electron gained from radio and television research. In 1939 he was able to demonstrate a fully developed electron microscope with which he subsequently attained magnifications on the order of 100,000 diameters—more than five times the magnification obtainable from the best compound microscope. In 1941 the influenza virus, magnified 65,000 diameters, was photographed for the first time at the University of Pennsylvania and in 1943 the electron microscope was put to use by RCA Laboratories in the study of atomic structure.

The list of present-day applications of electronics is seemingly endless—radio, television; facsimile; fluorescent and ultraviolet lighting; sound recording; voltage and current rectification; motor and generator control; induction and dielectric heating; temperature recording and control; sampling inspection and quality control; register control in printing; fever therapy and electronic surgery; x-ray photography; spectrometry; long-distance telephony; electronic computers; radar (detection and ranging) and loran (long-range navigation); guided missiles; electronic micrography; electronic welding; chronography; colorimetry; and last, but perhaps more important of all, electronic applications in the field of atomic energy. Most of these applications received tremendous stimulation from the urgency of the Second World War, and some of them are hardly out of the research stage and have no history as yet. Their impact on our society and their implications for the growth of science and industry cannot yet be formulated with certainty, but one can hardly overlook their enormous possibilities.

The Steam Turbine and Power Stations

As a result of the development of electricity, water power came into its own during the nineteenth century. The scientists set about to find the proper formula to design and construct water wheels. The mathematical approaches of Euler and Manoury in 1813 enabled Fourneyron to improve the water wheel and to make it once more a serious competitor of the steam engine. More efficient structures were developed by Henschel and Jonvel in 1837.

In the late 1860's, Bergier, a papermaker of Grenoble, France, began to use water from the mountains to move his water wheels. It was he who introduced the term *houille blanche* (white coal) to designate water power. The problem of using water wheels to drive electric generators was not easily solved. Its mathematical solution occupied the generations from Redtenbacher in 1844 to Zeuner in 1890; these calculations, together with practical experiments in Switzerland, England, and the United States, did much to introduce water power as a prime mover for the generation of electric power.

Hydroelectric power plants soon proved to be very efficient for the production of cheap power in the form of electricity. In 1911 the water-power stations of France already had a combined capacity of over 500,000 horsepower (372,750 kilowatts). This form of power production was tied up with efficient methods of transmission of electricity, but once this stage had been reached it was a boon to countries like Italy, where there is a grave shortage of coal. Here water power and proper transmission networks made possible the spread of electric power generated in the Alps to the whole region as far south as Rome. In 1890 Florence was one of the first cities in the world that could boast of an electric streetcar—only three years after Frank Sprague of the United States had made the first complete electrification of a streetcar line in Richmond, Va.

Both the generator and the turbine have high operating efficiencies, and were of great industrial importance in countries having abundant rainfall and facilities for storing water in dams. Foremost in the building of hydroelectric power stations were the United States, Canada, and Italy. These stations also contributed to the modern practice of building power networks over the whole country, coupling a number of power stations together for the more efficient production and distribution of electrical energy. Electrochemical plants began to congregate in the vicinity of hydroelectric plants for reasons of economy and efficient operation.

This cheap hydroelectric power does not mean that steam-driven generating plants will disappear in countries where hydroelectric power is available, for "thermoelectric" stations are still being improved constantly and now operate at high efficiencies. Steam-generated electricity used less than a third of the amount of coal, per unit of electricity generated, in 1930 as compared with 1900 figures. This struggle for cheaper steam goes on. Hence steam-generated power, employing such fuel-saving devices as economizers, air preheaters, super-heaters, pulverizers, and improved types of turbines and generators may still retain its proper place in electric power production.

The water turbine was a logical development of a primitive form of water wheel, whereas the steam turbine was a new form of prime mover. Many fanciful designs of steam turbines had occupied the minds of inventors from the sixteenth to the eighteenth century, but none of these dreams had got further than a drawing or sketch of doubtful value. The steam turbine differs from the steam engine in that the steam moves the turbine blades by its impact or back pressure, while the piston of a steam engine is moved only by the expansion of the steam. The steam turbine may therefore be said to be a "steam windmill."

The Swedish scientist De Laval built his first steam turbine on the impact principle in 1882. Then it took him more than eight years to turn it into a practical machine. In 1890 he finally perfected the high-speed helical gear, which enabled him to use the highly efficient steam turbine to move low-speed generators, pumps, ships, propellers, and other types of rotating machinery.

In the meantime, Charles Parsons had invented his reaction turbine in 1884. This type of turbine uses the reaction of steam escaping through an opening to push back the blades of a turbine wheel. The first reaction turbine of ten horsepower divided the expansion of the steam into many smaller stages, using the expansion much more efficiently than a steam engine does. The application of the reaction principle, which was already known to Heron of Alexandria, limited the rotor's speed and thus made it possible to use the turbine to move other machines directly.

The reaction turbine as designed by Parsons shows a rotor

composed of a series of disks mounted on a common shaft. Each disk has blades alternately along the rim fitting closely to the adjoining disk, through which the steam escapes, moving the disk. The steam then impinges on the next disk, to which is fitted a ring carrying blades, and the impact of the steam on these blades moves that disk also. Thus the rotors are alternately moved by impact and reaction. The success of this combining of two principles was soon apparent when Parsons constructed a turbine in 1891 that moved a generator.

In the early turbine Parsons still employed a condenser, for he could not yet use the expansion of low-pressure steam efficiently. This was finally achieved when Curtis invented his "velocity compounding" in 1898. The first commercial Parsons steam turbine was introduced into America by Westinghouse about 1895, and the first 120-kilowatt direct-current unit was built at Pittsburgh in 1896. In the following year, Parsons built his first ship, the *Turbinia*, of 100 tons, which was powered by a 2,000-horsepower steam turbine. The remarkable speed of this ship, and her capacity for maneuvering, quickly drew much attention to her in naval circles. The *Turbinia* contributed to the swift introduction of the steam turbine in warships and in the merchant marine.

The early ships had turbines that moved the screw directly, which did not allow the steam turbine to run at full efficiency. However, Parsons in 1910 succeeded in designing a speed-reducing gear, which enabled the steam turbine to run at full speed and efficiency. This invention made it into a very efficient prime mover for generators, ships, and for such industries as paper and textile manufacture. Curtis and Emmert had designed their first turbines in the laboratories of the General Electric Company at Schenectady by 1900. In 1903 a vertical turbine rated at 5,000 kilowatts was installed in the Fisk Street Station at Chicago, which for a long time remained the largest generating plant driven by a steam turbine.

The gas turbine, the development of which really dates back only to the 1920's, had many early forerunners. As early as 1648 Bishop Wilkins, in his *Mathematical Magick*, proposed a kind of gas turbine to move a cradle or turn a roasting spit. In 1791 John Walker even took out a patent on a gas turbine and compressor. But the earliest practical models were designed by Lemale and Armangaud in 1906 and by Holzwarth and Körting in 1908.

The modern prime movers, therefore, are water turbine, steam turbine, steam engine, gas engine, Diesel engine, and air-jet turbine. They form the backbone of our modern machine age. We may have atomic power in the near future, but prophecies on its form and applications are useless at this point. These prime movers are used to operate, either directly or indirectly, our modern machine tools, textile machinery, pumps, cranes, and many other forms of machinery. Generally we do not couple one prime mover directly to a separate piece of machinery, except, for example, in the case of generators. Usually the prime mover drives a line shaft and a system of countershafts, which in turn drive the separate machines, although this is giving place to the complete electrification of all types of moving machinery, combined with servomechanisms and other forms of fully automatic control.

The mechanical transmission of power through belts, pulleys, links, and gears was not studied seriously before the nineteenth century. The older link chains, gears, and toothed wheels remained in use, but belts and ropes were added as valuable and flexible forms of transmission. Rope drives were introduced in 1856 by James Combe of Belfast, and the firm he founded still produces ropes for this purpose. Combe's ropes compared favorably when tested against belts at Lille in 1894, belt drives having been introduced in 1893 by F. W. Taylor largely as a result of his brilliant study of power transmission published in the *Transactions* of the American Society of Mechanical Engineers. As early as 1851 C. F. Hirn of Colmar in Alsace had successfully used wire ropes running on wheels and pulleys to transmit power for fairly long distances, but electricity has made this form of power transmission practically obsolete.

At the same time the problem of reducing friction received more attention. Forced lubrication of steam engines was introduced by A. C. Pain in 1864 and was gradually applied to other machinery. Ball bearings were fairly old by this time; Benvenuto Cellini had used them in moving the statue of Jupiter three centuries earlier. In 1772 Varlo of London had constructed nonadjustable ball bearings, but with the advent of the new types of steel these were now made more adaptable. The cup and cone type of bearing dates from 1880. The new petroleum industry contributed largely to the more specific and more expensive demand for lubricants for the new machines.

The Canning and Shipping of Food

As MANKIND spread over the entire face of the globe and transportation facilities increased, food from different climates became more easily available. The problem of food supply had grown very serious in the nineteenth century, when large towns and cities sprang up and dense populations were concentrated in industrial areas where food could not be produced locally in sufficient quantities but had to be imported mainly from agricultural districts and countries. Hence the transport, and above all the preservation, of food became a major problem. It has been speculated that Napoleon would have conquered Russia had he adopted canned food for his army, but of course such speculations are useless.

The oldest ways of preserving food were salting, smoking, and drying. Drying alone is hardly ever sufficient, for three quarters of the food eaten by man has too high a fat content and unless preserved becomes spoiled in a very short time. Hence sterilization by heat alone will not suffice unless air is kept away from the heated food, as in canning. As long as the biological reasons underlying the decomposition of food were not completely understood, the various means that were devised for preserving food could not be completely successful.

It was, however, well understood that heating and salting together did help to preserve meat and fish. As the latter was the staple food of the poor in the Middle Ages, we can see why the inventor who introduced the salting of fish—more particularly, herrings—became famous even in his own lifetime. This Willem Beukelszoon of Biervliet, Holland, who died in 1283, is said to have been the first to cure herrings by gutting and salting them.

This invention was of prime importance to Holland, as herrings were exported in large quantities by the Dutch fishermen, and salt became one of the main products that the Dutch merchant navy obtained in France in exchange for Swedish corn and timber. By the eighteenth century the process of curing with salt was somewhat better understood, for it was realized that partly spoiled food could not be cured. Hales introduced the method of draining the blood from large joints of meat and then forcibly injecting salt water into the tissues. This method never became popular, though it has been revived with great success quite recently.

Sterilization by heat alone was too imperfectly grasped to be done effectively. It was actually the cause of many an epidemic in ancient times. As soon as it was realized that air should be excluded after sterilization, the search for a suitable container was on. The canning of food dates back to the Napoleonic Wars. The French confectioner Appert, inspired by the experiments of Gay-Lussac and Papin, had invented the process about 1795. Papin, who was the inventor of the autoclave (the prototype of the modern pressure cooker), had succeeded in canning beef jellies by excluding air from the glass containers. An Appert canning plant was built at Bermondsey in 1812.

Not until Pasteur and his pupils had completed their work on bacteria was the background of sterilization and canning properly understood. Hence we need not wonder that Appert was only partly successful, and that the food he canned often started to spoil in the bottle, and was partly preserved only by the fortuitous absence of certain bacteria, not by perfect sterilization.

Cans were not available in Appert's day, and had to await

the development of cheap, mild-steel sheets and electroplating processes as well as the increase in the supply of tin ores from Bolivia and other countries. Until then, preserved food in bottles or jars was used only by sailors, soldiers, and explorers.

Nevertheless the idea caught on. By 1840 fish and fruit were successfully bottled and preserved for much longer in-

Canning room of the Borden factory at Brewster, New York, 1879. (*From* Frank Leslie's Illustrated Newspaper, *April 12, 1879.*)

tervals. When cans were perfected they rapidly displaced bottles and jars because of their relative cheapness and durability, and because they afforded protection to certain types of food by excluding sunlight. In this period South American countries became suppliers of wool, bones, and hides to the European markets, but there were no suitable methods for preserving the enormous amounts of meat that, as a result, had to be thrown away. However, the German scientist von Liebig in 1850 succeeded in developing a process in which the meat was cooked and the extract evaporated after salt had been added. This evaporated liquid or solid extract could then be transported and kept indefinitely. The practical experi-

313

ments were conducted by Max von Pettenkofer. In 1865 G. Griebert, with English capital, founded the Liebig Company at Fray Bentos, Uruguay.

Evaporated milk was first produced by Gail Borden of Texas, whose process of "evaporating milk in vacuum" dates back to 1853. Not until 1855 was powdered milk produced by Grimwade in England. Then this method of preserving developed very rapidly along different lines, and now forms the basis of an important branch of the industry. Malted milk, marketed for the first time in 1877, consists of a powdered product made from whole milk, whole wheat, and barley malt. Many other powdered foods followed, and recently cereals that can be kept for a long period have been added to our growing list of processed foods.

The freezing of foods was well known to the ancients and had been advocated by Francis Bacon. Arctic people like the Eskimos had used refrigeration for centuries, and are said to have brought the first frozen meat to England in 1826. Yet however ideal freezing might be, Australian and other exports of the 1860's consisted of meat extracts and canned food.

Frozen food had to wait until refrigeration technique had developed sufficiently for practical use. In 1867 Reece invented an ammonia freezing plant, and Sutcliffe Mort, a Sydney wool broker, grasped this opportunity to start the first freezing works in the world in New South Wales. On February 2, 1880, the *Strathleven* brought the first cargo of frozen mutton to England. Chilled meat had been imported from Chicago a few years earlier, but this meat was still cooled by natural ice. Freezing was soon adopted in the United States and railroad cars and ships were built especially for the transport of frozen food.

In Europe the evolution of freezing equipment took great strides under the leadership of Carl von Linde, while the first experimental slaughterhouse with a freezing plant was built at Wiesbaden in 1883. In the meantime Charles Tellier had followed up von Linde's experiments. He had the *Frigorifique* built to his specifications and equipped with refrigerating machinery, and this ship in 1876 made its first trip from Rouen to Buenos Aires. This was the beginning of a period of prosperity for the meat packers in South America and Australia. The American meat exports to Europe diminished rapidly after 1907, and in their stead came increasing imports from South America.

Modern deep-freezing methods were instituted by the biologist Birdseye, who had studied the fauna of Labrador and knew from the experiments of Pictet and others in 1907 that freezing quickly to very low temperatures does not even destroy life in certain cases. This new method may well prove to be a major invention in the field of food preservation.

Synthetic Raw Materials

THE chemical technology of the nineteenth century is characterized by the manufacture of many synthetic products. Chemistry had a long way to go before it was ready to undertake successful synthesis. It all began in the eighteenth century, when a long battle on the nature and composition of air and other gases occupied the best minds. This involved research into the nature of combusion phenomena, and its outcome was the now-familiar definition of molecules and atoms. It also meant the establishment of quantitative measurement in chemistry, which once and for all abolished much of the speculation of the ancient alchemists.

After these conquests of Lavoisier and his generation, the early nineteenth-century chemists sat down to study the quantitative composition of chemicals. They found the rules according to which atoms of the elements combine to form complex molecules of chemical compounds. The next generation—during the middle of the nineteenth century—set about to perfect the analytical tools necessary to determine the composition of thousands of chemical compounds.

Whereas the older chemists had concentrated their activity in the inorganic world of minerals and had created what we call "inorganic chemistry," attention was now drawn to the products of vegetable and animal origin. It was soon found that these products form a class of chemicals of their own, being mainly composed of carbon combined with hydrogen, nitrogen, and oxygen, and sometimes containing small amounts of other elements like sulfur or silicon. This "organic chemistry" started on its way when Wöhler succeeded in making an organic chemical, urea, from inorganic materials. This wholly unexpected feat disproved the idea that man would never be able to make these organic chemicals synthetically.

Gradually the new analytical tools and methods allowed man, prompted by his great interest in biology, to penetrate this extremely interesting organic world, for the latter part of the nineteenth century was dominated by biological research and discussions on such fundamental theories as the evolution of man and the origin of species.

One of the first materials to be produced synthetically was rubber. In 1860 Williams had discovered that the decomposition of rubber gave an organic compound, isoprene, a colorless liquid having the formula C_5H_8, which under the influence of light and air forms a rubberlike mass. This compound is what we now call a polymer—a complex molecule formed from a simpler one. That is, isoprene combined with itself a number of times to form a substance having a more complex molecular structure. Bourchardet in 1879 was the first to recognize this fact and he therefore taught that raw rubber consists of "polymerized" isoprene, although at that time it was still difficult for him to prove it. In 1901 Kondakow succeeded in preparing a chemical, called dimethyl-butadiene, which was very closely related chemically to isoprene. Kondakow observed that his new product polymerized into a rubberlike mass also. The solution of the problem came from Harries (between 1902 and 1904), who by applying his so-called "ozone technique" succeeded in proving definitely that rubber is a polymer of isoprene.

In 1906 Karl Hofmann of the well-known firm of Bayer finally produced butadiene, a close relative of isoprene, from a common chemical, acetylene. Hofmann continued his researches on the polymerization of butadiene, investigating what catalysts should be used to speed up the reaction and what chemicals were suitable to vulcanize the polymer to prevent its aging and oxidation. In 1892 Tilden had already observed that sodium would help the polymerization of isoprene, and in 1909 Hofmann and Coutelle synthesized rubber from isoprene. During the First World War the Germans made a synthetic rubber called Buna, following up the results of Hofmann's work.

In the meantime, however, Harries discovered how to polymerize the so-called dienes with the help of sodium in 1902, his work being duplicated simultaneously and independently by that of Matthews and Strange. This process was the basis for the production of the different types of Buna, known as Buna-N, Buna-S, and Buna-SS. This synthetic product had all the disadvantages of a man-made product, for nature is much more versatile.

Natural rubber has many different properties and it has proved impossible, as in the case of their synthetic products, to reproduce all these properties in the man-made article. Most synthetic products may be far better for certain applications than the natural product; generally, however, they will not be as universally applicable. Hence synthetic products are usually made to fit only specialized applications, wherein they may often surpass the natural product.

The different types of Buna were far from satisfactory until Nieuland of the University of Notre Dame devised a better process. Starting from acetylene, he built up a compound called monovinylacetylene, which he converted with hydrochloric acid into chloroprene. This last compound when polymerized yielded a much superior product, neoprene, which du Pont began manufacturing in 1931. These superior products, such as neoprene, thiokol, and duprene, helped considerably to overcome the shortage of natural rubber during the Second World War, and they have certainly proved their usefulness in a variety of applications.

The coming of the automobile and the airplane meant that at last the lighter fractions of crude oil could be put to some use. In the early days, the petroleum industry had concentrated on making kerosene for oil lamps from crude petroleum. The lighter fractions had been burned or thrown away because they were too inflammable and dangerous. Now the situation changed rapidly and early in the present century the natural gasoline content of crude oil was no longer sufficient to meet the growing demand.

Hence so-called cracking processes were introduced in which, by the application of heat and pressure, heavier components were cracked up into lighter gasoline fractions. Soon more efficient ways of increasing the gasoline yield were found. Hydrogenation was introduced, in which the cracked products were treated with hydrogen to form more stable compounds.

Soon chemists began to experiment with the production of synthetic gasoline from coal. The first to be successful was Friederich Bergius, who in 1913 developed a process by which he could treat heavy fractions of petroleum or tar together with coal, peat, and other nonpetroleum products to form gasoline. A thick paste of powdered coal and heavy oil was introduced into steel drums and heated to about 400° C under about 200 atmospheres of pressure. Hydrogen was forced into the paste, together with a catalyst. The resulting mixture contained gasoline along with heavy oil, and thus a liquefaction of coal had been achieved.

The early troubles of this process were largely due to the fact that high-pressure apparatus could not yet be made satisfactorily. In 1916 Bergius started his first experimental plant. He soon sold his patent rights to the Badische Anilin und Soda Fabriken, who in turn sold them to the I. G. Farben concern. In 1927 the first commercial plant was built in the Leuna Werke at Merseburg. The competing Fischer-Tropsch process is wholly synthetic and no longer depends on the heavy oil used by Bergius. This process, first devised in 1925, was adopted for commercial purposes by the Ruhr-chemie

A. G. in 1934. The *Kogasin* produced there was synthesized from coke, air, and water. Water gas was first produced from coke and air, and part of the hydrogen recovered was synthesized with the rest of the water gas to form a kind of crude oil. Refining this synthetic oil produced gasoline, kerosene, and lubricants. This process, which attracted much attention during and after the Second World War, may solve the problem of producing additional synthetic gasoline from coal.

The plastics form another new family of chemical compounds. They were born when John Hyatt, an Albany printer, together with his brother Isaiah, entered a competition to find a good substitute for ivory billiard balls. In the course of lengthy experiments the Hyatts blended camphor and cellulose nitrate and, though failing to win the prize, they obtained the product now known by the trade name Celluloid. Using cellulose acetate, they later obtained a transparent material in 1869 which they called cellon (now manufactured under the du Pont trade name, Cellophane). Shortly afterward casein and formaldehyde were found to polymerize to form artificial horn or gallalith. This polymerization of two or more chemicals into a polymer plastic is called condensation.

The first wholly synthetic plastic was discovered by Baekeland, who from 1905 to 1909 experimented on the condensation of phenol (from coal tar) and formaldehyde together with fillers and pigments to form a plastic, which he called Bakelite. It proved to belong to the class of plastics we call thermosetting, as they receive their definite form in the hot presses in which the powder is molded. Other plastics, called thermoplastics, may be molded by the application of heat and pressure but unlike the thermosetting types they can be remelted and remolded after they have cooled.

Bakelite proved a new substance of very good qualities, for instance, as an insulating material in the electrical industry. As it could be molded into different shapes, it became extremely useful. Baekeland could synthesize his phenol and formaldehyde from coal, lime, water, and air, and thus he produced the first wholly synthetic plastic.

Another group of wholly synthetic resins was discovered in 1918. Starting from ammonia and carbon dioxide, artificial urea was made, which together with formaldehyde forms resins marketed as Plaskon, Beetle, Scarab, etc. Other plastics, such as methacrylate resins (Plexiglas, Lucite), vinyl resins (Vinylite, Saran), and polystyrene resins (Styron) followed the synthesis of urea, and the possibilities are far from being exhausted. Proteins like milk casein can be condensed with formaldehyde to form a protein plastic, which can also be made from cashew nuts and even from the protein in animal blood.

Closely related to the plastics are the substances we know as synthetic fibers. Indeed, several are simply plastics in fiber form. The experiments of Schönbein with solutions of nitrocellulose, obtained by treating cellulose with nitric acid, revealed certain strange properties which attracted attention to these new compounds in 1845. Working from these basic facts, Count de Chardonnet, a pupil of Pasteur, who had assisted him in his researches on silkworms, discovered a method of producing artificial silk. Taking out his first patent in 1884, he completed his process in 1889. Chardonnet dissolved nitrated cellulose in alcohol and ether. The solution was then pumped through the very fine openings of a "spinneret" into a bath, which took away the solvents and left a thread of what we now call rayon. The first dress of artificial silk was shown at the Paris Exhibition of 1887.

A competitive process, which was soon to become far more important than that of Chardonnet, was discovered in 1882 by Cross and Beven. They used cellulose treated with lye and then with carbon disulfide to form cellulose xanthate solution, or viscose. This viscose is then forced through the pinholes of the spinneret into a setting bath, where sulfuric acid and sodium sulfate harden the viscose into filaments. These can then be spun into viscose rayon fiber, a good substitute for cotton.

When cellulose acetate is used instead of cellulose in the above process, we obtain the so-called acetate rayon, better known as Celanese, Koda, or Teca. Schützenberger knew the fundamental reactions of this process in 1865, but commercial realization had to wait until 1904.

Italian chemists have recently developed a new fiber, called lanital, by treating casein, a milk product, in the same way as the cellulose in the old Chardonnet process. But all these processes use such composite organic materials as cellulose or casein. Wholly synthetic fibers were developed from chemicals derived from coal, petroleum, water, and air. One of the first to be marketed was nylon (now a generic name) which the E. I. du Pont de Nemours Company announced in 1939. Another fiber of this type is the P.C. yarn developed by the I. G. Farben chemists.

After the First World War, the idea was conceived of using synthetic fibers to compete with cotton and wool by cutting the synthetic yarn into small lengths. Fabrics made from lengths of fiber, spun and woven like wool, were first produced in Germany by the Köln-Rottweil A.G. in 1919 at Premnitz. In 1920 this firm, together with the Dynamit A.G. "A. Nobel," founded the Vistra, which continued to produce these materials, but which was later absorbed by I. G. Farben, the German Dye Trust whose full name may be of interest— *Interessengemeinschaft Farbenindustrie Aktien-Gesellschaft,* which freely translated means "community of interests in the dye manufacturing companies."

Transforming Natural Products: Rubber and Oil

THE impact of increased scientific knowledge on nineteenth-century industry can be illustrated here in somewhat greater detail by reference to the history of rubber and petroleum and their respective technologies. These two important natural products have been mentioned earlier in the course of our brief history in connection with other developments.

When Columbus landed in the New World he found the natives playing with heavy black balls made of some sort of vegetable gum. Later explorers found that the Aztecs used

similar balls in a game that was a kind of cross between basket-
ball and tennis, played by the emperor and nobles for very high
stakes. Though many other visitors to these parts reported on
this material, it remained more or less unknown for nearly
three hundred years. Then in the eighteenth century a
Frenchman, de Fresneau, took a great interest in its production and application and stimulated others to study the material. The English chemist Priestley discovered its first practical use—the erasing of pencil-marks—from which its English
name "rubber" was derived. The main difficulty hampering
further applications was the problem of producing a uniform,
stable product from the milky latex that oozed from the
rubber tree.

This difficulty was solved only when rubber plantations
took up the study of latex in the latter part of the nineteenth century. In 1873, seeds of rubber-producing plants had
been sent from the Amazon region to the botanical gardens
at Kew, England, whence they were forwarded to Ceylon and
Singapore and eventually formed the beginnings of the new
rubber plantations in India, Malaya, and the East Indies.

In the meantime, scientists had tried to adapt this resil-
ient material to technical uses. In 1834 Thomas Hancock had
discovered a primitive type of vulcanization—a process of
transforming the soft, perishable natural rubber into a harder,
more durable solid. Vulcanization was greatly improved when
catalysts such as zinc oxide were used, but in 1839 a fortunate accident led to the perfection of a more efficient method
when Charles Goodyear dropped a mixture of soft rubber and
sulfur on a hot stove. Much later it was discovered that the
most important accelerators of the vulcanization process
were the organic chemicals called amines, which were first
applied to this purpose by Georg Oenslager of Akron, Ohio,
in 1906.

Rubber vulcanized in this way, however, is hardly suitable
for making tires for automobiles, bicycles, and airplanes—applications that became increasingly important shortly after the
turn of the century. The problem was solved by compounding

crude rubber with mineral powders, oils, waxes, tars, asphalts, and fibers to suit individual requirements. Mixes were made, poured into a mold, and heated under pressure to form rubber objects having the required composition. Before long, however, the automobile-tire industry was looking for greater supplies of rubber to meet the fast-rising demand, which became crucial during both World Wars.

This demand was partly met by the recovery of scrap rubber. A. H. Marks had discovered in 1889 that scrap rubber could be reused if heated with a dilute solution of caustic soda. This and similar processes were employed but they did not provide a complete solution to the problem. The hardpressed rubber technologists then began an extended research into the chemistry of synthetic rubber, with results that have already been described in a previous section.

A further step in rubber technology was the combining of rubber with structural compounds such as textile fabrics, metals, wood, and asbestos so as to obtain a product having the resilience of rubber and the structural strength or special properties of the other component. This phase of research not only benefited the tire industry but greatly increased the potential uses of rubber in the chemical-process industries, in road building, and in other fields of engineering.

The petroleum refining industry also changed markedly under the impact of scientific research. From 1859, when Colonel Drake first demonstrated the possibility of tapping underground sources of crude oil by drilling instead of relying only on seepages, to 1900, when the infant automobile industry was barely getting started, the petroleum industry had been virtually a producer of kerosene only. Petroleum refining processes and apparatus had been mostly adapted from other industries, such as the coal-tar and alcohol industries. The evolution of petroleum refining in the United States was purely an experimental process and no fundamental research was started before the turn of the century.

Its status was somewhat different in Europe, where small

refineries had been struggling valiantly for many years until the much larger fields in Galicia, Rumania, and Russia were opened up. Western technicians wandered to the East in the closing decades of the nineteenth century and helped to found the Russian oil industry, which soon vied with the United States in production and range of products. For the Russian oil industry took up scientific research at the very beginning of its career, with such great names as Ipatieff, Ragusin, Mendelyeev, and Gurwitsch dominating petroleum science up until the outbreak of the first World War.

Gradually the oil industries of other nations achieved more scientific methods of distilling and refining petroleum. This change was prompted by the rising demand for products other than kerosene—lubricants, paraffin wax (for candles and waxed paper), asphalt (for road building), fuel oil (for marine and Diesel engines), and, above all, gasoline, which was now needed in ever-increasing quantities for the automobile and airplane.

The first important technical improvement was achieved in the field of distillation. Trumble, an American, had devised a system in 1912 whereby the oil was first superheated in a series of pipes and then pumped into a distilling column. Here all the light fractions needed were evaporated from the residue and recovered by fractional condensation—that is, condensing each fraction in a separate part of the column. This combination of a pipe-still and distilling columns plus evaporators proved a most flexible system for adapting distilling units to the variety of crudes available.

Then chemical refining, originally a batch process, was made automatic and converted into a continuous operation in closed vessels, which avoided the dangerous and wasteful evaporation of lighter parts. However, the days of refining with sulfuric acid, caustic soda, and the like were over once it was realized that no single refining process would suit the treatment of crudes that varied widely in chemical composition. Hence in the 1920's extraction processes came to the fore, first using sulfur dioxide, a gas that could be liquified under pressure. Then followed combinations of other solvents, such as acetone and benzene, which now permit the refiner to extract the unwanted components and market them separately for other purposes. This proved a suitable means of changing the original chemical composition of the oil considerably.

The natural gasoline content of the crude oil soon proved insufficient to meet the increased demand. Therefore the experimental cracking processes of the past were studied more closely and were much improved. In 1913 William M. Burton and Robert E. Humphreys of the Standard Oil Company of Indiana produced their high-temperature, high-pressure cracking still. The heated oil was prevented from evaporating by pressure and the liquid thus overheated cracked into lower-boiling compounds. This was the first of a series of "liquid phase" cracking systems, the most prominent of which were the systems of Jesse A. Dubbs (1909) and William M. Cross.

When natural gas came to supply the shortage of fuel, valuable low-boiling compounds like propane and butane could be extracted. This was impossible without proper distillation to remove the dissolved "wild" gases; accordingly, technicians were prompted to devise new types of distilling columns. MacCabe's original contribution to this problem in 1924 was the first step in the scientific design of distillation units, and proved to be a major advance when new cracking systems came to the fore about 1936. In these "vapor phase" cracking processes the oil was evaporated and circulated with catalysts. They soon became very important for the manufacture of special chemical compounds from petroleum. First, attention was drawn to the production of such chemicals as iso-octane, which made gasoline more efficient in aircraft engines. Later, other chemicals could be made that were suitable as solvents or as base materials for the production of glycerine, detergents, antibiotics, and synthetic fibers. Thus the oil industry is slowly expanding to include the manufacture of basic organic chemicals. Here, as in the rubber industry, scientific research has led the way for technological improvements.

EPILOGUE

TECHNOLOGY AND PROGRESS

OUR account has led us from the darkness of prehistoric times to our modern technical age. Had space permitted, we might have extended the list of principal discoveries and inventions almost to infinity and followed up more threads within the general fabric of their development. Further examples might have illustrated further the adaptation of our social order to the new technical developments, and the practical consequences of this for technology, but the essential picture of man's conquest of the physical world which we have given in this short survey would not have been altered.

Actually, if we study the history of technology carefully we shall find that many fundamental changes have occurred in technology itself. This not only means that modern society has made new demands of technology, but also that the modified technical forms make their influence felt on the social system in a new way and, by reason of their much greater intensity, constitute a more powerful factor in our civilization than ever before. This will be clear if we take another look at the principles which have come to govern our modern technology since the Industrial Revolution.

In the forefront stands the development of machinery which produces energy. The steam engine, the water turbine, the steam turbine, the internal combustion engine and the dynamo raised considerably the level of energy available in the nineteenth century. As with the advent of the watermill and the windmill at an earlier date, these facilitated the processing of larger and more complicated workpieces and enabled dreams of new technical horizons to be realized.

The higher level of energy produced by the new machinery would not in itself have led to the almost explosive development of technology during the past two centuries had not, in addition, the practical application of electricity brought about a form of transport of energy. Actually, until this time, machinery had always been dependent on fuels such as coal, oil or wood, which sometimes had to be transported over long distances. Consequently, there had always been a tendency for industries to be located at places within easy reach of fuel. Mass production methods for moving coal and gas, and central location of industries near these main sources, served to reduce the costs of transport, it is true, but the development of industrial towns remained in large measure bound up with the source of fuel.

The introduction of electricity quickly changed all this. The invention of the transformer enabled this form of energy to be temporarily transformed into a form which could be economically transported and reconverted on the spot into the required type of energy. In this way it was possible to exploit the enormous quantities of "white coal," the potential energy of mountain streams and waterfalls. It was no longer necessary to locate industries in these remote districts, with all the disadvantages consequent upon the difficulty of transporting the finished products. It was even possible to transmit energy in a concentrated form to places where the technical products could be quickly and smoothly marketed. Factories could now be established and run profitably at places where the basic materials were available, but fuels for the machinery lacking.

In short, it is due to the increased supply of energy, combined with the possibility of transporting it, that man, despite the unequal distribution of natural wealth and sources of fuel, has managed to arrive at a rational exploitation of the material world on behalf of the common good. What this has meant for mankind in the past, and still means today, cannot, in actual fact, be easily imagined. Unfortunately, we have but few reliable figures regarding the supply of energy in former times. But it has been calculated that in 1953 the average American citizen had at his disposal 2,000 times as much energy as his counterpart in 1776. And, due to the estimated 5% increase in energy available per year, the present level (1958) may now be well over 2,300 times the energy per head of that time. Undoubtedly, the situation in other parts of the world is much less favorable, but we can state with certainty that modern man has some hundred times more energy available than his forefathers of six or seven generations ago. Since the beginning of this century sufficient figures have been available to establish that the standard of living, likewise the expression in monetary value of industrial production, is proportional to the energy available per head of population.

That this development of technology concerns us all directly is clear when we realize that in the United States no less than half the available energy is used by the individual members of the population for purposes of heating, lighting and transport, and for driving the appliances in their homes. Only 20% is expended on the manufacture of new products, while approximately 30% is lost by the conversion of one kind of energy into other forms.

The development of technology has accordingly had a very direct effect upon our standard of living.

Expressing the above figures in terms of manpower, the American of 1776 used the help of one servant for two weeks in the year, while today he is the owner of sixty slaves. This colossal advance may best be imagined by visiting the palace of the French King at Versailles or any other residence of the wealthy in the eighteenth century and comparing such a castle with our own modern flats. Faced with the choice of living in the style of the wealthiest of the eighteenth century, only a few of the poorest among us would be willing to exchange our material living conditions for those of seven generations back.

This development is not only the result of the craftsman's accumulated experience and knowledge in the course of the centuries. It is due too, to a change in his role, as a result of a deliberate choice by Western man. In the Middle Ages the task of harnessing nature to man's needs was but dimly perceived. Francis Bacon gave clear expression to these subconscious aspirations and pointed the way.

According to him, science was the meeting ground of human knowledge and skill. The final aim of science was the conquest of nature: not only her comprehension, but also the practical application of knowledge for the benefit of mankind.

> "Therefore Truth and Profit are on here and the Works themselves are of greater value than Assurances of the Truthfulness (of Theories) because they add to the Pleasures of Life."

What Bacon time and again advocated (but never put into practice himself) was an empirical science which would build up a new world, for "we have many reasons to believe that Nature still carries many Secrets of great Profit, which are hardly related to those already known, which are still unperceived and beyond the Scope of our Imagination."

The new "empirical philosophy," as Bacon and his contemporaries called the natural sciences, expressed for the first time what several generations had been haltingly trying to put into words. The learned societies of the seventeenth century practised this new science with the benefit of society at large in mind, as is evident from their publications and treatises. Here, then, for the first time, science came to the aid of the craftsman, and the Industrial Revolution may accordingly best be seen as a period of growing co-operation between science and the crafts, in which process the latter is transformed into applied science.

Advances in the handicrafts were due to pursuit of the difficult path of trial and error. Now, these blind gropings were replaced by scientific research. The application of science to the handicrafts resulted not only in better methods of manufacture, but also in the more effective inspection of the basic material and finished product, and called for a completely new type of training for the skilled worker. We have already referred to the gradual replacement of the craftsman by the specialized worker, a process speeded up towards the end of the eighteenth century by the establishment of numerous technical schools and institutes. In particular, during the nineteenth century in France and Germany, workers were systematically given a scientific training with a view to providing torch-bearers of the new technology, and all due care was expended on the training of skilled workers. This example was later followed by the United States, after it had first sent its sons to France and Germany for training.

By the application of the natural sciences with their ever-increasing store of information and knowledge, pure and applied research was gradually taken out of the hands of the individual specialist and inventor. In modern technology the role of the individual inventor is only a minor one, although not altogether unimportant. Most improvements and inventions, however, result from the teamwork of a number of specialists in related fields.

The individual worker is already virtually excluded by the cost of purchasing the necessary instruments and financing laboratory research, frequently of several years' duration, which precedes the development of a new product such as synthetic gasoline, synthetic rubber or synthetic fibres. The large enterprises of our time frequently expend 5% or more of their total budget on research and it is clear that the private inventor stands small chance of competing on these terms.

Modern industrial research is very systematic and does not always operate directly in a field in which the possibilities are capable of immediate practical application. The large laboratories of the world carry on a considerable amount of pure scientific investigation in the course of which hitherto unknown fields of science are opened up, in the hope of course that the discoveries may ultimately be put to some useful purpose.

In this way modern technology has gradually come more and more within the sphere of operation of the universities. These, however, on account of limited funds, are frequently unable to pay for either the men or materials necessary to pursue modern research. Yet it is in the interests of modern science, and consequently of technology as well, that this pure scientific research work should not be taken out of the hands of the universities.

This fact is well understood by industry, which now supports the universities by means of donations and assignments, as may be seen from the figures quoted below. For example, if we consider the amounts expended on research in the United States, we shall find that in 1935 $200,000,000 was allocated for research purposes. While in 1953 this sum had risen to the enormous figure of $5,370,000,000, 44% contributed by industry itself, 52% by the State, and the rest by universities and other institutions. Of the total amount, 72% was expended on industrial research laboratories, 18% on State laboratories, 1% on miscellaneous agencies, and 9% on university laboratories. The latter figure, which has grown since the war, reflects appreciation for the role of the university in our modern technical development. Since that time, the sum total spent on research has risen considerably and will doubtless continue to rise. Certainly, the breakdown of percentages will also vary. This does however give us some idea of the present direction of growth.

Formerly, theoretic developments emanated chiefly from the universities and the laboratories in the Old World, while the New World excelled above all in practical experiments and in the application of theories which European scientists regarded as practicable. Today, theoretic research is beginning to make its voice heard in the United States as well.

As a result of scientific research and the contributions of the natural sciences, hand labor accordingly underwent increasing mechanization and the job of the artisan was taken over by the machine. Particularly since the middle of the last century a rapidly rising industrial production has been achieved in fewer working hours with less and less human and animal labor, but with an ever-increasing amount of machine-generated energy; and there are no signs to indicate that this process of eliminating human and animal labour will not continue. Undoubtedly, there are still many sectors, such as agriculture and fisheries, which mechanization has still barely touched. But here, too, the signs of the times are becoming clearly visible and the increasing research work which is being carried out in these fields—precisely where it is so necessary on account of the rapid growth of world population—will certainly speed up this process of mechanization.

It is not only the mechanization of working processes, however, which is so characteristic of our modern age. Formerly, the skilled artisan had to master the production process from beginning to end, whereas in modern technology the work process is dissociated into a number of operations, split up into phases, each of which is treated and built up as an independent process. Each individual process such as pressing, rolling, distilling, drying, annealing, etc. whether of a mechanical or chemical nature, becomes a specialized sector of operations which is not only subjected to scientific research but is also regarded as a unit in the enterprise and is supervised by specialists. The working process from base material to finished product is split up into a number of these units and each finished product must have undergone several such processes. In our modern industry, therefore, constructors of special units such as drying installations, distillation units, heating installations, etc., have come into being who call in the help of other producers, if they wish to employ a definite cycle of processes, not all of their own making, in order to manufacture a new product.

At the beginning of the Middle Ages, as we have already seen, the textile industry actually constituted a cycle of operations performed by skilled workers, who washed, dried, carded, spun, wove, fulled, etc., such operations being financed by a banker-moneylender. Until well into the eighteenth century, these operations tended to become integrated in one enterprise, but with the coming of modern technology the various units within the enterprise were to some extent separated and made independent operations again. A clear example of such a split-ting-up process may be seen in the large chemical concerns, where distillation, extraction and other units stand ready to play their part in the individual manufacturing cycle of the numerous products supplied.

Each of these basic processes has become a specialized field. Towards the end of last century, processes such as drying, dis-tilling, etc., had already begun to be studied as units and in-dividual problems. Hausbrand, Sorel and a number of other European scholars compiled handbooks on the subject. More-over, each of these manufacturing units was controlled more and more automatically, mostly by electrical apparatus, result-ing on the one hand in a marked reduction in manual control, but on the other, necessitating designers and engineers in the field of measuring technique. James Watt's indicator was the forerunner of our measuring instruments which, by register-ing fluctuations in the enterprise, make workmanship possible of such precision as would have appeared fantastic to our fore-fathers.

In addition to this strict supervision of the various stages of manufacture, a tendency is noticeable to assemble the finished product on a conveyor belt or assembly line from prefabricated parts. This form of mechanization has been particularly advan-tageous in the production of cheap motor vehicles, but it has become an integrating process in many other branches of in-dustry as well. In former times the keel of a new ship was laid in the shipyard and the framework constructed on this keel, the entire ship inside and out completed on the spot by many groups of experts. Great changes took place, however, shortly before and during the second world war. It has become increas-ingly the practice to weld ships instead of riveting the ship's plates. Modern welding offers sufficient security for this pur-pose and the welded construction is smoother and accordingly conducive to higher speeds. New ship designs were introduced. For instance, in the case of tankers, a longitudinal bulkhead with many transverse bulkheads was no longer used to divide the ship into many tanks; instead, the modern tanker has two longitudinal bulkheads, which invention considerably reduces the total weight of the ship and raises the speed without risk to the sturdiness of the vessel. However, it is even more important to note that the different parts of the modern ship are constructed in separate sheds and later welded together in the shipyard. This method results in a considerable saving in material and building time.

This rational planning of the manufacturing process has helped perhaps more than any other factor to reduce the cost price of goods and to further mass production for the benefit of the broad masses.

The strict inspection of the manufacturing processes, the specialized worker and the planned co-ordination of the various phases of manufacture play a very important part in modern technology. But of no less importance is the standardization of the parts used. Actually, in a modern enterprise the basic materials are exactly known beforehand. They are ordered on the basis of standards and must comply with certain closely defined requirements and dimensions. The screws, nuts, bolts, bars and steel strips with which a modern machinery factory constructs its machines, are made to exact measurements by special firms; these parts are interchangeable, so that, in general, our modern machine consists of units which in case of need may easily be replaced.

We scarcely ever pause to consider this important change which has taken place in technology, the production of large quantities of parts according to closely defined specifications, from which other enterprises assemble their final products. But this again is one of the *raisons d'être* of our modern technology. To us, the idea is hardly conceivable that a machine should be constructed from start to finish in one enterprise. Yet this was one of the greatest difficulties with which even the builders of the first steam engines had to contend. James Watt, Bolton and his entire generation were forced to construct each new machine as a separate entity and fashion all the various parts in their own workshops if they wanted them to fit properly.

Under the pressure of circumstances, the standardization of

parts was introduced. Perhaps the oldest examples of such standardization are the various types of calibrated nozzles which Roman waterworks engineers constructed in place of our modern water meters to check domestic water consumption. More systematic standardization began with the introduction of cannon into the armies of the Middle Ages. It is clear that for the long-term waging of war it was unsatisfactory to have to use cannon or fire-arms which were constructed as separate units and for which everyone had his own non-interchangeable ammunition. The artillery manuals and schools of the fifteenth and sixteenth centuries were powerful in the carrying out of this standardization. The introduction of severe disciplinary drills and uniforms in the armies may also be regarded as examples of standardization in warfare.

Similarly there arose a strong demand among the fleets and arsenals of the times for the manufacture of standard parts such as ropes, cables, anchor chains, sails, etc., since in those days long sea voyages necessitated taking along spare parts for use in places where no replacement could be expected from local factories. For instance, the East India Company established many stations along the route to India where it was not only possible to take in stores of fresh vegetables and food supplies, but also to find parts to replace worn or broken parts of the ship's rigging.

In the course of the following centuries, particularly towards the end of the eighteenth century, manufacturers and instrument-makers turned more and more to the manufacture of specialized and standardized products, which others purchased and assembled into new workpieces. As a result of the measuring and testing technique which was being developed, it was possible to construct these standard parts to very precise specifications and deliver them in accordance with previously stated characteristics, so that constructors could take this into account in designing the machines, but not need to spend time on manufacturing them. Hence, we can now purchase, for instance, screws and bolts from any manufacturer whatsoever since, by careful standardization, they are interchangeable. In this way, modern technology has made possible the mass (thus cheap) production of parts, which at the same time comply with closely defined specifications. The builders of a bridge no longer need to trouble about the manufacture of bolts, screws, sectional iron and steel plates; instead, they buy the standardized products and frequently even have them finished by specialists to certain specified dimensions. In the chemical industry, the selection of the type of standard auxiliary and base materials saves the industry the trouble of having to manufacture these itself.

The above described processes of mechanization, splitting up and standardization have been constantly inspired by the experience of former generations whose numerous earlier ventures and experiments have now borne fruit. A typical case in point is the harvesting machine which, according to the description by Palladius in his *De Re Rustica*, was used on Roman farms in Gaul. Its description was included by John Loudon in his *Encyclopaedia of Agriculture* (1825), where it was read by John Ridley. What he read inspired him to construct his stripper, which appeared in the fields of South Australia in the summer of 1843–44. It remained in general use there until approximately 1885, when it was replaced by more modern American agricultural machines. Standardization has not resulted in fewer kinds of machines or products, as was feared, but it did result in a saving of labor, and guaranteed a safe foundation upon which the modern engineer could base his own constructions.

In the last few centuries, then, the old handicrafts have been transformed at an accelerating tempo into modern technology. This change, which we are still witnessing, will in all probability receive still further strong stimuli from the new sources of energy released by the splitting of the atom and the action of the sun's rays and the tides, the use of which we are only beginning to learn. We are still in the middle of this process which, consequently, has not yet become history. At this point, therefore, where he is unable to compare our aims and achievements so far realized with accomplished facts, the historian

must perforce lay down his pen, if he wishes to avoid errors and prophecies which in the past appear to have existed all too frequently alongside reality.

It has no doubt become clear to us from the historical development of technology that each new technique is born of the questions and needs of the times, and that applied science is coming to occupy an ever more important place in the development of our civilization. From a purely scientific point of view, we can be satisfied with the answers which our specialists and engineers have given to these questions. But were our questions, seen from the social angle, always the right ones? Have we technically speaking actually subjugated nature and used her in such a way as to enable the broad masses to enjoy the fruits of our labors? Are the technical inventions handled in the correct way? Must, in the general interest, other new techniques and technical products be developed?

These questions bring the technologist to a plane broader than the narrow one of the specialist. Perhaps the triumph of technology has led to its disproportionally rapid development at the expense of other material and spiritual advances. The technologist, who is often called upon to fill high posts in our social system, would do well to ask himself whether, historically speaking, the development of his technical skill has been directed into the right channels, guided as it so often has been in the past by persons who, as specialists, were unable to envisage the broader possibilities of technical developments. Particularly towards the end of the last century, it was thought that all social problems could be solved with the aid of the sciences and technology. The structure of our modern technology as revealed in this survey has taught us differently.

The modern technologist or engineer has become rather modest. He realizes that man's problems cannot be understood by simple calculations and chemical reactions or physical changes alone. His science, he believes, teaches him no more than the properties of matter and its different forms.

He can and should, of course, apply these conquests of science and technology to avoid waste, and distribute the

fruits of his scientific work all around the globe according to need. He should also conserve the minerals and soils given man by nature, and use them in the most efficient way for the benefit of mankind. He should join hands with everybody willing to outlaw the exploitation of man's labor and all forms of destructive competition.

/ Unfortunately these aims are not purely scientific or technological. They cannot be achieved by the application of scientific principles alone, for they have pronounced sociological and economic aspects. As soon as we follow up the achievement of the engineer, we find that he is led into other domains of human life and activity if he tries to make others benefit from his inventions and discoveries.

The proper conditions for the realization of such a scientific world program are not too far off. From the time when the Royal Society and other national academies began to flourish and periodicals and letters started to spread scientific ideas, the exchange of views and the growth of science have been constantly stimulated. Notwithstanding the efforts of some countries or groups during certain periods of history, science and technology have become a field of international cooperation.

We live in a stage of human history in which the answers to the common problems that occupy men's attention at every point of the globe are no longer limited to certain areas and artificial lines on a map. The new science has established an international brotherhood of scientific thought.

In the foregoing pages we have found no rigid barriers of race, color, creed, or language between engineers and scientists of good will. During certain periods, especially in the more distant past, some of the barriers were effective for a time. A closer look at the historical development will prove, however, that the barriers were successfully broken down in the end.

If we take a long view of the story of science and engineering, it is clear that no discovery can be kept a secret; news of it spreads more or less quickly throughout the world. Ma-

terial progress itself has broken down the artificial barriers that certain groups or creeds may have tried to erect in their own interests.

For, with material progress, the different groups of mankind have come much closer together in the past few centuries. Geographical and political boundaries have been surmounted. The airplane, telephone, telegraph, and radio have established wider avenues of communication than the written word. Larger and larger circles have access to the news of what is going on in the inner circle of scientists and engineers.

Although this information is not always passed on unmodified and with complete accuracy, it still works effectively by drawing the attention of men working in other fields, anxious to find a solution to problems of their own and to obtain what aid science can proffer. Skills and techniques are pooled, mutual problems are discussed and solved in every part of the world. As our story unfolded we observed the increasing frequency of simultaneity and duplication of inventions and discoveries. Not only have individuals come to live in closer contact with their neighbors, but the economy and social structure of the greater part of the globe has become so interrelated that one can no longer speak of national economy, national politics, or national social structure in the strict sense of the term.

All over the world man has recognized this essential unity of mankind. It has been achieved more fully in the world of science and engineering than perhaps in any other field of activity. Growing numbers of people realize that this unity of mankind is deep-rooted and has become a permanent part of our social make-up. The barriers between groups and nations begin to fall under this growing conviction that all men have common goals and interests, and the cooperation rather than competition is the key to human progress.

We have also found that achievements in science are closely bound up with other aspects of human activity. The scientist today is no longer so certain, as was the scientist a few generations ago, that the world of the future will be founded on the material achievements of the past without the necessity for constant effort in the present. He knows that each generation is faced with a new set of problems peculiar to its times and that it must shape its science and technology so as to obtain the answers to these problems itself.

We know that science has not yet attained the complete conquest of nature. The heralding of the Atomic Age has rudely awakened us to the fact that, to paraphrase the words in which Newton summarized his life's achievements, we have picked up but a few pebbles on the shores of a great ocean that still remains to be explored. We seem to have only awakened to the danger of allowing our scientific and technological advances to outstrip our social and spiritual progress.

For it is clear that the conquest of the material world has caused the organic and spiritual world to fall behind, sometimes into almost complete oblivion. In order to build a really new and better world, more harmonious forms of progress must be achieved. We must apply our achievements and our knowledge of the material world to research into our biological and psychological activities in order to build the world of the future. Our science and technology must be consciously directed toward the accomplishment of this higher unity of mankind. No world can be built on the basis of material progress alone. We must supplement our material gains with a deeper understanding of the mind and spirit. Using the science of matter to implement the science of man is the task of present and future generations.

BIBLIOGRAPHY

THE serious student wishing to explore more fully the history of technology and engineering will be somewhat hindered by the fact that much of the evidence is still buried in periodicals and original documents in many languages. A number of gaps in our knowledge still remain to be filled by the scholar's patient research and evaluation of the abundant material. Interesting articles on the subject can be found in such periodicals as *Isis* (Cambridge, Mass.), *Annals of Science* (London), *Transactions of the Newcomen Society* (London), *Technikgeschichte* (Berlin), *The Journal of Chemical Education*, and the larger engineering journals.

There is yet no satisfactory and comprehensive history of technology and engineering, with the possible exception of Abbot P. Usher's *A History of Mechanical Inventions* (Harvard University Press, 1954), which is, however, somewhat weak in the sections on antiquity, and provides little historical background. Professor Charles Singer, Dr. E. J. Holmyard and Dr. A. R. Hall are now, however, publishing the first handbook on this subject with the financial aid of the I.C.I. (Imperial Chemical Industries, England). The first of three volumes of this *History of Technology* (Clarendon Press, 1955/56/57) have been published; two more are to follow. In the field of the history of science two of the best modern books are Charles

Singer's *A Short History of Science* (Oxford, 1946) and F. Sherwood Taylor's *Science, Past and Present* (London, 1945).

George Sarton's *Study of the History of Science* (Cambridge, 1950) is an excellent guide to students of both science and engineering.

It cannot be sufficiently stressed, however, that the serious student should study the original texts himself, for translations are often faulty and passages quoted by later authors may be distorted when torn from their context. Above all, the student of this subject should make himself conversant with the historical background of the period he is dealing with, for only in this way can he fully evaluate the evidence.

A list of selected readings, arranged by chapters, is given below.

CHAPTER I

An excellent little book on the material covered in this chapter is R. U. Sayce's *Primitive Arts and Crafts: An Introduction to the Study of Material Culture* (New York, 1933). The lecture of S. C. Gilfillan's article on "Invention As a Factor in Economic History" (Journal of the Patent Office Society, April 1947, pages 262–288) will be as stimulating as his *Sociology of Invention* (Chicago, 1935); also interesting are H. Stafford Hatfield's *The Inventor and His World* (Pelican Books, London, 1948) and André Leroi-Gourhan's *Evolution et Techniques* (Albin Michel, Paris, 1943/45, 2 vols.).

CHAPTER II

The historical background to Chapters II–VI can be found in J. H. Breasted's *Ancient Times* (Chicago, 1935) and J. Finnegan's *Light from the Ancient Past* (Princeton, 1946).

A simple discussion of the facts is given in H. J. Peake's *Early Steps in Human Progress* (London, 1932) and in J. G. D. Clark's *Prehistoric Europe* (London, 1952), while V. Gordon Childe's *What Happened in History* (London, 1942) will be found stimulating and provocative, but a bit dogmatic on certain points. See also George F. Renard, *Life and Work in Primitive Times* (New York, 1929), and A. H. J. Goodwin's *Communication Has Been Established* (London, 1937).

CHAPTER III

The older books by A. Neuburger (*The Technical Arts and Sciences of the Ancients*, New York, 1930) and F. M. Feldhaus (*Kulturgeschichte der Technik*, Berlin, 1928, etc.) are not recommended, because they are mainly compilations from other works and the authors have not always taken the trouble to verify the original sources. Much useful information is to be found in J. R. Partington's *Origins and Development of Applied Science* (London, 1935) if the reader will take the trouble to study for himself the evidence cited. Interesting information is given in T. A. Rickard's *Man and Metals*, Vol. I (New York, 1932), though some of the details may not be completely correct. There is an excellent chapter on Egyptian science and engineering in S. R. K. Glanville's *The Legacy of Egypt* (Oxford, 1943). A particular industry is discussed in R. J. Forbes's *Bitumen and Petroleum in Antiquity* (Leiden, 1936) and *Metallurgy in Antiquity* (Leiden, 1950).

CHAPTER IV

A. P. Gest's *Engineering* (London, 1930) and W. H. Burr's *Ancient and Modern Engineering* (New York, 1907) are still the best little summaries of the achievements of the classical engineers. H. Blümmer's four-volume work, *Technologie und Terminologie* (Leipzig, 1900) is still very valuable, as is Brunet and Mieli's *Histoire des Sciences: Vol. I, Antiquite* (Paris, 1935). H. Diels's *Antike Technik* (Leipzig, 1924) and H. Lamer's *Wörtebuch der Antike* (Leipzig, 1936) contain interesting evidence. Cohen and Drabkin's *A Sourcebook In Greek Science* (New York, 1948) gives valuable extracts from ancient authors. Specific industries are discussed in J. Hornell's *Water Transport* (Cambridge, 1946), Th. Ashby's *The Aqueducts of Rome* (Oxford, 1935) and the various volumes of R. J. Forbes's

Studies in Ancient Technology (Leiden 1955/56, 4 vols., volume V in the press).

CHAPTER V

The only satisfactory summary of the technical achievements of the Arabs is given in the relevant chapter of T. W. Arnold's *The Legacy of Islam* (Oxford, 1945), which is also an excellent introduction to the historical background. Volume I of George Sarton's *Introduction to the History of Science*, noted above, contains a good account of Arabic science. See also S. Runciman, *Byzantine Civilization* (London and New York, 1933), A. Mez, *Die Renaissance des Islam* (Heidelberg, 1922), H. J. J. Winter, *Eastern Science* (London, 1952), J. Needham, *Science and Civilization in China* (Cambridge, vol. I, 1954; vol. II, 1956) and A. L. Basham, *Wonder that was India* (London, 1954).

CHAPTER VI

The period covered in this chapter is not very adequately treated in histories of engineering and technology. The only book that gives any well-digested facts is P. Boissonnade's *Life and Work in Medieval Europe: Fifth to Fifteenth Centuries* (New York, 1927). There are, however, several excellent books on the historical background; see Eileen Power's *Medieval People* (London, 1937); S. Baldwin's *Business in the Middle Ages* (New York, 1937); F. Harrison, *Medieval Man* (London, 1947); G. G. Coulton, *Life in the Middle Ages* (Cambridge, 1929), and the same author's *Medieval Panorama* (Cambridge, 1938); H. Pirenne, *Medieval Cities* (Princeton, 1925). See also the monumental six-volume work of Lynn Thorndike, *A History of Magic and Experimental Science During the First Sixteen Centuries of Our Era* (New York, 1923–1941), a detailed and well-documented history of the rise of scientific thought based on an examination of original documents hitherto inaccessible to most scholars. For the influence of Jewish thought on the Middle Ages, see Bevan and Singer's *The Legacy of Israel* (Oxford, 1944). Theophilus's work on the various arts in the tenth century has been partly translated into German and annotated by W. Theobald (Berlin, 1933). For an analysis of intellectual development in the Middle Ages, see H. O. Taylor's *The Medieval Mind* (New York, 1925). See also B. Gille, *Esprit et Civilization Technique au Moyen Age* (Paris, 1952), B. Gille, *Les Origines de L'industrie Métallurgique en France* (Paris, 1949) and R. J. Forbes, *A Short History of the Art of Distillation* (Leiden, 1950), and M. Mercier, *Le Feu Gregeois* (Paris, 1952).

CHAPTER VII

The background of engineering progress discussed in this chapter is excellently outlined in J. H. Randall, Jr.'s *Making of the Modern Mind* (Boston, 1926). The subject is more amply covered in W. B. Parsons's *Engineers and Engineering in the Renaissance* (Baltimore, 1939) and in A. Wolf's *A History of Science, Technology, and Philosophy in the 16th and 17th Centuries* (London and New York, 1935).

The relation between science, technology, and society is admirably presented in M. Ornstein's *The Role of Scientific Societies in the 17th Century* (Chicago, 1938); in D. Stimson's *Scientists and Amateurs* (New York, 1948), and in G. N. Clark's *Science and Social Welfare in the Age of Newton* (Oxford, 1937). See also G. N. Clark's *The Seventeenth Century* (London, 1947); F. Sherwood Taylor, *The Alchemists* (New York, 1948); Ivor B. Hart, *James Watt and the History of Steam Power* (New York, 1949).

Excellent editions of originals are H. C. and L. H. Hoover's translation of Agricola's *De Re Metallica* (New York, 1912), and Smith and Gnudi's translation of Biringuccio's *Pirotechnica* (New York, 1943). C. Briggs's *A Short History of the Building Crafts* (Oxford, 1925) is also worth looking into.

CHAPTERS VIII, IX, AND X

The historical background is well presented in P. Mantoux's *The Industrial Revolution in the Eighteenth Century* (London, 1947); A. Birnie's *Economic History of Europe, 1760–1939* (London, 1944); E. P. Cheyney's *An Introduction to the Industrial and Social History of England* (New York, 1925); F. C. Dietz's *The Industrial Revolution* (New York, 1927); H. Heaton's *Economic History* (New York, 1936), and Randall's book mentioned above. H. Hamilton's *History of the Homeland* (London, 1947) is worth consulting though it deals with England only and from a special point of view. See also J. L. and Barbara Hammond, *The Rise of Modern Industry* (New York, 1926), which is also based more or less exclusively on British material but is scholarly and penetrating.

General books on the science and technology of this period are A. Wolf's *History of Science, Technology, and Philosophy in the 18th Century* (London, 1939), and H. T. Pledge's *Science Since 1500* (London, 1946). H. P. Vowles's *The Quest For Power* (London, 1932) makes somewhat dull reading but contains valuable data. See also W. T. Sedwick and H. W. Tylor, *A Short History of Science* (New York, 1917) and A. E. Shipley, *The Revival of Science in the Seventeenth Century* (Princeton, 1914).

There are a number of excellent books on special subjects covering the period treated in these three chapters:

Anderson, O. E., *Refrigeration in America* (Harvard, 1953)
Ashton, T. S. & Sykes, J., *The Coal Industry of the Eighteenth Century* (Manchester, 1929)
Baker, M. N., *The Quest for pure Water* (New York, 1948)
Boumphrey, G. M., *The Story of the Wheel* (London, 1932)
Browne, C. A., *A Sourcebook of Agricultural Chemistry* (Waltham, 1944)
Burlingame, R., *March of the Iron Men* (New York, 1938)
———, *Engines of Democracy* (New York, 1940)
Chandler, D. & Lacy, A., *The Rise of the Gas Industry in Britain* (London, 1949)
Chapman, E. H., *Wireless Today* (Oxford, 1936)

BIBLIOGRAPHY

Clow, A. & Clow, N., *The Chemical Revolution* (London, 1952)
Cressy, Edward, *A Hundred Years of Mechanical Engineering* (New York, 1937)
Davy, M. H. B., *Interpretative History of Flight* (London, 1937)
Dickinson, H. W., *A Short History of the Steam Engine* (London, 1938)
——, *Matthew Boulton* (London, 1936)
——, *James Watt* (London, 1935)
——, *Robert Fulton* (London, 1912)
——, and A. Titley, *Richard Trevithick* (London, 1934)
Fester, G., *Entwicklung der chemischen Technik* (Berlin, 1932)
Finch, J. K., *Engineering and Western Civilization* (New York, 1951)
Fletcher, B., *A History of Architecture* (New York, 1943)
Frazer, G. Lovat, *Textiles in Britain* (London, 1948)
Gibson, C. E., *The Story of the Ship* (New York, 1948)
Giddens, P. H., *Pennsylvania Petroleum 1750–1872* (Titusville, 1947)
——, *Early Days in Oil* (Princeton, 1948)
Himsworth, J. B., *The Story of Cutlery* (London, 1954)
Howard, Frank A., *The Birth of an Industry Buna Rubber* (New York, 1947)
Kirby, R. S. & Lawson, P. G., *The Early Years of Modern Civil Engineering* (Oxford, 1932)
Kirby, R. S., *et al.*, *Engineering in History* (New York, 1956)
Lippman, E. O. von, *Geschichte der Zuckers* (Berlin, 1929)
MacLaren, M., *The Rise of the Electrical Industry during the 19th Century* (Princeton, 1943)
MacLaurin, W. R., *Invention and Innovation in the Radio Industry* (New York, 1949)
McMahon, J. R., *The Wright Brothers* (Boston, 1930)
Magoun, F. A. & Hodgins, E., *A History of Aircraft* (New York, 1931)
Maxim, H. P., *Horseless Carriage Days* (New York, 1937)

347

Morgan, A. P., *A Pageant of Electricity* (New York, 1939)

Mumford, L., *Technics and Civilization* (New York, 1934)

Parsons, R. H., *The Early Days of the Power Station Industry* (London, 1940)

Passer, H. C., *The Electrical Manufacturers 1875–1900* (Harvard, 1953)

Phillips, C. J., *Glass, the Miracle Maker* (London, 1948)

Rhodes, F. L., *Beginnings of Telephony* (New York, 1929)

Rickard, T. A., *The Romance of Mining* (Toronto, 1945)

Schubert, P., *The Electric Word; the Rise of Radio* (New York, 1928)

Scoville, W. C., *A Short History of Marine Engineering* (London, 1927)

Storck, J. & Teague, W. D., *Flour for Man's Bread* (Univ. of Minnesota, 1952)

Straub, H., *Die Bauingenieurskunst* (Basel, 1949)

Thompson, G. N. V., *A Short History of American Railroads* (New York, 1925)

Thompson, G. N. V. & Edgar, J. H., *Canadian Railway Development* (Toronto, 1933)

Veen, Joh. van, *Dredge, Drain, Reclaim* (The Hague, 1955)

Abundant literature on the evolution of modern chemical technology is given in B. Jaffe's *New World of Chemistry* (New York, 1947); comprehensive bibliographies on American technology and invention are given in R. Burlingame's two volumes, *March of the Iron Men* (New York, 1938) and *Engines of Democracy* (New York, 1940).

INDEX

Academie des Sciences, 139
Accademia del Cimento, 139
Accademia dei Lincei, 139
achromatic lens, 227
Advancement of Learning, The,
138
aeolipile, 68
Agamemnon, 299
Age of Projects, 140
Age of Reason, 173-176
Age of Steam, 172-231
Agricola (Dr. Georg Bauer), 165-
168, 172
agricultural revolution, 110
agriculture, Arabian, 92; 18th and
19th century, 229-231; medieval,
110-112; primitive, 17
air brake, 253
airplane, development of, 266-271
air pump, 140, 143
Alberghetti, 141
Alberti, Leon Battista, 157
Albertus Magnus, 106
Al-Bīrūni, 95
alchemy, 86-88; Arabian, 95
alcohol, 87, 100; medieval distillation of, 124; 19th century, 218
Alexander the Great, 48, 50, 59, 61,
67, 69, 82, 85
Alexandrian science, 62 *ff.*
algebra, 92
alizarine red, 219
Al-Kindī, 92
alloy steel, 208, 279; *see also* steel
alloys, early determination of composition, 32
alternating current, 288-290
alternating-current motor, 295
alum, 170
aluminum, 281
amber, 29
Amenemhet III, 48
America, discovery of, 133

America, 265
Amman, Jost, 162
Ampere, André Marie, 285
Amsterdam chain dredger, 159
Anaxagoras, 60
aniline dyes, 218-219
animals, domestication of, 22
anthracene, 219
anthracite, 199
antimony, isolation from ore, 31;
uses, 167
antiseptics, 218
Apollonius, 49
Appert, Francois, 312
Appian Way, 76
Appius Claudius, 76, 78
applied science, in classical Greece,
62
aqua ardens, 124
aqua vitae, 125
aqueducts, Egyptian, 47; European
water supply and, 156; on Island
of Samos, 66-67; Persian invention, 50; Roman, 78-81
Aquinas, Thomas, 106
Arabian Nights, 132
Arabian science and engineering,
89-102
Arabian technology, 96-102
Arabic names, English terms derived from, 97, 100
Arabic notation, 92
arch, masonry, 242; steel, 242
archeology, 8
Archimedean screw, 65
Archimedes, 65, 68
Archimedes, 264
architects, earliest, 43-46
architecture, Egyptian, 44-46;
Mesopotamian, 44
Argand, Aimé, 214-215
Aristotle, 61-62, 92, 106, 136
Arkwright, Richard, 116, 192, 210

349

armature, 287
armorer, medieval, 118
Armstrong, Major Edwin, 303
Artemon, 82
artesian wells, Arabian, 93
Art of Glassmaking, The, 169
artillery, development of, 122 *ff.*
arts and crafts, of classical Greece, 64
Augustus, 70
Aspdin, Joseph, 238
asphalt roads, 236
asphaltic concrete, 238
aspirin, 218
astrolabe, 133; Arabian development of, 95
astrology, medieval, 106
astronomical tables, 133
astronomy, Arabian, 95; Egyptian and irrigation, 20; Renaissance, 139; Sumerian, 50-51
Athenaeum, 68
Atlantic cable, 299
audion, 303
Auleander, 144
automatic machines, beginnings of, 108
automobile, development of, 258-262; electric, 284; mass production of, 260; road building and, 237
Avicenna, 95

Babcock & Wilcox boiler, 195
Babylonian measurement, 21
Bacon, Francis, 107, 138, 139, 183, 314
Bacon, Roger, 106
Baghdad, 90
Baird, John Logie, 304
Baker, Benjamin, 245
Bakewell, Robert, 230
Bakker, 162
ballista, 84
ballistics, science of, 124
balloon, 266-267
bankers, medieval, 116
Baptists, 176
barbarian tribes, 103

barometer, 140
battery, electric, 283
Baumé, Antoine, 174
beam engines, 184-188
beehive oven, 199-200
Beekman, Isaac, 141
beet sugar, 223-224
Bell, Alexander Graham, 300
Belopoïka, of Philon, 84
belt drives, 310
benzene, 217
Bergbücherlein, 165
Bergier, Nicolas, 152
Bergius, Friederich, 318
Berlin Academy of Sciences, 139
Berthollet, Philippe J. L., 214
Bessemer, Henry, 275
Bessemer converter, 275
Besson, Jacques, 142
Beukelszoon, Willem, 312
Bible, authority of, in Middle Ages, 105; earliest printed, 135; illustrated scenes from, 129; lessened authority of, 136
bicycle, 255-258
Birdseye, 315
Biringuccio, Vanuccio, 165
bismuth, discovery of, 167
bituminous coal, 199
Black, Joseph, 187
Black Death, 125, 137, 165
blast furnace, 117, 198; modern, 207; preheated, 206; 16th century, 166
bleaching, 126, 213
block printing, Chinese, 134
block signal system, 253
blueing, 171
Blumenthal, Cellier, 218
Boccaccio, Giovanni, 136
boilers, steam, 194
bombards, first cast-iron, 119
Bonrepos, Pierre Paul du, 159
bookbinding, Arabian, 98
books, first printed, 134
Borden, Gail, 313
Bosch magneto, 260
Boston and Sandwich Glass Company, 226